The Charlton Standard Catalogue of

CHINTZ

First Edition

By
Linda Eberle
and
Susan Scott

W.K. CROSS
Publisher

Birmingham, Michigan • Toronto, Ontario

Canadian Cataloguing In Publication Data

Scott, Susan Joan, 1948-

The Charlton Standard Catalogue of Chintz

Includes index.

ISBN 0-88968-179-1

1. Chintz - Catalogs. I. Eberle, Linda

II. Title.

NK8806.S36 1996 746.6 C96-930481-1

Printed in Canada
in the Province of Quebec

The Charlton Press

Editorial Office
2010 Yonge Street
Toronto, Ontario M4S 1Z9
Telephone: (416) 488-4653 Fax: (416) 488-4656
Telephone: (800) 442-6042 Fax: (800) 442-1542

EDITORIAL

Editor	Nicola Leedham
Editorial Assistant	Davina Rowan
Editorial Assistant	Sandra Tooze
Graphic Technican	Patrick Glassford

ACKNOWLEDGEMENTS

The Charlton Press wishes to thank those who have helped and assisted with the first edition of the Charlton Standard Catalogue of Chintz.

CONTRIBUTORS

The Publisher would like to thank the following individuals who graciously supplied photographs or allowed us access to their pieces for photographic purposes. We offer sincere thanks to:

Bill Brethour, Dr. Tony Burke, Debbie and Richard Chuback, Fritz Mueller, Cathy Nicho, Cindy Oliver and Valerie Smith.

A SPECIAL NOTE TO COLLECTORS

The Charlton Press has an ongoing commitment to excellence and completeness in the production of all its reference works. We will consider editorial additions or corrections regarding colourways, varieties, or dating of patterns. Your help in providing new or previously unobtainable data on any aspect of Chintz collecting will be considered for inclusion in subsequent editions. Those providing information will be acknowledged in the contributor's section of this catalogue.

Please send your contributions together with your name, address and phone number to our editorial offices in Toronto.

58 Tea Pot, 24's, $33 doz.

41 Salad Bowl, 9", $15 doz.

1 Teacup & Saucer, $9 doz.

14 Salad Plate, 8", $7.50 doz.

16 Dinner Plate, 10", $10.50 doz.

29 Fruit Saucer, 5⅞", $4.50 doz.

50 Coffee Pot, 36's, $22.50 doz.

78 Cov. Sugar & Cream $30 doz.

ENCORE

A war and the sulking British pound delayed the return of ROSALYNDE CHINTZ. Now it's here at devaluation prices. Chintzware aglow with red and yellow roses, blue-bells and bits of green—trimmed in gold. Its James Kent, Ltd. backstamp is your assurance that ROSALYNDE is a sound investment.

Suggestion: The ROSALYNDE replacement market is vast. A postcard advising ROSALYNDE purchasers that you have a fresh stock should prove a profitable mailing.

NOTE

To match the dinnerware, 25 giftware items in ROSALYNDE, such as nut dishes, bonbons, sugar and cream sets, comports, pitchers and sandwich trays are offered at attractive prices. These range from $4 per dozen for a small square nut dish or ashtray to $24 per dozen for a square cake plate (11"). As separate items, open stock or an assorted case, $115.25 value for $107.50 — case and packing, $2. Fancy goods list on request.

Immediate shipment from Philadelphia of all ROSALYNDE items.

NOT ILLUSTRATED

12 Bread & Butter Plate, 6½"	$ 5.00 doz.
15 Luncheon Plate, 9"	9.00 doz.
32 Cereal Bowl, 6⅜"	6.00 doz.
51 Coffee Pot, 24's	33.00 doz.
56 Tea Pot, 36's	24.00 doz.
57 Tea Pot, 30's	28.50 doz.

A special assortment of this dinnerware is available. Value $137.75 for $130 — case and packing, $2.

EBELING & REUSS CO.

Established 1886

707 CHESTNUT STREET, PHILADELPHIA 6, PA.

225 Fifth Avenue
NEW YORK 10

1557 Merchandise Mart
CHICAGO 54

527 W. 7th Street
LOS ANGELES 14

TABLE OF CONTENTS

PREFACE

Three years ago we met by telephone — Toronto to California. We spent almost a year chatting most Sunday nights about twentieth-century English china in general and chintzware in particular. Linda is the avid chintz collector and she was trying to find examples of all the different chintzes produced by the major factories from 1920 to 1960. Susan is the researcher who started off collecting Malingware and continued with bits of Susie Cooper, Clarice Cliff, Moorcroft, even chintzware. Three years ago she wrote her first article about attending Susie Cooper's ninetieth birthday in London and since then has written a number of articles on different English factories. While Linda is out looking for chintz Susan is in the archives looking for any bit of information she can find — a perfect partnership.

The first face-to-face meeting was at the huge antiques fair at Newark, England, in 1994 and the second when Susan gave a talk at the inaugural Chintz Collectors' Convention in Rancho Cordova in 1995. At the convention most of the collectors asked if we would please give them a general book for collectors with patterns and shapes identified, and we agreed to collaborate on such a book. We had no idea just how difficult it was going to be to find information and how many people would help us put this material together.

We would never have been able to write this book without the help of a long line of people. First and foremost we want to thank our long suffering husbands, Gene Eberle and Douglas Scott — neither of whom are particularly interested in ceramics, especially chintz — who have been wonderful. We have promised not to start another book for at least a year. John Klycinski and Walter Kennedy came to Linda's house in April of 1995 and took all the slides for the pattern record; since then they have been back several times and many of the photographs in the book are their work. Bob Ostrowski from Idaho spent days checking material and searching for obscure patterns for us. The members of the Chintz Collectors' Club have patiently turned over all their pieces to record the pattern numbers and the backstamps, they have photographed anything they thought we might be interested in and they have faxed lists of the prices they paid for any recent chintz finds. Club members Cindy Oliver, Cathy Nicho, and Sonia Moreno from California, Valerie Smith from Idaho, and Laurie Goldberg from Virginia spent hours photographing pieces for us. David and Barbara Shestak of Gold River, California, found a marked piece of **Clyde** for us last year and this year managed to find a marked piece of **May Festival** just in the nick of time. Bill Brethour of Toronto, Ontario, offered advice and loaned us several pieces. Fritz Mueller of Vancouver, British Columbia, has been the custodian of shapes for the Chintz Collectors' Club. He has been diligent in recording every new "sighting" and is responsible for many of the shapes on the lists and a number of the photographs in the book. Tollie Coales, daughter of the Canadian representative for Grimwades for fifty years, welcomed Susan into her home a number of times and regaled her with stories of her father's life with Grimwades. Cassidy's of Canada was willing to look through their files and Mr. Brodeur loaned us the company's 1954 trade catalogue with the chintz pages we have reproduced in this book. Marilyn Saunders, who doesn't even collect chintz, spent two days in Buffalo with Susan going through trade catalogues.

Our research in England was helped along by so many people. Long time chintz dealers like Joy Humphries, Diana Frost, Beverley and Beth Adams, were generous in sharing their knowledge. Ken and Diana Glibberey and Muriel Miller and her husband Dave were very hospitable and showed us a number of interesting pieces from their collections. Jocelyn Lukins, author of any number of books on Royal Doulton, gave us a bed in London and constant help and encouragement. Susan's cousin Wendy Watson and her husband Peter have been a home base for Susan for the five years she has been going to England to do research, and last year they welcomed Linda as well. Three years ago when Susan called Capper Rataud Ltd., ceramic transfer manufacturers, Mike Cleaver, a designer, searched their archive and found some original Winton transfers for patterns like **Nantwich, Pelham** and **English Rose**. Doreen Donegan, who worked for James Kent, Florrie Dennis, who worked for Royal Winton, Ivy Mayer, secretary to the export director of Grimwades — all these women welcomed us into their homes and shared their memories with us. We have often phoned Ivy to ask her the name of yet another shape. Through Ivy we met Dora Shaw who led us to Gerrard Shaw. Even though he is in the midst of writing a book on A. G. Richardson, he has been incredibly generous with his time. It is thanks to Gerrard that we learned about *The Pottery, Glass & Brass Salesman* and found the names of a number of Crown Ducal patterns.

Dr.Tony Burke of Australia sent photographs and identified **Floral Garden** and **Chelsea Rose** for us. Toni Cardwell of New Zealand sent photographs and information on "chintz down under" as well as providing that elusive piece of Lord Nelson **Anemone**. Sheryl Vogt of the Australian Royal Winton Collectors' Club sent photographs and information.

Finally, Bullers Staffordshire Ltd. which bought Royal Winton in 1995, gave us permission to use **Summertime** on the book cover and Debbie and Rick Chuback of Toronto, Ontario, loaned us their 16-inch platter to photograph.

Chintzware was relatively cheap and cheerful china meant for everyday use. It was never meant to last. Most of the people we met in the potteries —even those who had worked for Winton and Kent — had very little chintz in their cupboards; they had Royal Doulton figurines. Chintz rarely figured in any of the literature of the day, certainly there was no mention of chintz in any of the design books or *Studio Yearbooks*. Factories opened and closed, were taken over and then taken over again and records were usually discarded. There are remarkably few written records to do with any of the factories which produced chintzware. Royal Winton has absolutely nothing left — no molds, no pattern books, no clipping files. James Kent was sold to Hadida in the late 1980s but it would seem that all the records were destroyed at that time, if not earlier. Nothing of Elijah Cotton has been found. All the Myott records were destroyed in a disastrous fire in 1949. Roy Midwinter made every attempt to find the patterns books for the book on Midwinter but he became convinced they had been destroyed. It was believed that all the A. G. Richardson pattern books were destroyed years ago, but recently Gerrard Shaw has come to believe that they may be buried somewhere in the basement of the Hanley Museum. One can only hope he is able to find them.

We have gone through more than forty years of *Pottery Gazette & Glass Trade Review*, an equal number of *The Pottery, Glass & Brass Salesman*, a New York trade catalogue, and the later American publication, *Crockery & Glass Journal*. We have pored over American and Canadian decorating magazines and found very few mentions of chintz in thousands of pages. More importantly, we have had access to hundreds of collectors, each with large or small collections, and we have tried to build up a picture of chintz from the empirical evidence of what remains —not unlike archeologists sifting through ancient middens trying to cobble together a working history of a group of people from the artifacts they left behind.

The moment the book is at press, someone will turn up with proof that some of our suppositions are wrong. We look forward to hearing from anyone with new information, and we will open a file for the second edition the moment the first letter arrives.

Linda Eberle
Susan Scott

INTRODUCTION

The History of Chintz

The history of chintz goes back hundreds of years, although the chintz so eagerly sought today is very much a twentieth-century industrial product. Chintz — the Indian word was *chintes* — goes back to the fantastical fabrics imported into England from the India of the late seventeenth century. Richly hued flowers and brightly plumed mythical birds decorated both the persons and the houses of the early 1700s to such an extent that it threatened domestic weavers. Even before 1800 chintz had come to mean homey, cozy, overstuffed furniture and a certain English country house look. An advertisement in *The Pottery Gazette* as late as 1957 describes "the homely rustle of chintz, the warm welcoming design of flowered pattern."

Inevitably the china manufacturers created hand-painted tableware which captured the feel of Indian chintz. The development of the process of transfer printing was very important in the popularizing of chintz ceramics. By the 1820s there were a number of Staffordshire factories producing chintz that was meant for everyday use. This chintz is recognizable by the very Victorian shapes to which it was applied and by the loose patterning and more subtle colouring than the twentieth-century versions.

Around 1912 Royal Doulton produced several versions of an all-over pattern called **Persian,** which remained in production until the second world war and was used mainly on cabinet pieces. However, chintzware was not really produced to any extent by any of the carriage-trade pottery firms. The firms which catered to the middle classes and to the masses were the firms which came to personify chintz. In 1918 A. G. Richardson developed their first chintz — a pattern so far identified only as A500 — but followed with **Rose and Motifs** and **Delhi** in the same year. Most of these early Crown Ducal chintzes were used for vases and trinket boxes, not for dinnerware. In dating chintz ware to the 1920s, it is useful to study the patterns produced by Richardson's, since they seem to exemplify that exotic 1920s look. They were particularly popular in America, and a long article in *The Pottery, Glass & Brass Salesman* extolls Richardson's work:

. . . there is always a steady demand for the chintz patterns . . . these come in many variations of colour background, and the subdued brilliance of the realistic flowers and plumaged birds makes an ever-delightful note. ***Festival*** *decoration with its intertwined lanterns hanging over blithely frolicsome scenes seems to have the ability to capture the fancy of many who like its vivacity. Crown Ducal ware is a beautiful piece of industrial accomplishment with none of the slight faults of immaturity.*

It is useful to place this tableware against a broader historical background. The 1920s were the Jazz Age, the time of the exotic and art deco. Yet the world had barely survived the war to end all wars and the Russian Revolution. The January 1927 advertisement for the new Crown Ducal chintzes describes them as "bordering on the sensational . . . novel indeed and radically different, but not bolshevik." Chintzes somehow managed to be both different but cozy, exotic but not revolutionary. Books on twentieth-century design never contain references to chintz. They were intended for "seaside cottages and bungalow furnishings," not avant garde houses in New York.

From 1918 through the first half of the 1920s, most of the Crown Ducal chintz pieces were vases and console sets (candle sticks and bowls), as well as toilet sets. A 1929 report pointed out that ten years before the Crown Ducal Works in England had produced only a few vases of various shapes and some odd pieces of decorative earthenware. "Today a tremendous volume business in dinnerware is theirs — and they serve the American market chiefly, for this ware appeals immensely to the value-loving and thrifty native housewife, in whom more for the money awakens instant response. . . .the early examples of CD ware consisting of chintz all-over pattern vases and similar items gained great favor with all who saw them . . . . " A steady stream of requests for individual breakfast sets to match, for tea sets and salad services flowed into the offices of Maddock & Miller, exclusive agents for Crown Ducal. In 1925 the manufacture of dinner services began "the first specimens were of the popular chintz effects which are still in steady demand especially for subsidiary sets." The Americans calculated that a Crown Ducal dinner service would cost about $100, while a comparable bone-china service would be over $500. After a strange gap of almost ten years, Crown Ducal produced a series of chintzes in the 1930s such as **Primrose**, **Priscilla** and **Pansy** but these have never achieved the popularity with collectors of the earlier patterns.

Other firms that were producing chintz very like the 1920s Crown Ducal were Samuel Ford & Company, Burslem and Wood & Sons, Burslem. All these firms were geographically very close together and exhibited at the same trade shows. It is not surprising to find that soon after one firm produced something marketable, the others followed. For most of them, however, these all-over patterns were simply one out of the many lines they produced.

Throughout this same period Grimwades Ltd. was producing a wide range of products; the company was noted for their ewers and basins amongst other lines. At this time their chintzes were closer to the Victorian versions than to the Crown Ducal "fantastical" and seem somewhat old-fashioned in comparison. Gradually their patterns changed, and in 1928 Grimwades introduced their first "modern" chintz, **Marguerite**, which was an instant success. The pattern was available on an amazing assortment of articles; it has even been found on a ceramic hot-water bottle.

As the decade ended and the world-wide depression deepened, the production of decorative pieces was replaced more and more with useful items at reasonable prices more suited to the hard economic times. Clearly there were still decorative items made but the prices had to be low. Grimwades is first mentioned in *The Pottery, Glass & Brass Salesman* in March 1933. Ebeling & Reuss, china and glass importers, is praised for importing fancy chintz earthenware baskets, vases, flatware and even short sets. Buyers are urged to look at the cake plates which they should be able to retail for $1.00 or possibly $1.25.

The July 1932 *Gazette* discussed the reorganization of Grimwades' lines during recent months — "occasioned no doubt by the fact that certain lines which were at one time very largely manufactured by Grimwades such as ornamentals and toiletware are less in demand than formerly and therefore these have had to be substituted by other creations more in keeping with the demand of the times." In addition, the improvements that had been made in sanitation spelled the end of the broad production of toiletwares for all but a limited market. Tollie Coales, the daughter of the Canadian representative for Grimwades, recalled her father having ewers and basins shipped directly to the Canadian Maritime provinces. He took orders and then sold off the samples since there was little or no market for them in the rest of Canada. He travelled with his sample cases by train from coast to coast of Canada and was always surprised by the success of his chintz lines.

The first British Industries Fair was held in 1915, and each year firms mounted displays of their newest lines and hoped to capture the attention of the buying public, as well as trade publications. Ceramics designers were forced to come up with hundreds of new patterns every year to keep up with their competitors and attract publicity. The Grimwade's pattern **Summertime** dates to 1932 and is numbered 775, and the pattern **Clyde** is numbered 5637 and probably dates to 1939. Grimwades therefore came up with something close to a thousand patterns a year throughout the 1930s. Obviously most of these were not chintz patterns but it is not surprising that in their constant search for new patterns, Grimwades took patterns such as **Welbeck** (2204) and redid them in different colourways like **Hazel** (2208) and **Spring** (2506). It is said that the first chintz pattern **Marguerite** was copied from a cushion cover embroidered by the wife of Leonard Grimwade, the owner of the factory. Other patterns came from clothing worn by staff, from pictures in books, from anywhere and everywhere. They were known throughout the 1930s and indeed through the 1950s as the "acknowledged pre-eminent house for chintz patterns."

Publicity was eagerly sought by all the Staffordshire firms. In the early 1930s Elijah Cotton supplied dealers who carried a sufficient range of Lord Nelson Ware with a five-foot-tall ceramic Nelson monument like the one in Trafalgar Square, made up of plates, sandwich trays and egg cups drilled and bolted together. Even today occasionally you run across drilled Nelson Ware chintz plates in the street markets around Stoke-on-Trent.

Having a "controlled" pattern was an expensive business; it meant buying the whole run from the lithographic firm and keeping it on premises. Some of the chintz patterns were clearly "open" stock patterns and could be used by anyone. James Kent's **Mille Fleurs** was used by Lord Nelson and called **Marigold.** Pieces have been found with an A.G. Richardson backstamp, several other Staffordshire potteries and several German factories. Similarly, James Kent's **Harmony** and Lord Nelson's **Anemone** have been found produced by other factories. Very few Royal Winton patterns came out of the open stock books; **Rose Du Barry** has been found as James Kent's **Chelsea Rose** and recently a piece of James Kent's **Silverdale** turned up with a Royal Winton backstamp. These factories were all close, and many of the workers were related or acquainted. Inevitably, strange pieces will have been produced.

Not only did the factories turn out new patterns on a weekly basis; they attempted to create new and interesting shapes regularly. In 1922 Crown Ducal were lauded in the American press for their chintz "trays and cups" which have come to be known as tennis or hostess sets. In 1923 it was their 12-inch lily bowls with matte black interiors which won approval. By the late 1920s it was Grimwades that were leading the way in innovative chintz designs and shapes. In 1933 it is Grimwades who are noted in the American trade journals for their plates with plain embossed borders and chintz centers (these plates are known to American collectors as Wedgwood plates). The 1932 *Pottery and Glass Record* noted that Grimwades' "latest design among sets is the small tray with a toast rack, sugar, cream and little teapot, all fitted into grooves but detachable. . . this being called the Bed-side set. It is also supplied with an irregular oblong shape and including a little groove for butter."

The square Ascot shape and the deco Norman shape were introduced in 1932. In 1936 the Athena shape was introduced and described in the *Gazette* as "hexagonal sided in rectangular form with a fancy handle." In 1940 the whole Rosebud line was introduced to great acclaim, and although initially produced in a solid colour with hand-painted handles and finials, it was not long before chintz was applied to the whole line. One of the most popular of the post-war shapes was the Albans with its clean lines and acorn finial. Interestingly the stacking teapot, which is so incredibly popular in North America, never appears to have been mentioned in the British press and has rarely been seen by British dealers. One of the first mentions of the stacker was in an advertisement in the Canadian Birk's catalogue for 1941, where a plain pink, blue and green "three-in-one Breakfast set" is advertised for sale for $2.00. In the same catalogue a Countess Bedside set is offered for $3.50.

By 1940 the British government had imposed restrictions on the decoration and production of pottery and these remained in force for the home market until 1952. As a result, patterns such as **Morning Glory** and **May Festival** often appear in England without hand painting and are presumably pre-1952. By the time the war ended, the Canadian representative alone had two years of back orders, which the factory simply could not supply. Shipments went around the world as fast as they could be packed, but often there were mix ups and pieces intended for Canada landed in New Zealand or elsewhere. Sheryl Vogt, the founder of the Australian Royal Winton Collectors' Club, heard from a New Zealand dealer that "the US buyers would not accept old or outmoded designs so the newest ware was kept for the Americans and the government insisted on 75% of production being exported, up to 1952 . . . so as much old stock as could be mustered from warehouses was sent out to Australia and New Zealand up until that time. This has turned out to be most fortunate as we still have a good range of pre-war ware from what was essentially a small family pottery."

The wartime production of plain white utility ware created a craving for colour and warmth, which resulted in a tremendous upsurge in the sales of chintzware both at home and abroad throughout the 1950s. Considering the direction of the design movement during this decade, this is quite surprising. Firms like Midwinter Ltd. produced a tremendous amount of chintzware from just after the war until the 1970s, yet a recent book on the company devotes one line to chintz. James Kent Ltd., under the able management of Ruth Kent, exported containers full of **Dubarry**, **Apple Blossom** and **Rosalynde** to North America through the 1950s and the 1960s. Although very few advertisements appeared for Royal Winton chintz after 1952, there were suddenly advertisements for **Cottonwood** by Langdale Pottery Company, for **Wild Rose Chintz** by Winterton Pottery, for **Springtime** by John Shaw & Sons Ltd. and for **Summer Flowers** by Myott Son & Company. The prices remained quite low. For example, a Barker Brothers Royal Tudor Ware cake plate and server was advertised in the *Montreal Gazette* in May of 1954 for $2.35, while a Royal Winton chintz stacking teapot is noted in the Christmas 1951 *Canadian House & Home* for $2.50.

Although many of the patterns that we think were produced after the war are similar to the pre-war patterns, such as **Marion**, **Nantwich** and **Cheadle**, there are others that are very much in the 1950s mold, such as **June Festival**, **Spring Glory** and **Peony**. Suddenly, from being new and fresh, all-over floral prints came to be described very differently in the 1950 *Crockery & Glass Journal*: "Dinner sets with small rosebuds or other tiny all over motifs 'crawling' have lost stature as the stock-in-trade of foreign-made wares. In their stead are larger floral motifs . . . sophisticated stylized versions." Just as the 1920s chintzes have a certain look, so do the 1950s versions. The flowers are much larger and further apart and the ground colours tend to be black, navy and burgundy. Even with these changes chintz could not be made to enhance the look of Scandinavian blond wood furniture and the amoeba shapes of the modern dishes. Gradually the potteries phased out their chintz lines and moved on to a completely different style.

Grimwades was bought by the Howard Group in 1964 and moved their operation to Norfolk Street where, after many setbacks, they are once again in operation. At the time of the takeover, Canada was the largest single overseas market with Australia and New Zealand not far behind. Ivy Mayer says that whenever she thinks of chintz she thinks of Canada, and when she thinks of Rosebud she thinks of Australia. After the move there was little room in the new location for the production of chintzware. Although chintz was not produced to any great extent after 1964, Ivy remembers a room with shelves full of sheets of chintz lithographs and she says good customers could still order chintz and if the sheets were available, the factory would fill the orders. We found two invoices from Grimwades to J.L. Bradshaw Ltd. in Stratford, Canada, one dated March 24, 1969, and the other June 5, 1969. The one invoice is for 215 "two tier" Tid Bit sets in **Cheadle**, **Victorian Rose** and **Old Cottage Chintz**. Everything else on the invoice appears to be in later non-chintz patterns, such as **Thistle** 1594. The backstamp used by Royal Winton after 1964 is easily recognizable and the earthenware has a whiter cast than before.

Although MIKASA turned out a complete line of James Kent's **Dubarry** in the mid 1980s, Staffordshire potteries have largely ignored the returning popularity of chintz. Crownford China Company Ltd., with the trade name Queen's China are now manufacturing a fine bone china they call **English Chintz**. When we went to watch the lithographs being applied, we were told that most workers find the transfers too difficult and prefer not to work with chintz. Spouts and handles are left plain since there is no one left with the skills of a Florrie Dennis to do the job.

The Human Face of Chintz

There were no records that we could find to tell us more about chintz ware. Finally we advertised in the *Evening Sentinel* in Stoke-on-Trent. Several letters came in response. One was from Florrie Dennis who worked for Royal Winton from the age of fourteen. "I worked for two weeks and didn't receive any pay until the end of the third week which was five shillings and nine pence a week." They were told "we must always decorate a piece of ware how we would like to buy it . . . perfect."

Florrie wrote a long letter describing the process of applying the lithograph to the pottery. It will be easier to understand her remarks if you think of wall papering around windows and difficult corners and try to imagine how hard it must have been to do toast racks and lamps. Large sheets of patterned paper were kept in a separate room and the girls had to go and get pieces and cut them into the appropriate size for the ware they were decorating.

"We had a pot of size which we then brushed on the piece of ware with a camel haired brush which we had to buy for one shilling old money so of course used to clean them every night. We applied the size onto the piece of ware then wafted it until nice and tacky. In front of us was placed a pattern of whatever piece of ware you were going to practise on. We had to fetch our litho from a little decorating shop. We applied the litho onto the piece of pottery looking closely at the pattern in front of you then we were shown a geyser at the bottom of the shop and given a chamber pot to carry very hot water to the bench and a piece of waste rag and a hard sponge and a soft sponge and a piece of hard yellow soap. When we had applied the litho sprays to the piece of ware we then dipped the hard sponge into the hot water then rubbed the sprays of litho on the ware then a little harder then of course it was very wet then taking the soft sponge which we have rubbed onto the hard soap began to sponge off the wet paper which by now had fastened the floral sprays onto the ware. Then taking the piece of soft cloth gently dabbed the piece of ware to be passed as perfect...the most popular pattern was Summertime which consisted of all summer flowers . . . also we did a chintz called Black Hazel and a lot of tea ware which was called ajax ware (this was a shape range). We were not allowed to cut into flowers and used a razor blade to decorate round the handles and teapot spouts and cup and cream handles. All the patterns we used were all set out and each had a number."

"...after six months you were expected to go on piece work to earn your wages. The prices then were very low. I worked in my dinner hour many days." When we went to see Florrie she told us much more about her life. She left school at fourteen on a Friday and she started at Royal Winton on the Monday. She started in 1928 and the first pattern she worked on was Marguerite the first real all over chintz at Winton. Out of her wages, she gave all but a shilling to her father. One week she worked every lunch hour and made an extra shilling which she hid in the toe of her shoe. When she went to bed she forgot about it and it hit the floor when she took her shoe off. Even at eighty she can remember vividly the beating her father gave her that night.

The decorating manager was a man called Mr. Parry and he could be very unkind to the young girls who worked for him. Florrie told us you always got more for your fittings but only if they were perfect (fittings were pieces like teapots and coffee pots).You had to do the pieces that were assigned to you. She still remembers girls sitting crying over their benches because they could not manage to do the spouts of the teapots or coffee pots and at the end of the day might have nothing to show for their efforts. They didn't get paid as a result and could be beaten when they came home empty handed. She remembers staying late to help girls with their spouts and handles. "I was only small and can remember how difficult it was to handle putting the border on the inside and outside of the large wash basins . . . ."

Grimwades were considered the pre-eminent producers of chintz ware and when you look at the products from the various factories you will begin to understand why. Elijah Cotton simply did not attempt to cover the handles and spouts with the chintz and were therefore able to sell their product at a lower price. The chintz ware which is produced today also has undecorated spouts and handles even though the slide-off method is now used whereby the transfer is dipped in water and then put on the ware. The method is much easier but spouts and handles are still beyond the skills of most workers.

It was — and is — "hard work for small wages." When you are enjoying your special **Welbeck** coffee pot, think of the fourteen year old who decorated it, and if it isn't perfectly done think of her sitting on her three-legged stool weeping as she tries to achieve perfection with materials that were far from perfect. They did it so well that thousands around the world still seek out and enjoy the "cheap and cheerful" product of their labors.

Advice for Collectors

We have heard wonderful stories of great treasures and we have also heard sad tales of disappointment, so we have put together a list of hazards and questions to ask for those who are new to chintz buying or, indeed, for those who are buying over the telephone.

One of the most common complaints is the size of the teapot or coffee pot — what was expected and what arrived. There are many ways of measuring size. Sometimes when you read an advertisement, such as Ebeling & Reuss for James Kent, and see that a teapot 30 is more expensive than a teapot 36 you may be confused. Often the number refers to the number of pieces which will fit into the kiln for firing, so the larger the number the smaller the piece. When you are offered a two- cup, or four-cup, or six-cup teapot or coffee pot, be sure that you are clear what that means. Usually a two-cup teapot means two six-ounce cups of tea and four cup means four six-ounce cups; if you are expecting a normal eight-ounce cup measurement you will be disappointed.

Another common complaint is trays which are meant to house various bits and come either incomplete or incorrect. If you are offered a divided tray, make sure it is a divided tray and not simply a tray with indentations for egg cups and salt and pepper which are not in evidence — Linda has first hand experience with this particular problem. A long-time collector was offered a complete breakfast set, but after some discussion discovered that although there was a teapot, toast rack, and cup, there was a salt and pepper in the place of the cream and sugar!

If you are offered a cruet set, make sure that the mustard has a lid if it ought to have one and that you are sent one pepper and one salt — not two of either one. Sometimes when you are at a show and in a hurry, you will buy what you think is a great bargain and discover that you got what you paid for. Some patterns are very similar and sadly sometimes tops and bottoms do not really go together once you get them into the light of day. The most common mismatch is the various cruet sets.

Always ask for the measurements of whatever piece you are buying. Royal Winton plates were made in four-inch to ten-inch sizes, and prices go up correspondingly. Trays came in all shapes and sizes. Cake plates came with and without cutout handles — since the cutout handles cracked more often, the price is usually a little higher. Jugs came in sizes ranging from three to nine inches and every conceivable shape, so make sure of the dimensions.

There are two sizes of cheese keeps and two sizes of Ascot butter dishes, — five and six inches — and mistakes are easily made. Make a habit of carrying a measuring tape to the telephone, as well as to shows, so that you can be sure of the dimensions.

There are at least ten different cream and sugar shapes in Royal Winton and a variety in all the other makers. Both the Winton Ascot shape and the Globe shape cream and sugar came with two versions of the sugar bowl, so if it matters to you, be sure that you are getting the shape you want.

Midwinter, James Kent and Howard Potteries Royal Winton coffee pots, teapots, cream and sugars and cups and saucers sometimes come with a plain white foot. Some people do not like the look of the white rim; remember to ask.

Both **Summertime** and **Old Cottage Chintz** were made from the early 1930s until well into the 1960s. The lithographs changed over the intervening thirty years. The pinks and reds in **Summertime** and the pinks and blues in **OCC** are quite different, and if you are trying to make up sets it is important to find out which decade you are talking about. There are several Winton patterns, in particular **Sweet Pea** and **Julia**, where pieces can vary tremendously in the depth of colour. Ask how strong the colours are to make sure you will not be disappointed when a faded vase arrives.

The most fragile colour in chintz is the blue, and if someone bleaches a teapot to remove the stains, sometimes the blues fade quite badly. Relish dishes that have been used for something acidic such as pickles may be very faded where the juices bleached out the colours. Fruit bowls that have been used for pineapple or grapefruit may also have faded in the bottom of the bowl.

People often ask which cup should be on the breakfast sets because they are concerned about having the "right" one. Ivy Mayer, the secretary of Royal Winton's export director, told us that the breakfast sets were always sold with the buyer's "cup of choice," so any cup could be considered correct since who knows what a Philadelphia importer chose forty years ago. The exception to this is the breakfast sets in **Lily, Rosebud** and **Petunia**, where normally you would expect everything on the tray to match.

Sauce boats and jam pots normally come with an under plate, and you should expect to pay less if it is missing. Some of the Royal Winton and the Midwinter jam pots came with chrome lids, some with ceramic. The ceramic lid is inset and the chrome fits over the pot with a protruding rim. Look carefully to make sure that you have the right lid. The Winton Rheims jam pot came in a short and tall version, and the short version usually sells for less because the pattern does not display as well as on the tall pot. Many collectors prefer the all-ceramic jam pots, which usually makes the price higher.

If you are buying a bowl or compote ask if the pattern is on both the inside and the outside of the piece. There is always a premium for pieces which are completely covered with the pattern.

Many of the 1930s chintzes were used for what Americans call "Wedgwood" plates. The pattern covers the center of the plate and the rim is white and embossed. The plates came in several sizes — round and square plates in nine and 12 inches. The 1950s versions had no embossing and were available with solid colour bands in maroon, green or yellow in eight and ten inch square plates.

Sometimes new collectors become very concerned about the crazing on many of the pieces, especially Royal Winton. This was not fine bone china but earthenware, and often the glaze will become crazed over a number of years. Unless a hairline crack has appeared, this should not greatly effect the value. An Australian collector recommends that you keep a dish of water in the china cabinet to prevent further crazing. Even if you are paying more for your chintz these days than for Royal Worcester, do not forget that it was cheap and cheerful when it started life. The ill-fitting lid is not necessarily the wrong lid — it may never have fit properly.

As the price of chintz goes up and up, there are more and more repaired pieces on the market. Look very closely at the spouts of teapots and coffee pots, since they are the most vulnerable to chips. Always check finials to make sure they haven't been reattached. As long as the piece is marked restored and the price has been adjusted accordingly, if you want the piece buy it by all means — especially if it is for display and you don't have that particular shape or pattern. If you are buying the teapot for use, do not buy a restored pot since you may find the repair vanishing as the boiling tea is poured through the spout.

Sometimes the lithographs are very badly applied, especially with some of the James Kent and Lord Nelson Ware. The joins are supposed to be invisible and some of the Royal Winton pieces are remarkably well done. If this is important to you, look carefully, especially around awkward corners. Some people like the hominess of the badly done pieces. Susan's Lord Nelson **Rosetime** bud vase looks as though a young girl, thinking about her date on a Friday night, just threw the litho onto the vase — nothing matches, but it has its own peculiar charm.

How to Use This Price Guide

Prices

We have tried, in this book, to provide collectors with a useful "price guide," but we have tried to make it not just a price guide.

We have tried to give a selection of the pieces that are most commonly found by the collector. Royal Winton and James Kent made a great variety of bonbon dishes and footed compotes, some large, some small, and the prices will vary accordingly. Crown Ducal made an amazing assortment of vases in every conceivable shape and size, and we have included only a few to give you an idea of the prices for a particular shape or size.

The majority of collectors used to be American, and several years ago it is fair to say that prices were much higher there than in the rest of the world. In the last year prices have tended to equalize and fewer bargains are available. Prices are still somewhat lower in Canada, since Canadian collectors are dealing with a weaker currency and a smaller market. English prices are very much on par with American prices, particularly for Royal Winton chintzes. Elijah Cotton, James Kent and Crown Ducal, as well as some of the lesser-known manufacturers have been lower both in England and in Canada but the gap is narrowing as more collectors enter the market and fewer pieces are available. Prices in New Zealand and Australia may have been lower a year ago but recent prices there as well, particularly for Royal Winton, are again on a level with the American market place.

As any of you who have used a price guide know, they are always subject to fierce debate. In the case of something like chintzware, where the collecting field is very new and prices have gone up dramatically in the past two years, the debate is even more heated. A price guide is exactly that: a guide to recent prices which have been paid for the pieces described. Chintz collecting is so new that many dealers and collectors are unsure what to charge and what to pay. We heard from a collector who found a stacking teapot in **Sweet Pea** somewhere in Washington State for $125 and we also heard from a collector in New York City who had paid $1200 for a stacking teapot! Which price reflects the truth? The price in any market is what one person asks and another person is willing to pay.

In the final analysis Oscar Wilde's trenchant comment about pricing is probably true: "A cynic is a man who knows the price of everything and the value of nothing."

In this book we share with you what we know about the prices of chintz, but we also try to talk about its value — as a pleasing collectable, as a part of our shared history and as a product of the ingenuity of the men and women who worked in the potteries in hard times.

Numbering System

The system we have in place enables every piece of chintz to have an exclusive letter and number.

Pattern Letters

The letter codes represent the pattern; for example "GT" is **Green Tulip.** A.G. Richardson presented special problems, since there were more than a dozen patterns and we had names for only **Primula** and **Marigold** when we started working on this project. With Gerrard Shaw's guidance, Susan found copies of forty years of the *Pottery Glass & Brass Salesman* and discovered advertisements for a number of the Crown Ducal patterns, including pattern names. We were able to identify **Ascot**, **Blue Chintz**, **Festival**, **Florida** and **Ivory Chintz**. Gerrard was able to give us **Canton** and **Rose & Motifs** from his research in England. In order to make the collector's life easier, we decided to create appropriate names for the other five patterns until we are able to find the actual factory names: **"Grey Fruit," "Ivory Fruit," "Mauve Chintz,", "Pink Chintz,"**, and **"Purple Chintz."**

Wade **"Butterfly Chintz"** and Myott **"Spring Flower"** are also temporary names until factory names can be found. In other cases where there was only one or two examples we have left the pattern unnamed. We hope that someone will be able to supply us with the missing names in time for the second edition.

PATTERN CODES

Barker Brothers Ltd.

Pattern Letters	Pattern Name
Bab	Unnamed

Brexton

Pattern Letters	Pattern Name
Bx	Unnamed

Elijah Cotton Ltd. — Lord Nelson Ware

Pattern Letters	Pattern Name
AC	Anemone Chintz
BB	Black Beauty
BR	Briar Rose
GT	Green Tulip
He	Heather
MgC	Marigold
Ma	Marina
P	Pansy
R	Rosetime
RB	Royal Brocade
Sk	Skylark

Empire Porcelain Co. Ltd.

Pattern Letters	Pattern Name
LT	Lilac Time

Ford & Sons

Pattern Letters	Pattern Name
FS	Unnamed

Grimwades Ltd. — Royal Winton

Pattern Letters	Pattern Name
A	Anemone
Ba	Balmoral
Be	Bedale
Bee	Beeston
Chd	Cheadle
Chl	Chelsea
Chz	Chintz
Cl	Clevedon
Cly	Clyde
Co	Cotswold
Cr	Cranstone
Cro	Crocus (white and black background)
Crom	Cromer
De	Delphinium Chintz
Do	Dorset
El	Eleanor
ER	English Rose
Esl	Estelle
Est	Esther
Ev	Evesham
FiB	Fireglow Black
FiW	Fireglow White
FF	Floral Feast
FG	Floral Garden
Fl	Florence
H	Hazel
JL	Joyce-Lynn
J	Julia
JF	June Festival
JR	June Roses
Ke	Kew
Ki	Kinver
Maj	Majestic
Mag	Marguerite
Mar	Marion
May	Mayfair
MF	May Festival
MG	Morning Glory
N	Nantwich
OC	Old Cottage Chintz
O	Orient
Pe	Pekin
Pel	Pelham (Sampler)
Peo	Peony
QA	Queen Anne
Q	Quilt
Ri	Richmond
RD	Rose Du Barry
Ro	Royalty
Ru	Rutland
Sh	Shrewsbury
So	Somerset
Sp	Spring
SG	Spring Glory
Spt	Springtime
St	Stratford
Su	Summertime
Sun	Sunshine
SN	Sweet Nancy
SP	Sweet Pea
T	Tartans
V	Victorian
VR	Victorian Rose
W	Welbeck
WF	Wild Flowers
Wi	Winifred

James Kent, Ltd.

Pattern Letters	Pattern Name
AB	Apple Blossom
CP	Crazy Paving
D	Dubarry
F	Florita
Ha	Harmony
Hy	Hydrangea (white background)
HyB	Hydrangea (black background)
MgK	Marigold
MiF	Mille Fleurs
Pr	Primula
Ra	Rapture
Ro	Rosalynde
S	Silverdale
Tp	Tapestry

Midwinter

Pattern Letters	Pattern Name
Br	Brama
C	Coral
LD	Lorna Doone

Myott Son & Co.

Pattern Letters	Pattern Name
SF	*Spring Flower*
SuF	Summer Flower

A.G. Richardson Ltd. — Crown Ducal

Pattern Letters	Pattern Name
As	Ascot
BC	Blue Chintz
C	Canton
Fe	Festival
Fd	Florida
GF	*Grey Fruit*
IC	Ivory Chintz
IF	*Ivory Fruit*
MgR	Marigold
MC	*Mauve Chintz*
PC	*Pink Chintz*
PrR	Primula
PuC	*Purple Chintz*
RM	Rose & Motifs

Ridgway Potteries Ltd.

Pattern Letters	Pattern Name
RP	Unnamed

Royal Doulton Ltd.

Pattern Letters	Pattern Name
Per	Persian

Shelley Potteries Ltd.

Pattern Letters	Pattern Name
Mat	Maytime
Me	Melody
SuG	Summer Glory

Wade & Company

Pattern Letters	Pattern Name
Bu	*Butterfly Chintz*
Th	Thistle Chintz

Wood & Sons Ltd.

Pattern Letters	Pattern Name
WS	Unnamed

SHAPE NUMBERS

The number codes represent the shapes and are the same across all the factories for the same item; a round seven-inch plate, for example, is '104' whether it is Lord Nelson Ware or A.G. Richardson. We have left gaps in the numbering system to accommodate the variety of chintz pieces that will inevitably come to light.

Number	Shape
04	Bonbon dish
09	Bowl, 5"
10	Bowl, 6"
14	Bowl, 8″ soup
15	Bowl, 9"
17	Bowl, lily 12″ (matte black interior)
22	Bowl, octagonal, 7"
24	Bowl, octagonal, 8"
23	Breakfast set
28	Butter dish
30	Butter pat
35	Cake plate, open handles
36	Cake plate, tab handles
37	Cake plate, 8″ square pedestal
40	Cake stand, 2 tier
41	Cake stand, 3 tier
42	Cake plate, with server
43	Cake stand, chrome handle
44	Cake stand, chrome base
45	Canoe-shaped dish
50	Cheese keep
52	Coaster
53	Coffee pot, 3 cup
55	Coffee pot, 6 cup
60	Compote, footed
65	Condiment set on tray
70	Cream and sugar
71	Cream and sugar on tray
75	Demi-tasse
77	Egg cup, footed
80	Hot water jug
85	Jam pot with liner
90	Jug, 4" round
91	Jug, 4 1/2" round
92	Jug, 5" round
95	Jug, 5″ straight-sided
96	Jug, 7″ straight-sided
97	Nut dish
103	Plate, 6 1/2" round
104	Plate, 7" round
105	Plate, 8" round
106	Plate, 9" round
201	Plate, 4″ square
202	Plate, 5″ square
203	Plate, 6″ square
204	Plate, 7″ square
205	Plate, 8″ square
206	Plate, 9″ square
207	Plate, 10″ square
301	Plate, 4″ triangular
402	Plate, octagonal, 5"
406	Plate, octagonal, 9"
407	Plate, octagonal, 10"
112	Relish dish, small
115	Salad bowl, chrome rim
117	Salt and pepper
118	Salt and pepper on tray
120	Sandwich tray, 10" x 6"
121	Sandwich tray, 12" x 7"
122	Sandwich tray, 13″x 6″
125	Sauce boat and liner
130	Teacup and saucer
135	Teapot, 2 cup
136	Teapot, 4 cup
137	Teapot, 6 cup
140	Teapot, stacking
145	Tennis set
150	Toast rack, 4 slice
151	Toast rack, 2 slice
155	Trivet
160	Vase, bud
163	Vase, spill, 8"
162	Vase, trumpet 6"
165	Vase, 9″
169	Sugar shaker
170	Biscuit barrel

BARKER BROTHERS LTD.

In the Meir Works at Longton, the Barker Brothers factory became noted for its ability "to copy the best new ideas on the market quickly and efficiently." Although originally the company produced both china and earthenware, in 1925 they decided to concentrate on semi-porcelain, which is a high-quality earthenware. John Guildford created patterns for Barker Brothers that were remarkably like those of Clarice Cliff. Their hand-painted pieces looked very like those of Poole Pottery. Like Myott Son & Co. and Wade, they produced several chintz patterns in the 1930s, along with all the other product lines they created. To date none of the chintz patterns have been found with pattern names, but they were still producing chintz patterns in the 1950s for they were advertised in Canadian publications as late as 1957. The trade name "Tudor Ware" or "Royal Tudor Ware" was incorporated into several versions of the Barker Brothers backstamp from about 1937.

The company was acquired by Alfred Clough in 1961 and in turn they were bought up by Coloroll Housewares Group in 1987.

UNKNOWN

This is one of the more common Barker Brothers "Royal Tudor Ware" patterns.

Cat.No.	Shape	U.S. $	Can. $	U.K. £
BaB-42	Cake plate, with server	175.00	200.00	100.00

Cat.No.	Shape	U.S. $	Can. $	U.K. £
BaB-70	Cream and sugar	100.00	125.00	65.00

BREXTON

UNKNOWN

Cat.No.	Shape	U.S. $	Can. $	U.K. £
Bx-130	Teacup and saucer	50.00	65.00	30.00

ELIJAH COTTON LTD. (LORD NELSON)

The firm advertised themselves as being established since 1758, but it was not until 1889 that they were known as Nelson Pottery in Hanley. To date little has been written about Elijah Cotton. They were better than many of the lower echelon firms at self-promotion. They created a ceramic model of the Nelson Monument in Trafalgar Square — probably copied from the Clarice Cliff Bizooka — using sandwich trays, tea plates and egg cups from their product lines. As was widely reported in the press at the time, they made these models available to any retailer who bought the required amount of product.

Elijah Cotton certainly never had a light hand when it came to either the product or the decoration. During the 1930s the designs were heavily applied to chunky-shaped earthenware by paintresses working by eye and not by printed or sketched outlines. This was a utilitarian pottery and little or no time was spent on the production of bric-a-brac. The *Pottery Gaztte* reported in 1931 that they produced a range in domestic ware from plain white glaze upwards. They were big producers of kitchen and hospital plain white and their advertisements from the 1950s feature plain white jugs in a wide variety of shapes. Their chintzes were never applied to handles or spouts, since these required special skill. Often the work is sloppy enough that it is unlikely that another factory would have allowed it to pass.

Although **Marina** was reported a best-seller for Elijah Cotton in 1939, there is certainly never a mention of any member of the royal family taking home a teaset in Nelson chintz. Interestingly, it is Cotton in 1955 that came out with **Kaleidoscope**, an all-over, multi-colour snow crystal design more in keeping with the '50s style.

ANEMONE

The pattern number is 2446 . This chintz pattern was not a controlled pattern and was used by other companies such as John Shaw & Sons "Burlington Ware."

Photograph not available
at
press time.

Cat.No.	Shape	U.S. $	Can. $	U.K. £
AC-04	Bonbon dish	40.00	50.00	25.00
AC-28	Butter dish	125.00	150.00	75.00
AC-35	Cake plate, open handles	125.00	150.00	75.00
AC-36	Cake plate, tab handles	100.00	120.00	60.00
AC-41	Cake stand, 3 tier	135.00	165.00	85.00
AC-50	Cheese keep	200.00	250.00	115.00
AC-55	Coffee pot, 6 cup	425.00	500.00	255.00
AC-65	Condiment set on tray	150.00	175.00	100.00
AC-70	Cream and sugar	80.00	95.00	50.00
AC-71	Cream and sugar on tray	135.00	165.00	85.00
AC-85	Jam pot with liner	100.00	125.00	65.00
AC-92	Jug, 5" round	150.00	175.00	100.00
AC-96	Jug, 7" straight-sided	175.00	200.00	100.00

Cat.No.	Shape	U.S. $	Can. $	U.K. £
AC-301	Plate, 4" triangular	35.00	40.00	20.00
AC-104	Plate, 7"	40.00	50.00	25.00
AC-105	Plate, 8"	75.00	85.00	45.00
AC-112	Relish dish	150.00	175.00	85.00
AC-117	Salt and pepper	75.00	85.00	45.00
AC-118	Salt and pepper on tray	135.00	165.00	85.00
AC-122	Sandwich tray, 13" x 6"	85.00	100.00	50.00
AC-125	Sauce boat and liner	100.00	125.00	65.00
AC-130	Teacup and saucer	50.00	75.00	35.00
AC-137	Teapot, 6 cup	475.00	575.00	275.00
AC-140	Teapot, stacking	475.00	575.00	275.00
AC-145	Tennis set	85.00	100.00	50.00
AC-160	Vase, bud	75.00	90.00	45.00

BLACK BEAUTY

This is the only Nelson pattern with a black background and is considered the most desirable by many collectors.

Cat.No.	Shape	U.S. $	Can. $	U.K. £
BB-04	Bonbon dish	75.00	85.00	45.00
BB-28	Butter dish	225.00	275.00	130.00
BB-35	Cake plate, open handles	200.00	250.00	120.00
BB-36	Cake plate, tab handles	175.00	200.00	100.00
BB-41	Cake stand, 3 tier	225.00	275.00	135.00
BB-50	Cheese keep	325.00	400.00	200.00
BB-55	Coffee pot, 6 cup	750.00	900.00	450.00
BB-65	Condiment set on tray	250.00	300.00	150.00
BB-70	Cream and sugar	135.00	165.00	85.00
BB-71	Cream and sugar on tray	200.00	250.00	125.00
BB-85	Jam pot with liner	165.00	200.00	100.00
BB-92	Jug, 5" round	225.00	275.00	150.00
BB-96	Jug, 7" straight-sided	275.00	325.00	175.00

Cat.No.	Shape	U.S. $	Can. $	U.K. £
BB-301	Plate, 4" triangular	50.00	65.00	30.00
BB-104	Plate, 7"	85.00	100.00	50.00
BB-105	Plate, 8"	125.00	150.00	75.00
BB-112	Relish dish	250.00	300.00	150.00
BB-117	Salt and pepper	100.00	125.00	65.00
BB-118	Salt and pepper on tray	200.00	235.00	115.00
BB-122	Sandwich tray, 13" x 6"	150.00	175.00	90.00
BB-125	Sauce boat and liner	165.00	200.00	100.00
BB-130	Teacup and saucer	100.00	125.00	65.00
BB-137	Teapot, 6 cup	750.00	900.00	450.00
BB-140	Teapot, stacking	700.00	850.00	425.00
BB-145	Tennis set	135.00	165.00	85.00
BB-160	Vase, bud	125.00	150.00	75.00

BRIAR ROSE

We currently have no information available on this pattern.

Cat.No.	Shape	U.S. $	Can. $	U.K. £
BR-04	Bonbon dish	45.00	60.00	30.00
BR-28	Butter dish	140.00	175.00	85.00
BR-35	Cake plate, open handles	135.00	165.00	85.00
BR-36	Cake plate, tab handles	125.00	150.00	75.00
BR-41	Cake stand, 3 tier	150.00	175.00	90.00
BR-50	Cheese keep	200.00	250.00	125.00
BR-55	Coffee pot, 6 cup	500.00	600.00	300.00
BR-65	Condiment set on tray	165.00	200.00	100.00
BR-70	Cream and sugar	100.00	125.00	65.00
BR-71	Cream and sugar on tray	150.00	175.00	90.00
BR-85	Jam pot with liner	125.00	150.00	75.00
BR-92	Jug, 5″ round	165.00	200.00	100.00
BR-96	Jug, 7″ straight-sided	200.00	250.00	125.00

Cat.No.	Shape	U.S. $	Can. $	U.K. £
BR-301	Plate, 4″ triangular	40.00	50.00	25.00
BR-104	Plate, 7″	50.00	75.00	35.00
BR-105	Plate, 8″	85.00	100.00	50.00
BR-112	Relish dish	190.00	230.00	115.00
BR-117	Salt and pepper	75.00	85.00	45.00
BR-118	Salt and pepper on tray	150.00	175.00	85.00
BR-122	Sandwich tray, 13″ x 6″	100.00	125.00	65.00
BR-125	Sauce boat and liner	125.00	150.00	75.00
BR-130	Teacup and saucer	65.00	80.00	40.00
BR-137	Teapot, 6 cup	550.00	650.00	325.00
BR-140	Teapot, stacking	550.00	650.00	325.00
BR-145	Tennis set	100.00	125.00	65.00
BR-160	Vase, bud	80.00	100.00	50.00

GREEN TULIP

This pattern is rare in North America but found more often in New Zealand and Australia. It has recently become as sought after as **Black Beauty** is in North America.

Cat.No.	Shape	U.S. $	Can. $	U.K. £
GT-04	Bonbon dish	75.00	85.00	45.00
GT-28	Butter dish	225.00	275.00	135.00
GT-35	Cake plate, open handles	200.00	250.00	125.00
GT-36	Cake plate, tab handles	175.00	200.00	100.00
GT-41	Cake stand, 3 tier	225.00	275.00	135.00
GT-50	Cheese keep	325.00	400.00	200.00
GT-55	Coffee pot, 6 cup	750.00	900.00	450.00
GT-65	Condiment set on tray	250.00	300.00	150.00
GT-70	Cream and sugar	135.00	165.00	85.00
GT-71	Cream and sugar on tray	200.00	250.00	125.00
GT-85	Jam pot with liner	165.00	200.00	100.00
GT-92	Jug, 5″ round	235.00	275.00	150.00
GT-96	Jug, 7″ straight-sided	275.00	325.00	165.00

Cat.No.	Shape	U.S. $	Can. $	U.K. £
GT-301	Plate, 4″ triangular	50.00	65.00	30.00
GT-104	Plate, 7″	85.00	100.00	50.00
GT-105	Plate, 8″	125.00	150.00	75.00
GT-112	Relish dish	275.00	300.00	150.00
GT-117	Salt and pepper	100.00	125.00	65.00
GT-118	Salt and pepper on tray	200.00	250.00	125.00
GT-122	Sandwich tray, 13″ x 6″	150.00	175.00	85.00
GT-125	Sauce boat and liner	165.00	200.00	100.00
GT-130	Teacup and saucer	100.00	125.00	65.00
GT-137	Teapot, 6 cup	750.00	900.00	450.00
GT-140	Teapot, stacking	700.00	850.00	425.00
GT-145	Tennis set	135.00	165.00	85.00
GT-160	Vase, bud	125.00	150.00	75.00

HEATHER

The pattern number is 2750.

Cat.No.	Shape	U.S. $	Can. $	U.K. £
He-04	Bonbon dish	45.00	55.00	30.00
He-28	Butter dish	150.00	175.00	85.00
He-35	Cake plate, open handles	135.00	165.00	80.00
He-36	Cake plate, tab handles	125.00	150.00	75.00
He-41	Cake stand, 3 tier	150.00	175.00	90.00
He-50	Cheese keep	200.00	250.00	125.00
He-55	Coffee pot, 6 cup	500.00	600.00	300.00
He-65	Condiment set on tray	165.00	200.00	100.00
He-70	Cream and sugar	100.00	125.00	65.00
He-71	Cream and sugar on tray	150.00	175.00	90.00
He-85	Jam pot with liner	125.00	150.00	75.00
He-92	Jug, 5″ round	165.00	200.00	100.00
He-96	Jug, 7″ straight-sided	200.00	235.00	115.00
He-301	Plate, 4″ triangular	40.00	50.00	25.00
He-104	Plate, 7″	50.00	70.00	35.00
He-105	Plate, 8″	85.00	100.00	50.00
He-112	Relish dish	200.00	250.00	115.00
He-117	Salt and pepper	75.00	85.00	45.00
He-118	Salt and pepper on tray	150.00	175.00	85.00
He-122	Sandwich tray, 13″ x 6″	100.00	125.00	65.00
He-125	Sauce boat and liner	125.00	150.00	75.00
He-130	Teacup and saucer	65.00	80.00	40.00
He-137	Teapot, 6 cup	550.00	650.00	325.00
He-140	Teapot, stacking	550.00	650.00	325.00
He-145	Tennis set	100.00	125.00	60.00
He-160	Vase, bud	80.00	100.00	50.00

MARIGOLD

The pattern number is 2122.

Cat.No.	Shape	U.S. $	Can. $	U.K. £
MaG-04	Bonbon dish	45.00	60.00	30.00
MaG-28	Butter dish	125.00	160.00	80.00
MaG-35	Cake plate, open handles	125.00	150.00	75.00
MaG-36	Cake plate, tab handles	100.00	125.00	65.00
MaG-41	Cake stand, 3 tier	150.00	175.00	85.00
MaG-50	Cheese keep	200.00	250.00	125.00
MaG-55	Coffee pot, 6 cup	450.00	550.00	275.00
MaG-65	Condiment set on tray	150.00	185.00	100.00
MaG-70	Cream and sugar	90.00	110.00	50.00
MaG-71	Cream and sugar on tray	140.00	170.00	85.00
MaG-85	Jam pot with liner	100.00	125.00	65.00
MaG-92	Jug, 5″ round	200.00	250.00	125.00
MaG-96	Jug, 7″ straight-sided	225.00	275.00	135.00
MaG-301	Plate, 4″ triangular	30.00	35.00	20.00
MaG-104	Plate, 7″	45.00	55.00	30.00
MaG-105	Plate, 8″	75.00	90.00	45.00
MaG-112	Relish dish	175.00	225.00	125.00
MaG-117	Salt and pepper	65.00	80.00	40.00
MaG-118	Salt and pepper on tray	125.00	150.00	75.00
MaG-122	Sandwich tray, 13″ x 6″	90.00	110.00	50.00
MaG-125	Sauce boat and liner	125.00	150.00	75.00
MaG-130	Teacup and saucer	60.00	75.00	35.00
MaG-137	Teapot, 6 cup	525.00	625.00	325.00
MaG-140	Teapot, stacking	525.00	625.00	325.00
MaG-145	Tennis set	90.00	110.00	50.00
MaG-160	Vase, bud	75.00	90.00	45.00

MARINA

This chintz pattern was a best seller for Nelson ware in 1939. The pattern itself was registered in 1937, English registration number 821468. This pattern was also produced by Royal Albert in bone china.

Cat.No.	Shape	U.S. $	Can. $	U.K. £
Ma-04	Bonbon dish	45.00	50.00	30.00
Ma-28	Butter dish	150.00	175.00	85.00
Ma-35	Cake plate, open handles	125.00	150.00	75.00
Ma-36	Cake plate, tab handles	125.00	150.00	75.00
Ma-41	Cake stand, 3 tier	150.00	175.00	90.00
Ma-50	Cheese keep	200.00	250.00	125.00
Ma-55	Coffee pot, 6 cup	500.00	600.00	300.00
Ma-65	Condiment set on tray	165.00	200.00	100.00
Ma-70	Cream and sugar	100.00	125.00	65.00
Ma-71	Cream and sugar on tray	150.00	175.00	85.00
Ma-85	Jam pot with liner	115.00	150.00	75.00
Ma-92	Jug, 5″ round	165.00	200.00	100.00
Ma-96	Jug, 7″ straight-sided	200.00	250.00	115.00
Ma-301	Plate, 4″ triangular	40.00	50.00	25.00
Ma-104	Plate, 7″	50.00	75.00	35.00
Ma-105	Plate, 8″	85.00	100.00	50.00
Ma-112	Relish dish	200.00	225.00	125.00
Ma-117	Salt and pepper	75.00	85.00	45.00
Ma-118	Salt and pepper on tray	150.00	175.00	85.00
Ma-122	Sandwich tray, 13″ x 6″	100.00	125.00	65.00
Ma-125	Sauce boat and liner	125.00	150.00	75.00
Ma-130	Teacup and saucer	65.00	80.00	40.00
Ma-137	Teapot, 6 cup	550.00	650.00	325.00
Ma-140	Teapot, stacking	550.00	650.00	325.00
Ma-145	Tennis set	100.00	125.00	65.00
Ma-160	Vase, bud	75.00	95.00	50.00

PANSY

This was not a controlled pattern and was produced by other Staffordshire factories as well as by the Japanese. Royal Albert produced the pattern in bone china.

Cat.No.	Shape	U.S. $	Can. $	U.K. £
P-04	Bonbon dish	45.00	65.00	30.00
P-28	Butter dish	125.00	150.00	75.00
P-35	Cake plate, open handles	125.00	150.00	75.00
P-36	Cake plate, tab handles	100.00	125.00	65.00
P-41	Cake stand, 3 tier	150.00	175.00	85.00
P-50	Cheese keep	200.00	250.00	125.00
P-55	Coffee pot, 6 cup	450.00	550.00	250.00
P-65	Condiment set on tray	150.00	175.00	100.00
P-70	Cream and sugar	100.00	125.00	65.00
P-71	Cream and sugar on tray	150.00	175.00	85.00
P-85	Jam pot with liner	100.00	125.00	60.00
P-92	Jug, 5″ round	200.00	250.00	125.00
P-96	Jug, 7″ straight-sided	225.00	275.00	150.00

Cat.No.	Shape	U.S. $	Can. $	U.K. £
P-301	Plate, 4″ triangular	30.00	35.00	20.00
P-104	Plate, 7″	45.00	55.00	30.00
P-105	Plate, 8″	75.00	90.00	45.00
P-112	Relish dish	175.00	225.00	125.00
P-117	Salt and pepper	65.00	80.00	40.00
P-118	Salt and pepper on tray	135.00	165.00	85.00
P-122	Sandwich tray, 13″ x 6″	90.00	110.00	50.00
P-125	Sauce boat and liner	125.00	150.00	75.00
P-130	Teacup and saucer	60.00	75.00	35.00
P-137	Teapot, 6 cup	525.00	625.00	325.00
P-140	Teapot, stacking	525.00	625.00	325.00
P-145	Tennis set	100.00	125.00	65.00
P-160	Vase, bud	75.00	90.00	45.00

ROSETIME

The English registration number for **Rosetime** was 829287, and the pattern was registered sometime in 1938. This pattern was produced by Royal Albert in bone china.

Cat.No.	Shape	U.S. $	Can. $	U.K. £
Ro-04	Bonbon dish	50.00	75.00	35.00
Ro-28	Butter dish	175.00	200.00	100.00
Ro-35	Cake plate, open handles	150.00	185.00	100.00
Ro-36	Cake plate, tab handles	135.00	165.00	85.00
Ro-41	Cake stand, 3 tier	175.00	200.00	100.00
Ro-50	Cheese keep	250.00	300.00	150.00
Ro-55	Coffee pot, 6 cup	600.00	725.00	350.00
Ro-65	Condiment set on tray	200.00	250.00	125.00
Ro-70	Cream and sugar	100.00	125.00	65.00
Ro-71	Cream and sugar on tray	175.00	200.00	100.00
Ro-85	Jam pot with liner	135.00	165.00	85.00
Ro-92	Jug, 5" round	200.00	250.00	125.00
Ro-96	Jug, 7" straight-sided	225.00	275.00	135.00

Cat.No.	Shape	U.S. $	Can. $	U.K. £
Ro-301	Plate, 4" triangular	45.00	55.00	30.00
Ro-104	Plate, 7"	65.00	80.00	40.00
Ro-105	Plate, 8"	95.00	115.00	50.00
Ro-112	Relish dish	225.00	275.00	135.00
Ro-117	Salt and pepper	85.00	100.00	50.00
Ro-118	Salt and pepper on tray	165.00	200.00	100.00
Ro-122	Sandwich tray, 13" x 6"	100.00	125.00	65.00
Ro-125	Sauce boat and liner	135.00	165.00	85.00
Ro-130	Teacup and saucer	75.00	90.00	45.00
Ro-137	Teapot, 6 cup	650.00	775.00	400.00
Ro-140	Teapot, stacking	650.00	775.00	400.00
Ro-145	Tennis set	125.00	150.00	75.00
Ro-160	Vase, bud	100.00	125.00	65.00

ROYAL BROCADE

This pattern was also produced by Royal Albert in bone china.

Cat.No.	Shape	U.S. $	Can. $	U.K. £
RB-04	Bonbon dish	40.00	50.00	25.00
RB-28	Butter dish	125.00	150.00	75.00
RB-35	Cake plate, open handles	100.00	125.00	65.00
RB-36	Cake plate, tab handles	100.00	125.00	65.00
RB-41	Cake stand, 3 tier	125.00	150.00	75.00
RB-50	Cheese keep	175.00	200.00	100.00
RB-55	Coffee pot, 6 cup	400.00	475.00	250.00
RB-65	Condiment set on tray	135.00	165.00	85.00
RB-70	Cream and sugar	75.00	90.00	45.00
RB-71	Cream and sugar on tray	125.00	150.00	75.00
RB-85	Jam pot with liner	75.00	100.00	50.00
RB-92	Jug, 5″ round	150.00	175.00	90.00
RB-96	Jug, 7″ straight-sided	165.00	200.00	100.00

Cat.No.	Shape	U.S. $	Can. $	U.K. £
RB-301	Plate, 4″ triangular	30.00	35.00	20.00
RB-104	Plate, 7″	40.00	50.00	25.00
RB-105	Plate, 8″	65.00	75.00	40.00
RB-112	Relish dish	125.00	150.00	75.00
RB-117	Salt and pepper	65.00	75.00	40.00
RB-118	Salt and pepper on tray	125.00	150.00	75.00
RB-122	Sandwich tray, 13″ x 6″	75.00	90.00	45.00
RB-125	Sauce boat and liner	100.00	150.00	75.00
RB-130	Teacup and saucer	50.00	65.00	30.00
RB-137	Teapot, 6 cup	425.00	500.00	250.00
RB-140	Teapot, stacking	450.00	550.00	275.00
RB-145	Tennis set	75.00	100.00	50.00
RB-160	Vase, bud	65.00	80.00	40.00

SKYLARK

We currently have no information available on this pattern.

Cat.No.	Shape	U.S. $	Can. $	U.K. £
Sk-04	Bonbon dish	40.00	50.00	25.00
Sk-28	Butter dish	125.00	150.00	75.00
Sk-35	Cake plate, open handles	100.00	125.00	65.00
Sk-36	Cake plate, tab handles	100.00	125.00	65.00
Sk-41	Cake stand, 3 tier	125.00	150.00	75.00
Sk-50	Cheese keep	175.00	200.00	100.00
Sk-55	Coffee pot, 6 cup	400.00	475.00	250.00
Sk-65	Condiment set on tray	135.00	165.00	85.00
Sk-70	Cream and sugar	75.00	90.00	45.00
Sk-71	Cream and sugar on tray	125.00	150.00	75.00
Sk-85	Jam pot with liner	85.00	100.00	50.00
Sk-92	Jug, 5″ round	150.00	175.00	85.00
Sk-96	Jug, 7″ straight-sided	165.00	200.00	100.00

Cat.No.	Shape	U.S. $	Can. $	U.K. £
Sk-301	Plate, 4″ triangular	30.00	35.00	20.00
Sk-104	Plate, 7″	40.00	50.00	25.00
Sk-105	Plate, 8″	65.00	75.00	40.00
Sk-112	Relish dish	125.00	150.00	75.00
Sk-117	Salt and pepper	65.00	75.00	40.00
Sk-118	Salt and pepper on tray	125.00	150.00	75.00
Sk-122	Sandwich tray, 13″ x 6″	75.00	90.00	45.00
Sk-125	Sauce boat and liner	100.00	125.00	65.00
Sk-130	Teacup and saucer	50.00	65.00	30.00
Sk-137	Teapot, 6 cup	425.00	500.00	250.00
Sk-140	Teapot, stacking	450.00	550.00	275.00
Sk-145	Tennis set	75.00	100.00	50.00
Sk-160	Vase, bud	65.00	80.00	40.00

EMPIRE PORCELAIN COMPANY LTD.

This company was established at the Empire Works in Stoke around 1896 and continued in business until 1967. They produced a wide range of pottery and porcelain including several chintzes. One of their 1930s chintz patterns **Lilac Time** was very popular and was produced in more than one colourway.

The trade name "Empire Ware" or "Shelton Ivory" is often found within the backstamp. Backstamps from the late 1940s and 1950s usually incorporate numbers for the month and year of manufacture.

LILAC TIME

This pattern was produced in two colourways, green and ivory, the green being the most common.

Cat.No.	Shape	U.S. $	Can. $	U.K. £
LT-55	Coffee pot, 6 cup	425.00	500.00	250.00
LT-70	Cream and sugar	80.00	95.00	50.00
LT-75	Demi-tasse	50.00	65.00	30.00

Cat.No.	Shape	U.S. $	Can. $	U.K. £
LT-104	Plate, 7″	40.00	50.00	25.00
LT-130	Teacup and saucer	55.00	70.00	35.00
LT-137	Teapot, 6 cup	475.00	575.00	275.00

FORD & SONS

From 1893 until 1938 this company was known as Ford & Sons and the backstamp was minimal: "F & S" or "F & SONS LTD," or "F & SONS BURSLEM." They produced several of the exotic bird and flower chintzes during the 1920s and perhaps earlier. They do not appear to have produced the all-over floral chintzes in the 1930s style. Although the company name did not change to Ford & Sons (Crownford) Ltd. until 1938, the most common backstamp through the 1930s incorporated the trade name "Crownford Ware."

UNKNOWN

This was not a controlled pattern. It is sometimes found with a Bridgwood & Sons backstamp and it is sometimes unmarked.

Cat.No.	Shape	U.S. $	Can. $	U.K. £
FS-36	Cake plate, tab handles	150.00	175.00	85.00
FS-95	Jug, 7″ straight-sided	250.00	300.00	150.00
FS-130	Teacup and saucer	75.00	90.00	45.00

GRIMWADES LTD. (ROYAL WINTON)

In 1885 Leonard Lumsden Grimwade founded a pottery with his brother at the Winton Pottery, Stoke-on-Trent. Although the brothers started with a shed, they grew very quickly and by 1900, after the takeover of the Stoke Pottery, Grimwade Brothers had become Grimwades Limited. Atlas China was acquired in 1906, which enabled the Grimwades to produce quality teasets. Tollie Coales, daughter of the Grimwades representative in Canada, still has beautiful teaware which was hand-painted by the art director at Atlas and sent to her mother as a gift.

Export became a very important part of the Grimwades business. It was around this time that G.O. Coales came out to Canada to represent the company . By the time he retired almost fifty years later he had crossed the Atlantic more than sixty times. Every January he would leave central Canada and head to the Maritime Provinces. In February he would head west. During the summer he would repeat the journey. His daughter remembers the huge padded trunks that he would fill with Grimwades samples. The Coales family much preferred the fine china produced at the Atlas Works and Tollie said her father was always surprised at how well the chintz ware sold.

Grimwades Ltd. produced any number of chintzes earlier in the century, but it was not until 1928 with the production of the first "modern" chintz pattern, **Marguerite**, that Grimwades found the line which would become their particular specialty. **Marguerite** chintz was described in the November *Gazette* as "a treatment employing a very pleasing ground tint in natural colours and a theme expressive of the charm of the countryside, the shapes being new and unquestionably appealing." It is said to have come from a design worked by Leonard Grimwade's wife on a cushion. Over the next few years several chintz designs were introduced but in 1932 **Summertime** chintz brought even greater popularity for the firm. The *Gazette* waxed lyrical: "It is a sort of fantasia compounded of roses, daisies, violets, harebells and similar summertime flowers." Although we have been told that **Summertime** is not common in Australia, it was shipped in huge quantites to North America and even today dinner services for 12 turn up with some regularity. The pattern was applied to everything including, clocks, sick feeders for hospitals and even a souvenir plate with Niagara Falls lithographed in the center.

Throughout the 1930s vast quantities of chintz ware were produced and a number of new patterns were introduced at the British Industries Fair every year. Ivy Mayer, secretary to the export director Fred Seabridge for thirty years, remembers seeing big red pattern books with each pattern recorded by number. The books have long since disappeared, and dating the patterns has become an exercise in piecing together various bits of information. Every year when new ceramic lines were introduced at the B.I.F., trade publications including *Pottery Gazette* and *Glass Trade Review* might mention particularly popular patterns or patterns which were bought by members of the Royal family, who were staunch supporters of British industry.

It is important to remember that **all** patterns were recorded in order in the pattern books and not simply chintz patterns. There are, therefore, large gaps between the various chintz pattern numbers since many numbers were allocated to the non-chintz patterns produced by Grimwades. We know that the first modern all-over-floral was **Marguerite** and that the pattern was introduced in 1928 with the number 9432 (although the *Gazette* quotes the pattern number as 9467, all the pieces we have seen have the number 9432). **Old Cottage Chintz** 9632 and **Delphinium Chintz** 9889 have a slightly old-fashioned appearance and are often featured on the older shapes. Similarly **Springtime** usually appears on older shapes and has been found with the pattern number 10017. Suddenly the number drops to 775 with **Summertime,** which we know from the *Gazette* appeared in 1932. It is logical to assume that Grimwades, like so many other factories, decided the pattern numbers were getting too long to record and started again in the low hundreds with their pattern numbering. **Clevedon** and **Kinver** were mentioned in January 1934 as new patterns intended for the spring of 1934 and the pattern numbers we have found for them are 1844 (**Clevedon**) and 2254 (**Kinver**).

With this theory and with the pattern numbers that collectors from around the world contributed, we were able to compile a list of patterns in the order in which they appeared in the pattern book. There are several anomalies with the patterns in the late 1930s. Unfortunately, in 1939 the last recorded pattern is **Sweet Nancy** at 5828 and the next is **Julia** at 109. Originally we assumed that this might have been pre- and post war, but **Crocus** is mentioned in the 1939 *Gazette* as a new pattern, and the number recorded for white **Crocus** is 111 and black **Crocus** 112. We have been unable to find either of these patterns with a pattern backstamp. The next chintz patterns we have records for are **June Festival** at 137 and **May Festival** at 139, which appear to be different colourways of the same pattern. As far as we are aware, Grimwades always gave different names to alternate colourways of the same pattern (e.g. **Cleve-**

don and **Cranstone**) so perhaps the backstamp for **May Festival** was discontinued since most pieces in this pattern do not have a pattern backstamp. **Floral Garden** 4547 from the late thirties came in several colourways. To date only the green colourway has been found with a backstamp including the pattern name and only in Australia. **Rose du Barry** was advertised by Henry Morgans of Montreal in 1938 and has been found with no name, with the name **Chelsea Rose** and with **Rose du Barry**. The backstamp on **Rose du Barry** always has Henry Morgan & Co. Ltd.; perhaps the name **Rose du Barry** was exclusively given to Morgans.

With copies of chintz patterns from Japan becoming a serious problem, copyright became an issue in the late 1940s, and many of the new patterns were registered in Canada, the United States, New Zealand and Australia. Using information from Ivy Mayer along with the pattern number and the dates of the Canadian registration, it is possible to figure out which patterns appeared in the early 1950s. Both **Cheadle** and **Mayfair** were registered in 1951 and the pattern numbers seem appropriate — 311 for **Cheadle** and 392 for **Mayfair**. **Victorian Rose** and **Florence** which were registered in 1953 have later pattern numbers — 440 and 472 respectively. Although Australian researchers have dated **Evesham** to 1958 as the last chintz pattern registered, pieces found in North America are marked with Canadian registration 1951 and with the pattern number 404. This would seem to match the pattern number seequence. Companies usually advertise their newest patterns, which makes advertisements useful as confirmation. **Cheadle** was first advertised by Ebeling & Reuss in the United States in 1951 and **Nantwich** by Cassidy's in 1952.

By the time Howard Potteries took over Grimwades Ltd. in 1964, chintzware was not as important to the factory. Norfolk Street had little room for chintz production, according to Ivy Mayer, but special orders were still produced for long-standing customers such as John Bradshaw of Stratford, Canada. Grimwades' history from 1964 to the present is typical of so many of the factories which had competed successfully in a different time but found the second half of the twentieth century crippling. Although the company passed through several hands, Royal Winton continued. From the collapse of the Coloroll Group in 1990, the company has gone from crisis to crisis. Five owners in five years all but finished the firm. Bullers (Staffordshire) Ltd. bought the firm from the liquidators in mid-1995 and Royal Winton lives on.

Although we have prepared this preliminary list of the Royal Winton patterns in the order in which they appeared, many of the numbers were difficult to decipher and we are missing pattern numbers for the following patterns: **Morning Glory**, **Peony**, **Rose du Barry** and **Winifred**. We hope readers will be able to help us with these in time for the next edition.

LETTER CODE	PATTERN NAME	PATTERN NUMBER
Mag	Marguerite	9432 (1928)
OC	Old Cottage	9632
De	Delphinium Chintz	9889
Spt	Springtime	10017
Su	Summertime	775
Cr	Cranstone	1154
FF	Floral Feast	1394
So	Somerset	1420
Ru	Rutland	1470
Be	Bedale	1703
Cl	Clevedon	1844
JR	June Roses	1924
Crom	Cromer	2078
Pel	Pelham	2201
Bee	Beeston	2203
W	Welbeck	2204
H	Hazel	2208
Ki	Kinver	2254
Sp	Spring	2506
FiW	Fireglow (original)	2510
Chz	Chintz	2836
QA	Queen Anne	2995
SP	Sweet Pea	3030
Ro	Royalty	3079
WF	Wild Flowers	3149
V	Victorian	3164
Maj	Majestic	3311
Sun	Sunshine	4030
Ri	Richmond	4249
T	Tartans	4514
Q	Quilt	4515
FG	Floral Garden	4547

LETTER CODE	PATTERN NAME	PATTERN NUMBER
A	Anemone	4801
Cly	Clyde	5315 for green, 5637 for brown
SN	Sweet Nancy	5828
J	Julia	109
Cro	Crocus	111 for white 112 for black
JF	June Festival	137 for burgundy, 135 for navy
MF	May Festival	139
Ke	Kew	240
Do	Dorset	274
JL	Joyce-Lynn	275
N	Nantwich	291
Chd	Cheadle	311
Pe	Pekin	320 (1950s version)
Mar	Marion	324
Ba	Balmoral	374
El	Eleanor	375
ER	English Rose	381
May	Mayfair	392
SG	Spring Glory	402
Ev	Evesham	404
Co	Cotswold	408
Sh	Shrewsbury	418
Esl	Estelle	423
VR	Victorian Rose	440
Chl	Chelsea	455
O	Orient	471
Fl	Florence	472
Est	Esther	473
St	Stratford	493
FiB	Fireglow (black)	533

ANEMONE

The pattern number is 4801 and it was available with a light blue, navy blue and black background. Some of the large flowers are handpainted on top of the transfer.

Cat.No.	Shape	U.S. $	Can. $	U.K. £
A-04	Bonbon dish	40.00	50.00	30.00
A-09	Bowl, 5″	25.00	30.00	20.00
A-14	Bowl, 8″ soup	40.00	50.00	30.00
A-23	Breakfast set	550.00	650.00	375.00
A-28	Butter dish	125.00	150.00	75.00
A-30	Butter pat	35.00	40.00	25.00
A-35	Cake plate, open handles	125.00	150.00	75.00
A-36	Cake plate, tab handles	100.00	125.00	65.00
A-37	Cake plate, 8″ sq. pedestal	125.00	150.00	85.00
A-40	Cake stand, 2 tier	125.00	150.00	85.00
A-45	Canoe-shaped dish	165.00	195.00	115.00
A-50	Cheese keep	150.00	175.00	100.00
A-52	Coaster	30.00	35.00	25.00
A-55	Coffee pot	450.00	550.00	325.00
A-60	Compote, footed	100.00	125.00	75.00
A-65	Condiment set on tray	135.00	165.00	85.00
A-70	Cream and sugar	75.00	90.00	50.00
A-71	Cream and sugar on tray	135.00	165.00	85.00
A-75	Demi-tasse	50.00	65.00	35.00
A-77	Egg cup, footed	45.00	55.00	30.00
A-80	Hot water jug	200.00	235.00	125.00
A-85	Jam pot with liner	100.00	125.00	65.00
A-90	Jug, 4″	165.00	200.00	115.00
A-91	Jug, 4 1/2″	175.00	225.00	135.00
A-92	Jug, 5″	200.00	250.00	150.00

Cat.No.	Shape	U.S. $	Can. $	U.K. £
A-97	Nut dish	35.00	40.00	25.00
A-201	Plate, 4″ sq.	25.00	30.00	20.00
A-202	Plate, 5″ sq.	30.00	35.00	25.00
A-203	Plate, 6″ sq.	35.00	40.00	25.00
A-204	Plate, 7″ sq.	40.00	50.00	30.00
A-205	Plate, 8″ sq.	50.00	65.00	35.00
A-206	Plate, 9″ sq.	75.00	90.00	50.00
A-207	Plate, 10″ sq .	75.00	95.00	50.00
A-112	Relish dish, small	100.00	125.00	65.00
A-115	Salad bowl, chrome rim	100.00	125.00	65.00
A-117	Salt and pepper	50.00	75.00	40.00
A-118	Salt and pepper on tray	125.00	150.00	75.00
A-120	Sandwich tray, 10″ x 6″	75.00	90.00	50.00
A-121	Sandwich tray, 12″ x 7″	100.00	125.00	65.00
A-125	Sauce boat and liner	100.00	125.00	65.00
A-130	Teacup and saucer	50.00	65.00	35.00
A-135	Teapot, 2 cup	275.00	325.00	175.00
A-136	Teapot, 4 cup	325.00	400.00	225.00
A-137	Teapot, 6 cup	425.00	500.00	300.00
A-140	Teapot, stacking	450.00	550.00	325.00
A-145	Tennis set	75.00	85.00	50.00
A-150	Toast rack, 4 slice	165.00	200.00	125.00
A-151	Toast rack, 2 slice	135.00	165.00	85.00
A-155	Trivet	75.00	85.00	50.00
A-160	Vase, bud	75.00	90.00	50.00

BALMORAL

The pattern number is 374, and it was probably introduced in 1951

Cat.No.	Shape	U.S. $	Can. $	U.K. £
Ba-04	Bonbon dish	60.00	75.00	45.00
Ba-09	Bowl, 5″	45.00	55.00	35.00
Ba-14	Bowl, 8″ soup	75.00	85.00	50.00
Ba-23	Breakfast set	800.00	975.00	550.00
Ba-28	Butter dish	175.00	200.00	125.00
Ba-30	Butter pat	50.00	65.00	35.00
Ba-35	Cake plate, open handles	175.00	225.00	125.00
Ba-36	Cake plate, tab handles	150.00	175.00	100.00
Ba-37	Cake plate, 8″ sq. pedestal	175.00	225.00	125.00
Ba-40	Cake stand, 2 tier	175.00	225.00	125.00
Ba-45	Canoe-shaped dish	250.00	300.00	175.00
Ba-50	Cheese keep	225.00	275.00	150.00
Ba-52	Coaster	45.00	55.00	35.00
Ba-55	Coffee pot	675.00	800.00	475.00
Ba-60	Compote, footed	150.00	175.00	100.00
Ba-65	Condiment set on tray	200.00	250.00	125.00
Ba-70	Cream and sugar	100.00	125.00	65.00
Ba-71	Cream and sugar on tray	200.00	250.00	150.00
Ba-75	Demi-tasse	75.00	90.00	50.00
Ba-77	Egg cup, footed	65.00	80.00	45.00
Ba-80	Hot water jug	300.00	350.00	200.00
Ba-85	Jam pot with liner	150.00	175.00	100.00
Ba-90	Jug, 4″	250.00	300.00	175.00
Ba-91	Jug, 4 1/2″	275.00	325.00	175.00
Ba-92	Jug, 5″	300.00	350.00	200.00

Cat.No.	Shape	U.S. $	Can. $	U.K. £
Ba-97	Nut dish	50.00	65.00	35.00
Ba-201	Plate, 4″ sq.	45.00	55.00	30.00
Ba-202	Plate, 5″ sq.	50.00	65.00	35.00
Ba-203	Plate, 6″ sq.	50.00	75.00	40.00
Ba-204	Plate, 7″ sq.	75.00	100.00	50.00
Ba-205	Plate, 8″ sq.	115.00	150.00	75.00
Ba-206	Plate, 9″ sq.	135.00	165.00	85.00
Ba-207	Plate, 10″ sq.	150.00	175.00	100.00
Ba-112	Relish dish, small	150.00	175.00	100.00
Ba-115	Salad bowl, chrome rim	150.00	175.00	100.00
Ba-117	Salt and pepper	80.00	100.00	50.00
Ba-118	Salt and pepper on tray	150.00	175.00	100.00
Ba-120	Sandwich tray, 10″ x 6″	100.00	125.00	65.00
Ba-121	Sandwich tray, 12″ x 7″	125.00	175.00	100.00
Ba-125	Sauce boat and liner	150.00	175.00	100.00
Ba-130	Teacup and saucer	75.00	100.00	50.00
Ba-135	Teapot, 2 cup	325.00	400.00	225.00
Ba-136	Teapot, 4 cup	500.00	600.00	350.00
Ba-137	Teapot, 6 cup	600.00	725.00	425.00
Ba-140	Teapot, stacking	650.00	775.00	450.00
Ba-145	Tennis set	100.00	125.00	65.00
Ba-150	Toast rack, 4 slice	200.00	250.00	150.00
Ba-151	Toast rack, 2 slice	150.00	175.00	100.00
Ba-155	Trivet	100.00	125.00	65.00
Ba-160	Vase, bud	100.00	125.00	65.00

BEDALE

The pattern number is 1703, and it is an alternate colourway to **Summertime** 775. This is one of the patterns copied by the Japanese.

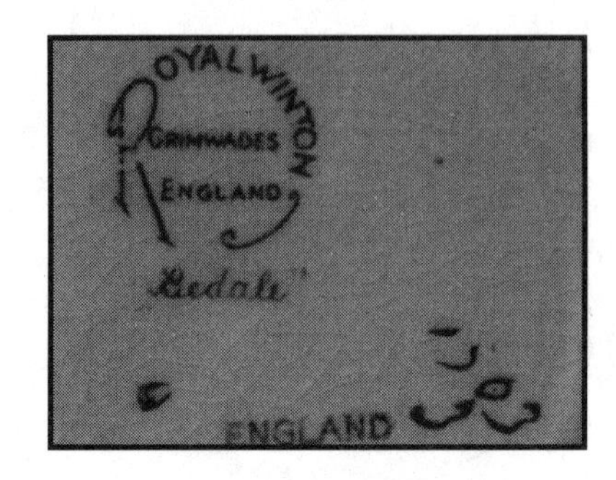

Cat.No.	Shape	U.S. $	Can. $	U.K. £
Be-04	Bonbon dish	50.00	65.00	35.00
Be-09	Bowl, 5″	40.00	50.00	30.00
Be-14	Bowl, 8″ soup	65.00	80.00	45.00
Be-23	Breakfast set	750.00	900.00	525.00
Be-28	Butter dish	140.00	175.00	100.00
Be-30	Butter pat	40.00	50.00	30.00
Be-35	Cake plate, open handles	175.00	200.00	125.00
Be-36	Cake plate, tab handles	150.00	175.00	100.00
Be-37	Cake plate, 8″ sq. pedestal	175.00	225.00	125.00
Be-40	Cake stand, 2 tier	150.00	175.00	100.00
Be-45	Canoe-shaped dish	200.00	250.00	150.00
Be-50	Cheese keep	175.00	225.00	125.00
Be-52	Coaster	35.00	40.00	25.00
Be-55	Coffee pot	625.00	750.00	450.00
Be-60	Compote, footed	125.00	150.00	75.00
Be-65	Condiment set on tray	165.00	200.00	100.00
Be-70	Cream and sugar	100.00	125.00	65.00
Be-71	Cream and sugar on tray	175.00	200.00	125.00
Be-75	Demi-tasse	65.00	80.00	45.00
Be-77	Egg cup, footed	50.00	75.00	40.00
Be-80	Hot water jug	250.00	300.00	175.00
Be-85	Jam pot with liner	125.00	175.00	100.00
Be-90	Jug, 4 1/2″	200.00	250.00	150.00
Be-91	Jug, 5″	225.00	275.00	150.00
Be-92	Jug, 5 1/2″	250.00	300.00	175.00

Cat.No.	Shape	U.S. $	Can. $	U.K. £
Be-97	Nut dish	40.00	50.00	30.00
Be-201	Plate, 4″ sq.	45.00	55.00	30.00
Be-202	Plate, 5″ sq.	50.00	65.00	35.00
Be-203	Plate, 6″ sq.	50.00	75.00	40.00
Be-204	Plate, 7″ sq.	65.00	75.00	45.00
Be-205	Plate, 8″ sq.	100.00	125.00	65.00
Be-206	Plate, 9″ sq.	100.00	125.00	65.00
Be-207	Plate, 10″ sq.	125.00	150.00	75.00
Be-112	Relish dish, small	125.00	175.00	100.00
Be-115	Salad bowl, chrome rim	100.00	125.00	75.00
Be-117	Salt and pepper	75.00	90.00	50.00
Be-118	Salt and pepper on tray	135.00	165.00	85.00
Be-120	Sandwich tray, 10″ x 6″	100.00	125.00	75.00
Be-121	Sandwich tray, 12″ x 7″	100.00	125.00	80.00
Be-125	Sauce boat and liner	125.00	150.00	75.00
Be-130	Teacup and saucer	65.00	80.00	45.00
Be-135	Teapot, 2 cup	300.00	375.00	225.00
Be-136	Teapot, 4 cup	400.00	500.00	300.00
Be-137	Teapot, 6 cup	500.00	625.00	375.00
Be-140	Teapot, stacking	600.00	725.00	425.00
Be-145	Tennis set	85.00	100.00	60.00
Be-150	Toast rack, 4 slice	200.00	250.00	150.00
Be-151	Toast rack, 2 slice	150.00	200.00	100.00
Be-155	Trivet	85.00	100.00	60.00
Be-160	Vase, bud	100.00	125.00	75.00

Unnamed — Marigold

Barker Brothers Ltd.

Barker -- Backstamp

Barker -- Unnamed

Brexton

Brexton -- Backstamp

Brexton -- Unnamed

Elijah Cotton Ltd. — Lord Nelson Ware

Anemone

Black Beauty

Briar Rose

Green Tulip

Heather

Marigold

Elijah Cotton Ltd.

Marina

Pansy

Rosetime

Royal Brocade

Skylark

Skylark -- Backstamp

Empire Porcelain Co. Ltd.

Lilac Time

Lilac Time -- Backstamp

Ford & Sons

Ford -- Unnamed

Ford -- Backstamp

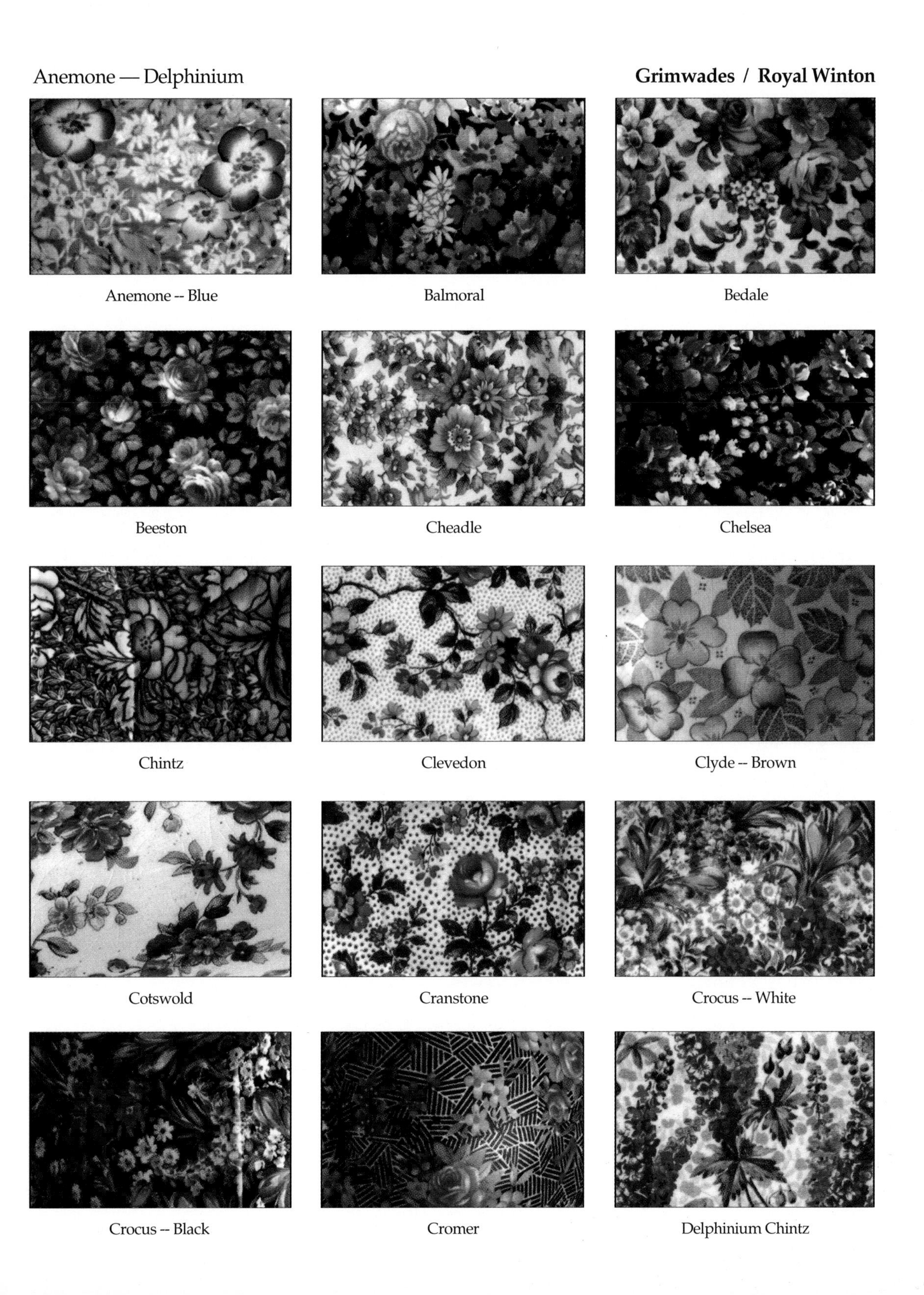

Anemone -- Blue

Balmoral

Bedale

Beeston

Cheadle

Chelsea

Chintz

Clevedon

Clyde -- Brown

Cotswold

Cranstone

Crocus -- White

Crocus -- Black

Cromer

Delphinium Chintz

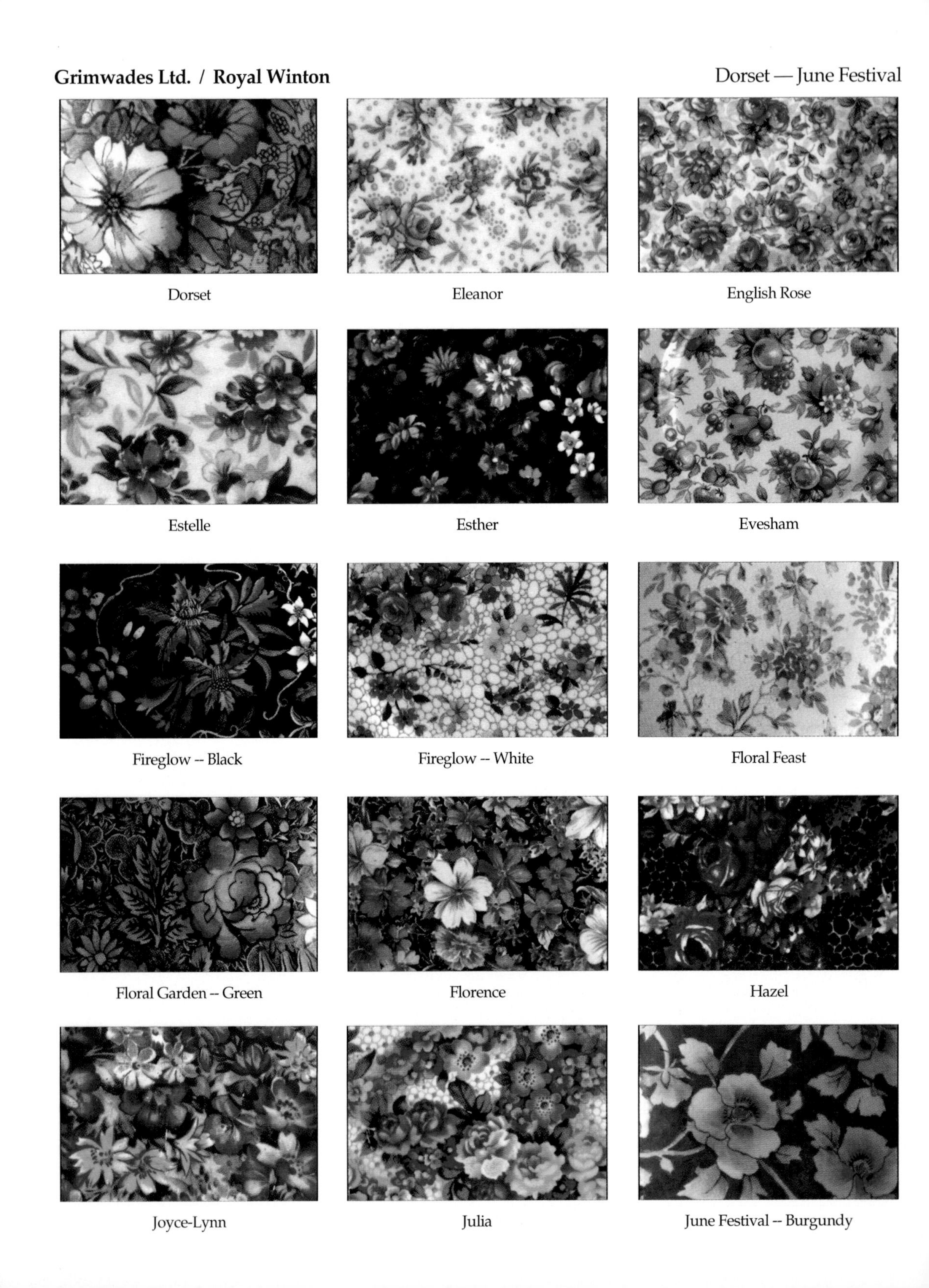

Dorset

Eleanor

English Rose

Estelle

Esther

Evesham

Fireglow -- Black

Fireglow -- White

Floral Feast

Floral Garden -- Green

Florence

Hazel

Joyce-Lynn

Julia

June Festival -- Burgundy

June Roses

Kew

Kinver

Majestic

Marguerite

Marion

Mayfair

May Festival

Morning Glory -- Black

Nantwich

Old Cottage Chintz

Orient

Pekin -- Black

Pekin -- Burgundy

Pelham

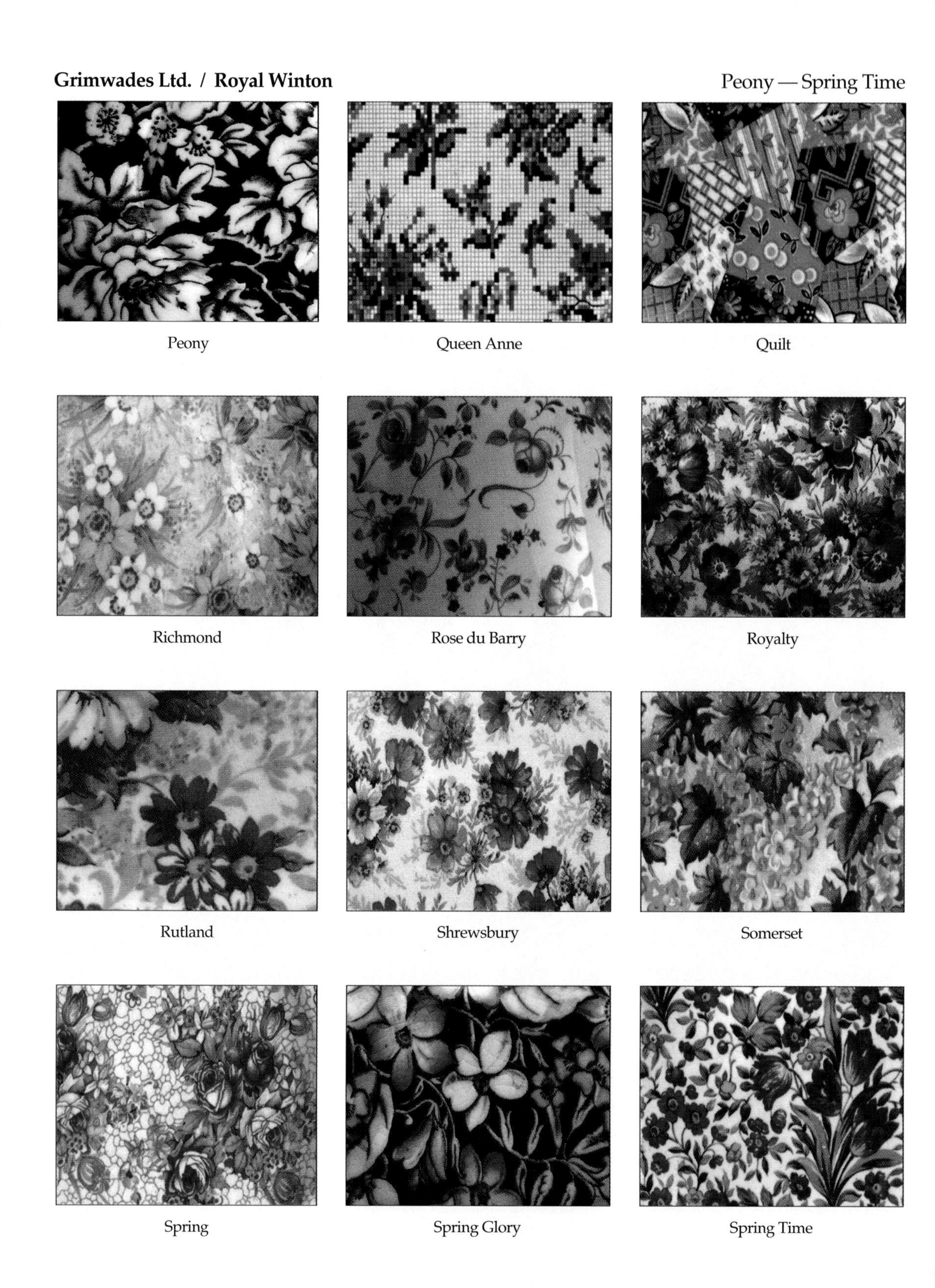

Peony

Queen Anne

Quilt

Richmond

Rose du Barry

Royalty

Rutland

Shrewsbury

Somerset

Spring

Spring Glory

Spring Time

Stratford

Summertime

Sunshine

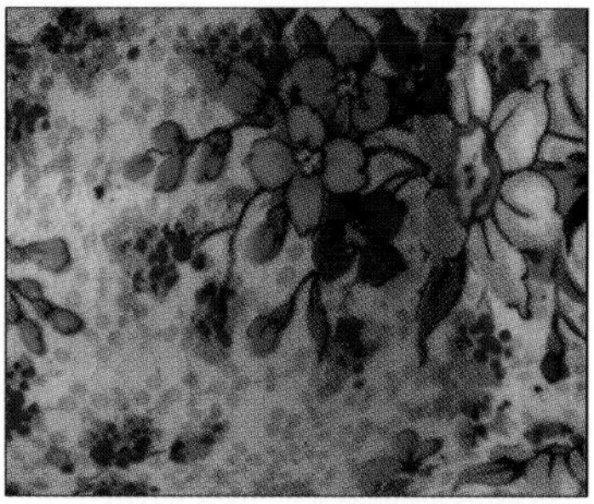

Sweet Nancy

Sweet Pea

Tartans

Victorian

Victorian Rose

Welbeck

Wild Flowers

Winifred

"Welbeck"
ROYAL WINTON
GRIMWADES
STOKE ON
TRENT.
ENGLAND

Welbeck -- Backstamp

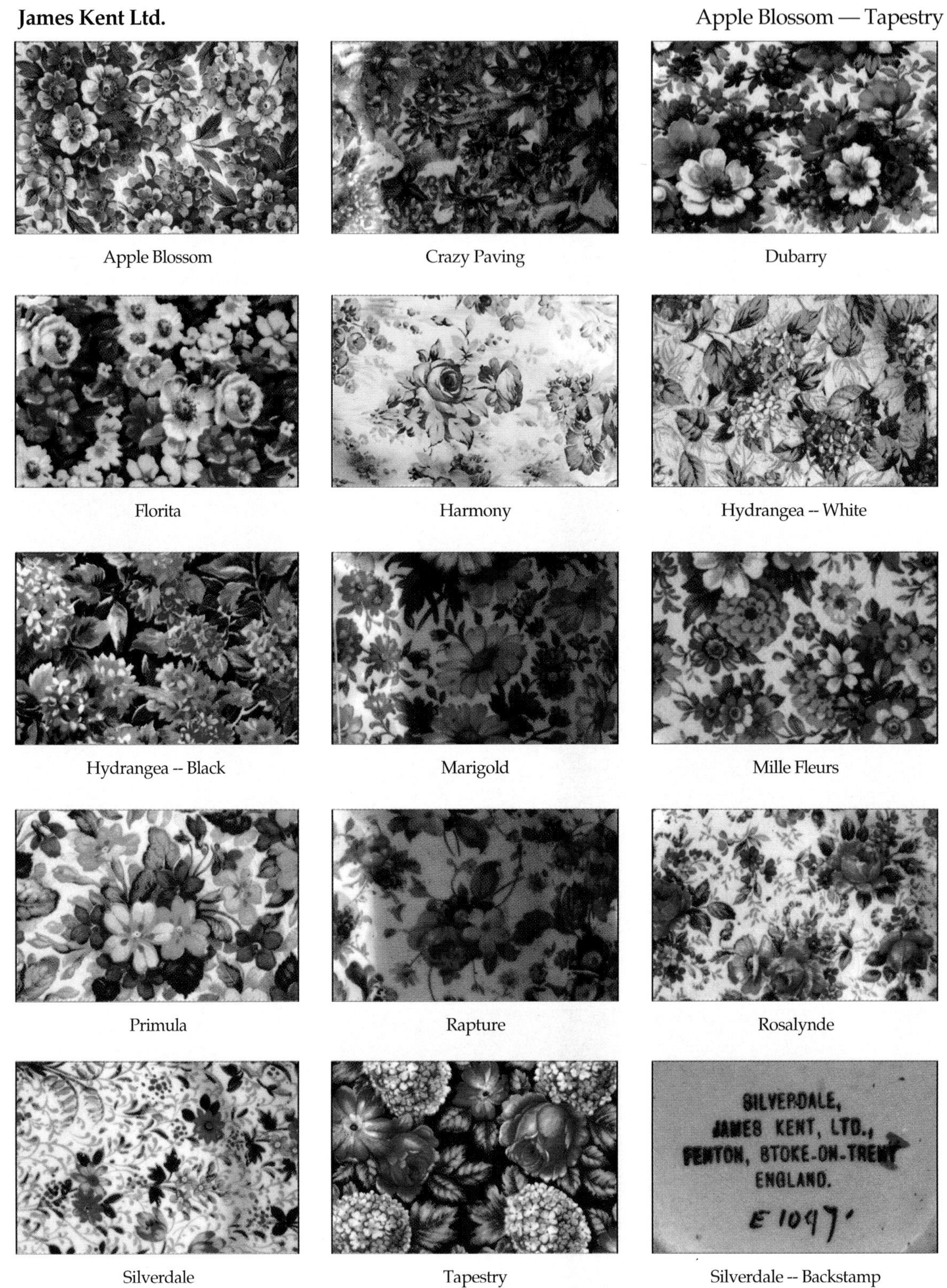

Apple Blossom

Crazy Paving

Dubarry

Florita

Harmony

Hydrangea -- White

Hydrangea -- Black

Marigold

Mille Fleurs

Primula

Rapture

Rosalynde

Silverdale

Tapestry

Silverdale -- Backstamp

W.R. Midwinter Ltd.

Brama

Coral

Lorna Doone

Myott Son & Co.

"Spring Flower"

Summer Flower

Summer Flower -- Backstamp

A.G. Richardson Ltd. — Crown Ducal

Ascot

Blue Chintz

Canton

Festival

Florida

"Grey Fruit"

A.G. Richardson Ltd. / Crown Ducal

Ivory Chintz

"Ivory Fruit"

Marigold

"Mauve Chintz"

"Pink Chintz"

Primula

"Purple Chintz"

Rose and Motifs

Ridgeway Potteries Ltd.

Unnamed

Royal Doulton Ltd.

Persian -- Backstamp

Persian

Shelley Potteries Ltd.

Maytime

Melody

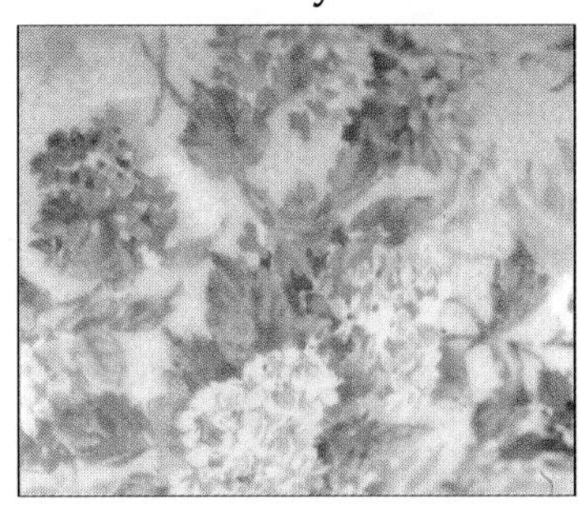

Summerglory

Wade & Company

"Butterfly Chintz"

Thistle Chintz

Wade -- Backstamp

Wood & Sons Ltd.

Wood & Sons -- Backstamp

Unnamed

Rosebud (Royalty) Diamond (Florence) Dutch (Fireglow — White)

Norman (Royalty) Norman (Royalty) Lily (Sweet Pea)

Countess (Sweet Pea) Countess (Sweet Pea) Elite (June Roses)

Rosebud (Welbeck) Snowdrop (Sweet Pea) Unnamed (Summertime)

Rowsley (Morning Glory) Rowsley (Shrewsbury) Etona (Majestic)

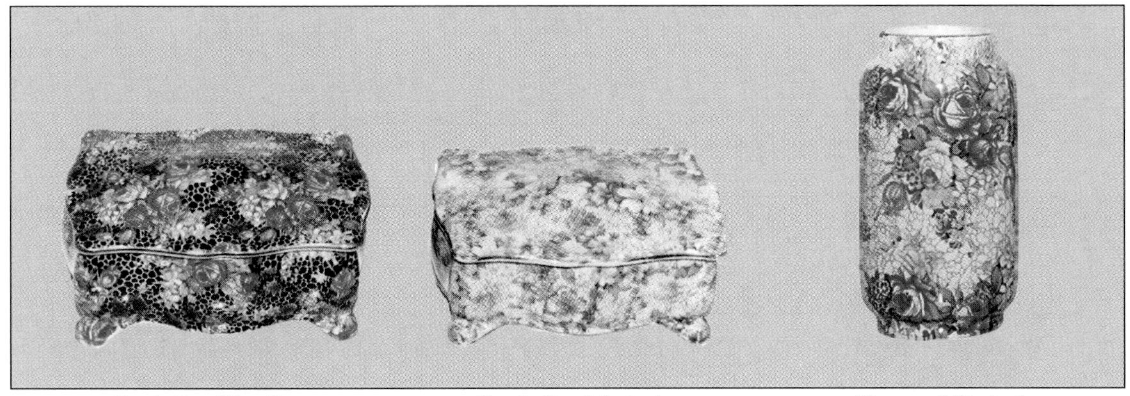

Candy Box (Hazel) Candy Box (Marion) Unnamed (Spring)

From Left: Ajax (Spring), Unnamed (Clevedon), Sexta (Welbeck), Gem (Majestic), Unnamed (Evesham), Unnamed (Old Cottage Chintz),Unnamed (Floral Garden), Tudor (Cotswold)

From Left: Unnamed (Sunshine), Unnamed (Floral Feast), Unnamed (Welbeck), Unnamed (Victorian), Neme(Julia), Unnamed (Peony), Clwyd (Sweet Nancy), Etona (Spring)

From Left: Fife (Victorian Rose), Leaf (White Crocus), Hampton (Welbeck), Candy Box (Joyce-Lynn), Candy Box (Hazel), Unnamed (June Roses)

From Left: Unnamed (Hazel), Albans (Royalty), Globe (Somerset), Globe (Sweet Pea), Globe (Summertime)

Back Row: Chelsea (L), Diamond (R) Bottom Left: Octagon (Dubarry) Bottom Right: Diamond (L), Kent (R)

Granville (Dubarry)

Cup Shape and Handle Variations (Dubarry) 4-slice Toast Rack (Hydrangea)

Vase 11" A/451 Deco (Ivory) — Flower Vase No. 3 (Beaumont) — Vase 9" No. 19 a/443 Deco (Rose & Motifs)

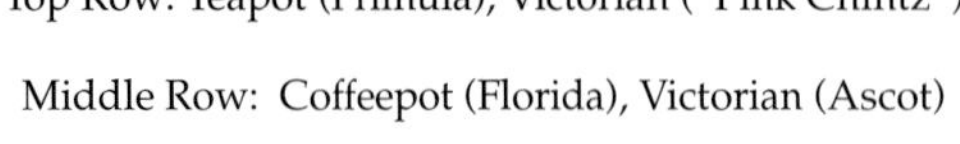

Top Row: Teapot (Primula), Victorian ("Pink Chintz")

Middle Row: Coffeepot (Florida), Victorian (Ascot)

Bottom Row: Teapot (Blue Chintz)

Top Row: Jug (Blue Chintz), Sugar Shaker (Ivory Chintz)

Middle Row: Rose Bowl No. 4 (Blue Chintz)

Bottom Row: Cruet (Blue Chintz)

BEESTON

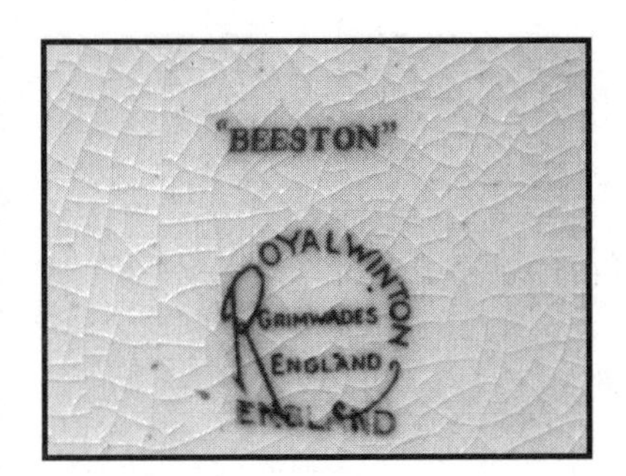

The pattern number is 2203. This pattern was copied by the Japanese.

Cat.No.	Shape	U.S. $	Can. $	U.K. £
Bee-04	Bonbon dish	75.00	90.00	50.00
Bee-09	Bowl, 5″	50.00	65.00	35.00
Bee-14	Bowl, 8″ soup	85.00	100.00	60.00
Bee-23	Breakfast set	950.00	1,150.00	675.00
Bee-28	Butter dish	225.00	275.00	150.00
Bee-30	Butter pat	65.00	80.00	45.00
Bee-35	Cake plate, open handles	225.00	275.00	150.00
Bee-36	Cake plate, tab handles	200.00	250.00	150.00
Bee-37	Cake plate, 8″ sq. pedestal	225.00	275.00	150.00
Bee-40	Cake stand, 2 tier	225.00	275.00	150.00
Bee-45	Canoe-shaped dish	325.00	375.00	220.00
Bee-50	Cheese keep	275.00	350.00	200.00
Bee-52	Coaster	50.00	65.00	35.00
Bee-55	Coffee pot	850.00	1,000.00	600.00
Bee-60	Compote, footed	175.00	225.00	125.00
Bee-65	Condiment set on tray	250.00	300.00	175.00
Bee-70	Cream and sugar	150.00	175.00	100.00
Bee-71	Cream and sugar on tray	250.00	300.00	175.00
Bee-75	Demi-tasse	100.00	125.00	75.00
Bee-77	Egg cup, footed	85.00	100.00	50.00
Bee-80	Hot water jug	375.00	450.00	250.00
Bee-85	Jam pot with liner	200.00	250.00	150.00
Bee-90	Jug, 4″	325.00	375.00	225.00
Bee-91	Jug, 4 1/2″	350.00	425.00	250.00
Bee-92	Jug, 5″	375.00	450.00	265.00
Bee-97	Nut dish	65.00	80.00	45.00
Bee-201	Plate, 4″ sq.	50.00	70.00	40.00
Bee-202	Plate, 5″ sq.	65.00	80.00	45.00
Bee-203	Plate, 6″ sq.	75.00	90.00	50.00
Bee-204	Plate, 7″ sq.	100.00	125.00	65.00
Bee-205	Plate, 8″ sq.	135.00	165.00	85.00
Bee-206	Plate, 9″ sq.	150.00	175.00	100.00
Bee-207	Plate, 10″ sq.	165.00	200.00	115.00
Bee-112	Relish dish, small	200.00	250.00	150.00
Bee-115	Salad bowl, chrome rim	175.00	200.00	125.00
Bee-117	Salt and pepper	100.00	125.00	65.00
Bee-118	Salt and pepper on tray	175.00	200.00	125.00
Bee-120	Sandwich tray, 10″ x 6″	150.00	175.00	100.00
Bee-121	Sandwich tray, 12″ x 7″	165.00	200.00	115.00
Bee-125	Sauce boat and liner	150.00	200.00	100.00
Bee-130	Teacup and saucer	100.00	125.00	65.00
Bee-135	Teapot, 2 cup	425.00	500.00	300.00
Bee-136	Teapot, 4 cup	625.00	750.00	450.00
Bee-137	Teapot, 6 cup	725.00	875.00	500.00
Bee-140	Teapot, stacking	800.00	950.00	550.00
Bee-145	Tennis set	130.00	160.00	100.00
Bee-150	Toast rack, 4 slice	275.00	300.00	175.00
Bee-151	Toast rack, 2 slice	200.00	250.00	125.00
Bee-155	Trivet	135.00	165.00	90.00
Bee-160	Vase, bud	135.00	165.00	90.00

CHEADLE

The pattern number is 311. This pattern was featured in an American advertisement in early 1950 and has been seen on an invoice as late as 1969. The pattern was registered in Canada in 1951.

Cat.No.	Shape	U.S. $	Can. $	U.K. £
Chd-04	Bonbon dish	60.00	75.00	45.00
Chd-09	Bowl, 5″	45.00	50.00	35.00
Chd-14	Bowl, 8″ soup	70.00	85.00	50.00
Chd-23	Breakfast set	800.00	950.00	575.00
Chd-28	Butter dish	175.00	200.00	125.00
Chd-30	Butter pat	50.00	65.00	35.00
Chd-35	Cake plate, open handles	200.00	235.00	150.00
Chd-36	Cake plate, tab handles	175.00	210.00	125.00
Chd-37	Cake plate, 8″ sq. pedestal	200.00	235.00	150.00
Chd-40	Cake stand, 2 tier	175.00	225.00	125.00
Chd-45	Canoe-shaped dish	250.00	300.00	175.00
Chd-50	Cheese keep	225.00	275.00	150.00
Chd-52	Coaster	45.00	50.00	35.00
Chd-55	Coffee pot	700.00	850.00	500.00
Chd-60	Compote, footed	150.00	175.00	100.00
Chd-65	Condiment set on tray	200.00	250.00	125.00
Chd-70	Cream and sugar	100.00	125.00	75.00
Chd-71	Cream and sugar on tray	200.00	250.00	125.00
Chd-75	Demi-tasse	75.00	90.00	50.00
Chd-77	Egg cup, footed	65.00	80.00	45.00
Chd-80	Hot water jug	300.00	375.00	200.00
Chd-85	Jam pot with liner	150.00	185.00	100.00
Chd-90	Jug, 4″	275.00	325.00	175.00
Chd-91	Jug, 4 1/2″	300.00	375.00	200.00
Chd-92	Jug, 5″	325.00	400.00	225.00
Chd-97	Nut dish	50.00	65.00	35.00
Chd-201	Plate, 4″ sq.	50.00	65.00	35.00
Chd-202	Plate, 5″ sq.	50.00	70.00	40.00
Chd-203	Plate, 6″ sq.	65.00	80.00	45.00
Chd-204	Plate, 7″ sq.	75.00	100.00	50.00
Chd-205	Plate, 8″ sq.	125.00	150.00	75.00
Chd-206	Plate, 9″ sq.	150.00	175.00	100.00
Chd-207	Plate, 10″ sq.	150.00	175.00	100.00
Chd-112	Relish dish, small	150.00	175.00	100.00
Chd-115	Salad bowl, chrome rim	135.00	165.00	85.00
Chd-117	Salt and pepper	75.00	100.00	50.00
Chd-118	Salt and pepper on tray	150.00	175.00	100.00
Chd-120	Sandwich tray, 10″ x 6″	100.00	125.00	65.00
Chd-121	Sandwich tray, 12″ x 7″	125.00	150.00	75.00
Chd-125	Sauce boat and liner	150.00	175.00	100.00
Chd-130	Teacup and saucer	75.00	90.00	50.00
Chd-135	Teapot, 2 cup	350.00	425.00	250.00
Chd-136	Teapot, 4 cup	550.00	650.00	375.00
Chd-137	Teapot, 6 cup	650.00	775.00	450.00
Chd-140	Teapot, stacking	750.00	900.00	525.00
Chd-145	Tennis set	100.00	125.00	65.00
Chd-150	Toast rack, 4 slice	200.00	250.00	135.00
Chd-151	Toast rack, 2 slice	150.00	175.00	100.00
Chd-155	Trivet	100.00	125.00	65.00
Chd-160	Vase, bud	125.00	150.00	75.00

CHELSEA

The pattern number is 455 and the name has been seen on an invoice as late as 1969. The pattern was registered in Canada in 1952.

Cat.No.	Shape	U.S. $	Can. $	U.K. £
Chl-04	Bonbon dish	75.00	100.00	50.00
Chl-09	Bowl, 5″	50.00	65.00	35.00
Chl-14	Bowl, 8″ soup	75.00	100.00	50.00
Chl-23	Breakfast set	850.00	1,100.00	600.00
Chl-28	Butter dish	200.00	250.00	135.00
Chl-30	Butter pat	60.00	75.00	45.00
Chl-35	Cake plate, open handles	200.00	250.00	135.00
Chl-36	Cake plate, tab handles	200.00	250.00	135.00
Chl-37	Cake plate, 8″ sq. pedestal	225.00	275.00	150.00
Chl-40	Cake stand, 2 tier	225.00	275.00	150.00
Chl-45	Canoe-shaped dish	275.00	325.00	200.00
Chl-50	Cheese keep	275.00	325.00	200.00
Chl-52	Coaster	55.00	75.00	40.00
Chl-55	Coffee pot	850.00	1,100.00	600.00
Chl-60	Compote, footed	175.00	200.00	125.00
Chl-65	Condiment set on tray	250.00	300.00	175.00
Chl-70	Cream and sugar	125.00	175.00	100.00
Chl-71	Cream and sugar on tray	250.00	300.00	175.00
Chl-75	Demi-tasse	100.00	125.00	65.00
Chl-77	Egg cup, footed	75.00	100.00	55.00
Chl-80	Hot water jug	350.00	425.00	250.00
Chl-85	Jam pot with liner	175.00	225.00	125.00
Chl-90	Jug, 4″	300.00	375.00	200.00
Chl-91	Jug, 4 1/2″	325.00	400.00	225.00
Chl-92	Jug, 5″	350.00	425.00	245.00

Cat.No.	Shape	U.S. $	Can. $	U.K. £
Chl-97	Nut dish	50.00	75.00	45.00
Chl-201	Plate, 4″ sq.	50.00	75.00	40.00
Chl-202	Plate, 5″ sq.	65.00	85.00	45.00
Chl-203	Plate, 6″ sq.	75.00	100.00	50.00
Chl-204	Plate, 7″ sq.	100.00	125.00	65.00
Chl-205	Plate, 8″ sq.	135.00	165.00	85.00
Chl-206	Plate, 9″ sq.	150.00	185.00	100.00
Chl-207	Plate, 10″ sq.	165.00	200.00	115.00
Chl-112	Relish dish, small	200.00	250.00	125.00
Chl-115	Salad bowl, chrome rim	165.00	200.00	115.00
Chl-117	Salt and pepper	100.00	125.00	65.00
Chl-118	Salt and pepper on tray	175.00	225.00	125.00
Chl-120	Sandwich tray, 10″ x 6″	135.00	165.00	85.00
Chl-121	Sandwich tray, 12″ x 7″	150.00	200.00	100.00
Chl-125	Sauce boat and liner	150.00	200.00	100.00
Chl-130	Teacup and saucer	100.00	125.00	65.00
Chl-135	Teapot, 2 cup	400.00	475.00	275.00
Chl-136	Teapot, 4 cup	600.00	725.00	425.00
Chl-137	Teapot, 6 cup	700.00	850.00	500.00
CHl-140	Teapot, stacking	800.00	950.00	550.00
Chl-145	Tennis set	125.00	150.00	75.00
Chl-150	Toast rack, 4 slice	250.00	300.00	175.00
Chl-151	Toast rack, 2 slice	200.00	250.00	125.00
Chl-155	Trivet	125.00	150.00	75.00
Chl-160	Vase, bud	135.00	165.00	85.00

CHINTZ

The pattern number is 2836 and was probably introduced in the mid 1930s. The pattern has elements of handpainting, including a butterfly.

Cat.No.	Shape	U.S. $	Can. $	U.K. £
Chz-04	Bonbon dish	30.00	35.00	25.00
Chz-09	Bowl, 5″	30.00	35.00	25.00
Chz-14	Bowl, 8″ soup	40.00	50.00	30.00
Chz-23	Breakfast set	450.00	540.00	325.00
Chz-28	Butter dish	100.00	125.00	65.00
Chz-30	Butter pat	25.00	30.00	20.00
Chz-35	Cake plate, open handles	100.00	125.00	65.00
Chz-36	Cake plate, tab handles	85.00	100.00	60.00
Chz-37	Cake plate, 8″ sq. pedestal	100.00	125.00	65.00
Chz-40	Cake stand, 2 tier	100.00	125.00	65.00
Chz-45	Canoe-shaped dish	135.00	165.00	85.00
Chz-50	Cheese keep	125.00	150.00	75.00
Chz-52	Coaster	25.00	30.00	20.00
Chz-55	Coffee pot	375.00	450.00	250.00
Chz-60	Compote, footed	80.00	95.00	50.00
Chz-65	Condiment set on tray	100.00	125.00	65.00
Chz-70	Cream and sugar	50.00	75.00	45.00
Chz-71	Cream and sugar on tray	100.00	125.00	65.00
Chz-75	Demi-tasse	40.00	50.00	30.00
Chz-77	Egg cup, footed	35.00	40.00	25.00
Chz-80	Hot water jug	160.00	200.00	125.00
Chz-85	Jam pot with liner	85.00	100.00	60.00
Chz-90	Jug, 4″	135.00	165.00	85.00
Chz-91	Jug, 4 1/2″	150.00	200.00	125.00
Chz-92	Jug, 5″	150.00	200.00	125.00
Chz-97	Nut dish	25.00	30.00	20.00
Chz-201	Plate, 4″ sq.	30.00	35.00	25.00
Chz-202	Plate, 5″ sq.	35.00	40.00	25.00
Chz-203	Plate, 6″ sq.	40.00	50.00	30.00
Chz-204	Plate, 7″ sq.	45.00	55.00	35.00
Chz-205	Plate, 8″ sq.	65.00	80.00	45.00
Chz-206	Plate, 9″ sq.	75.00	90.00	50.00
Chz-207	Plate, 10″ sq .	85.00	100.00	60.00
Chz-112	Relish dish, small	85.00	100.00	60.00
Chz-115	Salad bowl, chrome rim	100.00	125.00	65.00
Chz-117	Salt and pepper	50.00	75.00	40.00
Chz-118	Salt and pepper on tray	125.00	150.00	80.00
Chz-120	Sandwich tray, 10″ x 6″	60.00	75.00	45.00
Chz-121	Sandwich tray, 12″ x 7″	75.00	85.00	50.00
Chz-125	Sauce boat and liner	65.00	80.00	45.00
Chz-130	Teacup and saucer	40.00	50.00	30.00
Chz-135	Teapot, 2 cup	175.00	200.00	125.00
Chz-136	Teapot, 4 cup	275.00	325.00	200.00
Chz-137	Teapot, 6 cup	325.00	400.00	225.00
Chz-140	Teapot, stacking	400.00	475.00	275.00
Chz-145	Tennis set	55.00	70.00	40.00
Chz-150	Toast rack, 4 slice	150.00	200.00	100.00
Chz-151	Toast rack, 2 slice	135.00	165.00	85.00
Chz-155	Trivet	55.00	70.00	40.00
Chz-160	Vase, bud	60.00	75.00	45.00

CLEVEDON

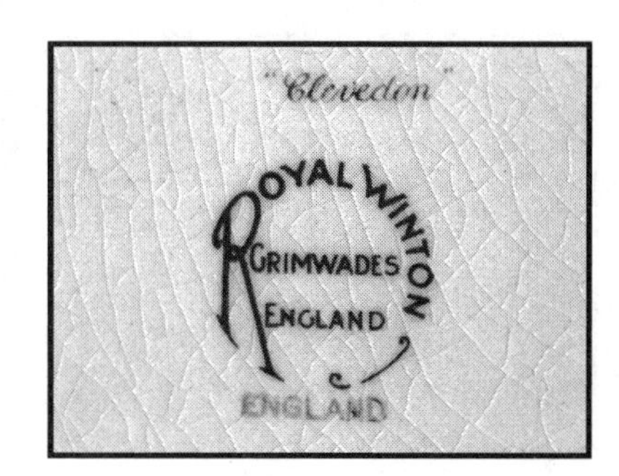

The pattern number is 1844. This pattern was introduced in 1934 and is an alternate colourway to **Cranstone** 1154, an earlier version. It also came with burgundy trim.

Cat.No.	Shape	U.S. $	Can. $	U.K. £
Cl-04	Bonbon dish	75.00	90.00	50.00
Cl-09	Bowl, 5″	50.00	65.00	35.00
Cl-14	Bowl, 8″ soup	85.00	100.00	60.00
Cl-23	Breakfast set	950.00	1,200.00	675.00
Cl-28	Butter dish	225.00	265.00	150.00
Cl-30	Butter pat	65.00	80.00	45.00
Cl-35	Cake plate, open handles	225.00	275.00	150.00
Cl-36	Cake plate, tab handles	200.00	250.00	125.00
Cl-37	Cake plate, 8″ sq. pedestal	225.00	275.00	150.00
Cl-40	Cake stand, 2 tier	225.00	275.00	150.00
Cl-45	Canoe-shaped dish	325.00	400.00	225.00
Cl-50	Cheese keep	300.00	350.00	200.00
Cl-52	Coaster	50.00	65.00	35.00
Cl-55	Coffee pot	850.00	1,100.00	600.00
Cl-60	Compote, footed	175.00	225.00	125.00
Cl-65	Condiment set on tray	275.00	325.00	175.00
Cl-70	Cream and sugar	150.00	175.00	85.00
Cl-71	Cream and sugar on tray	275.00	325.00	175.00
Cl-75	Demi-tasse	100.00	125.00	65.00
Cl-77	Egg cup, footed	85.00	100.00	60.00
Cl-80	Hot water jug	375.00	450.00	265.00
Cl-85	Jam pot with liner	200.00	250.00	150.00
Cl-90	Jug, 4″	325.00	380.00	225.00
Cl-91	Jug, 4 1/2″	350.00	450.00	250.00
Cl-92	Jug, 5″	375.00	450.00	250.00

Cat.No.	Shape	U.S. $	Can. $	U.K. £
Cl-97	Nut dish	65.00	80.00	45.00
Cl-201	Plate, 4″ sq.	50.00	75.00	40.00
Cl-202	Plate, 5″ sq.	65.00	80.00	45.00
Cl-203	Plate, 6″ sq.	75.00	100.00	50.00
Cl-204	Plate, 7″ sq.	100.00	125.00	65.00
Cl-205	Plate, 8″ sq.	135.00	165.00	85.00
Cl-206	Plate, 9″ sq.	150.00	175.00	100.00
Cl-207	Plate, 10″ sq.	165.00	200.00	125.00
Cl-112	Relish dish, small	200.00	250.00	125.00
Cl-115	Salad bowl, chrome rim	175.00	225.00	125.00
Cl-117	Salt and pepper	100.00	125.00	65.00
Cl-118	Salt and pepper on tray	175.00	200.00	125.00
Cl-120	Sandwich tray, 10″ x 6″	150.00	175.00	100.00
Cl-121	Sandwich tray, 12″ x 7″	165.00	200.00	125.00
Cl-125	Sauce boat and liner	165.00	200.00	125.00
Cl-130	Teacup and saucer	100.00	125.00	65.00
Cl-135	Teapot, 2 cup	425.00	500.00	300.00
Cl-136	Teapot, 4 cup	625.00	750.00	450.00
Cl-137	Teapot, 6 cup	725.00	875.00	500.00
Cl-140	Teapot, stacking	800.00	950.00	550.00
Cl-145	Tennis set	125.00	150.00	75.00
Cl-150	Toast rack, 4 slice	260.00	325.00	175.00
Cl-151	Toast rack, 2 slice	200.00	250.00	150.00
Cl-155	Trivet	135.00	165.00	85.00
Cl-160	Vase, bud	135.00	165.00	85.00

CLYDE

The pattern number 5315 is for the green-leaf version which was probably introduced late in 1939. The three versions of **Clyde** feature green, brown and blue leaves, but the brown and blue versions have not been found with a pattern name backstamp.

Cat.No.	Shape	U.S. $	Can. $	U.K. £
Cly-04	Bonbon dish	30.00	35.00	25.00
Cly-09	Bowl, 5″	30.00	35.00	25.00
Cly-14	Bowl, 8″ soup	40.00	50.00	30.00
Cly-23	Breakfast set	450.00	550.00	325.00
Cly-28	Butter dish	100.00	125.00	65.00
Cly-30	Butter pat	25.00	30.00	20.00
Cly-35	Cake plate, open handles	100.00	125.00	75.00
Cly-36	Cake plate, tab handles	85.00	100.00	60.00
Cly-37	Cake plate, 8″ sq. pedestal	100.00	125.00	65.00
Cly-40	Cake stand, 2 tier	100.00	125.00	65.00
Cly-45	Canoe-shaped dish	135.00	165.00	85.00
Cly-50	Cheese keep	125.00	175.00	100.00
Cly-52	Coaster	25.00	30.00	20.00
Cly-55	Coffee pot	375.00	450.00	250.00
Cly-60	Compote, footed	75.00	100.00	50.00
Cly-65	Condiment set on tray	100.00	125.00	65.00
Cly-70	Cream and sugar	60.00	75.00	45.00
Cly-71	Cream and sugar on tray	100.00	125.00	65.00
Cly-75	Demi-tasse	40.00	50.00	30.00
Cly-77	Egg cup, footed	35.00	40.00	25.00
Cly-80	Hot water jug	165.00	200.00	125.00
Cly-85	Jam pot with liner	85.00	100.00	60.00
Cly-90	Jug, 4″	135.00	165.00	85.00
Cly-91	Jug, 4 1/2″	150.00	175.00	100.00
Cly-92	Jug, 5″	165.00	200.00	125.00

Cat.No.	Shape	U.S. $	Can. $	U.K. £
Cly-97	Nut dish	25.00	30.00	20.00
Cly-201	Plate, 4″ sq.	30.00	35.00	25.00
Cly-202	Plate, 5″ sq.	35.00	40.00	25.00
Cly-203	Plate, 6″ sq.	40.00	50.00	30.00
Cly-204	Plate, 7″ sq.	45.00	50.00	35.00
Cly-205	Plate, 8″ sq.	65.00	80.00	45.00
Cly-206	Plate, 9″ sq.	75.00	90.00	50.00
Cly-207	Plate, 10″ sq.	85.00	100.00	60.00
Cly-112	Relish dish, small	85.00	100.00	60.00
Cly-115	Salad bowl, chrome rim	100.00	125.00	65.00
Cly-117	Salt and pepper	50.00	75.00	40.00
Cly-118	Salt and pepper on tray	115.00	140.00	80.00
Cly-120	Sandwich tray, 10″ x 6″	50.00	75.00	45.00
Cly-121	Sandwich tray, 12″ x 7″	75.00	100.00	50.00
Cly-125	Sauce boat and liner	65.00	80.00	45.00
Cly-130	Teacup and saucer	40.00	50.00	30.00
Cly-135	Teapot, 2 cup	175.00	200.00	125.00
Cly-136	Teapot, 4 cup	275.00	325.00	175.00
Cly-137	Teapot, 6 cup	325.00	400.00	225.00
Cly-140	Teapot, stacking	400.00	475.00	275.00
Cly-145	Tennis set	50.00	75.00	40.00
Cly-150	Toast rack, 4 slice	165.00	200.00	125.00
Cly-151	Toast rack, 2 slice	100.00	125.00	65.00
Cly-155	Trivet	50.00	75.00	40.00
Cly-160	Vase, bud	50.00	75.00	45.00

COTSWOLD

The pattern number is 408 and the pattern was registered in Canada in 1952.

Cat.No.	Shape	U.S. $	Can. $	U.K. £
Co-04	Bonbon dish	50.00	75.00	40.00
Co-09	Bowl, 5″	50.00	65.00	35.00
Co-14	Bowl, 8″ soup	75.00	100.00	50.00
Co-23	Breakfast set	775.00	930.00	550.00
Co-28	Butter dish	165.00	200.00	125.00
Co-30	Butter pat	45.00	50.00	35.00
Co-35	Cake plate, open handles	165.00	200.00	125.00
Co-36	Cake plate, tab handles	150.00	175.00	100.00
Co-37	Cake plate, 8″ sq. pedestal	175.00	225.00	125.00
Co-40	Cake stand, 2 tier	175.00	225.00	125.00
Co-45	Canoe-shaped dish	250.00	300.00	165.00
Co-50	Cheese keep	200.00	250.00	150.00
Co-52	Coaster	40.00	50.00	30.00
Co-55	Coffee pot	600.00	725.00	425.00
Co-60	Compote, footed	135.00	165.00	95.00
Co-65	Condiment set on tray	200.00	250.00	135.00
Co-70	Cream and sugar	100.00	125.00	65.00
Co-71	Cream and sugar on tray	175.00	225.00	135.00
Co-75	Demi-tasse	75.00	100.00	50.00
Co-77	Egg cup, footed	65.00	80.00	45.00
Co-80	Hot water jug	275.00	350.00	200.00
Co-85	Jam pot with liner	150.00	175.00	100.00
Co-90	Jug, 4″	200.00	250.00	135.00
Co-91	Jug, 4 1/2″	225.00	275.00	150.00
Co-92	Jug, 5″	250.00	300.00	175.00

Cat.No.	Shape	U.S. $	Can. $	U.K. £
Co-97	Nut dish	45.00	50.00	35.00
Co-201	Plate, 4″ sq.	50.00	65.00	35.00
Co-202	Plate, 5″ sq.	55.00	75.00	40.00
Co-203	Plate, 6″ sq.	60.00	75.00	45.00
Co-204	Plate, 7″ sq.	75.00	90.00	50.00
Co-205	Plate, 8″ sq.	125.00	150.00	75.00
Co-206	Plate, 9″ sq.	125.00	150.00	75.00
Co-207	Plate, 10″ sq.	135.00	165.00	85.00
Co-112	Relish dish, small	150.00	175.00	100.00
Co-115	Salad bowl, chrome rim	125.00	150.00	75.00
Co-117	Salt and pepper	75.00	90.00	50.00
Co-118	Salt and pepper on tray	150.00	175.00	100.00
Co-120	Sandwich tray, 10″ x 6″	100.00	125.00	65.00
Co-121	Sandwich tray, 12″ x 7″	125.00	150.00	90.00
Co-125	Sauce boat and liner	150.00	175.00	100.00
Co-130	Teacup and saucer	70.00	85.00	50.00
Co-135	Teapot, 2 cup	275.00	350.00	200.00
Co-136	Teapot, 4 cup	450.00	550.00	300.00
Co-137	Teapot, 6 cup	550.00	675.00	400.00
Co-140	Teapot, stacking	650.00	775.00	450.00
Co-145	Tennis set	100.00	125.00	65.00
Co-150	Toast rack, 4 slice	200.00	250.00	135.00
Co-151	Toast rack, 2 slice	135.00	165.00	85.00
Co-155	Trivet	100.00	125.00	65.00
Co-160	Vase, bud	100.00	125.00	65.00

CRANSTONE

The pattern number is 1154 and an example was purchased by the Queen at the 1935 British Industries Fair. The alternate colourway is **Clevedon** 1844.

Cat.No.	Shape	U.S. $	Can. $	U.K. £
Cr-04	Bonbon dish	80.00	95.00	55.00
Cr-09	Bowl, 5″	50.00	75.00	40.00
Cr-14	Bowl, 8″ soup	100.00	125.00	65.00
Cr-23	Breakfast set	950.00	1,200.00	675.00
Cr-28	Butter dish	225.00	275.00	160.00
Cr-30	Butter pat	65.00	80.00	45.00
Cr-35	Cake plate, open handles	225.00	275.00	150.00
Cr-36	Cake plate, tab handles	200.00	250.00	135.00
Cr-37	Cake plate, 8″ sq. pedestal	250.00	300.00	175.00
Cr-40	Cake stand, 2 tier	250.00	300.00	175.00
Cr-45	Canoe-shaped dish	350.00	400.00	225.00
Cr-50	Cheese keep	300.00	350.00	200.00
Cr-52	Coaster	60.00	75.00	45.00
Cr-55	Coffee pot	875.00	1,100.00	600.00
Cr-60	Compote, footed	200.00	250.00	135.00
Cr-65	Condiment set on tray	275.00	325.00	175.00
Cr-70	Cream and sugar	150.00	175.00	85.00
Cr-71	Cream and sugar on tray	275.00	325.00	175.00
Cr-75	Demi-tasse	100.00	125.00	65.00
Cr-77	Egg cup, footed	85.00	110.00	60.00
Cr-80	Hot water jug	400.00	475.00	275.00
Cr-85	Jam pot with liner	200.00	250.00	135.00
Cr-90	Jug, 4″	325.00	400.00	225.00
Cr-91	Jug, 4 1/2″	375.00	425.00	250.00
Cr-92	Jug, 5″	400.00	475.00	275.00

Cat.No.	Shape	U.S. $	Can. $	U.K. £
Cr-97	Nut dish	65.00	85.00	45.00
Cr-201	Plate, 4″ sq.	65.00	85.00	45.00
Cr-202	Plate, 5″ sq.	65.00	85.00	45.00
Cr-203	Plate, 6″ sq.	75.00	100.00	50.00
Cr-204	Plate, 7″ sq.	100.00	125.00	65.00
Cr-205	Plate, 8″ sq.	150.00	175.00	100.00
Cr-206	Plate, 9″ sq.	150.00	175.00	100.00
Cr-207	Plate, 10″ sq.	175.00	225.00	125.00
Cr-112	Relish dish, small	200.00	250.00	150.00
Cr-115	Salad bowl, chrome rim	175.00	225.00	125.00
Cr-117	Salt and pepper	100.00	125.00	65.00
Cr-118	Salt and pepper on tray	200.00	250.00	150.00
Cr-120	Sandwich tray, 10″ x 6″	150.00	200.00	100.00
Cr-121	Sandwich tray, 12″ x 7″	175.00	225.00	125.00
Cr-125	Sauce boat and liner	175.00	225.00	125.00
Cr-130	Teacup and saucer	100.00	125.00	65.00
Cr-135	Teapot, 2 cup	450.00	550.00	300.00
Cr-136	Teapot, 4 cup	625.00	750.00	450.00
Cr-137	Teapot, 6 cup	725.00	875.00	500.00
Cr-140	Teapot, stacking	825.00	1,000.00	575.00
Cr-145	Tennis set	150.00	175.00	100.00
Cr-150	Toast rack, 4 slice	275.00	350.00	200.00
Cr-151	Toast rack, 2 slice	225.00	275.00	150.00
Cr-155	Trivet	150.00	175.00	100.00
Cr-160	Vase, bud	135.00	165.00	85.00

CROCUS

Photograph not available at press time

The pattern number of the white background **Crocus** is 111 and the black 112. The pattern is mentioned in a 1939 article but it is the one Royal Winton chintz pattern that has never been found with a pattern name backstamp.

Cat.No.	Shape	U.S. $	Can. $	U.K. £
Cro-04	Bonbon dish	75.00	100.00	50.00
Cro-09	Bowl, 5″	50.00	65.00	35.00
Cro-14	Bowl, 8″ soup	80.00	95.00	50.00
Cro-23	Breakfast set	850.00	1,100.00	600.00
Cro-28	Butter dish	200.00	250.00	150.00
Cro-30	Butter pat	60.00	75.00	45.00
Cro-35	Cake plate, open handles	200.00	250.00	150.00
Cro-36	Cake plate, tab handles	175.00	225.00	135.00
Cro-37	Cake plate, 8″ sq. pedestal	225.00	275.00	150.00
Cro-40	Cake stand, 2 tier	225.00	275.00	150.00
Cro-45	Canoe-shaped dish	275.00	350.00	200.00
Cro-50	Cheese keep	275.00	350.00	200.00
Cro-52	Coaster	50.00	75.00	40.00
Cro-55	Coffee pot	850.00	1,100.00	600.00
Cro-60	Compote, footed	175.00	225.00	125.00
Cro-65	Condiment set on tray	250.00	300.00	175.00
Cro-70	Cream and sugar	135.00	165.00	85.00
Cro-71	Cream and sugar on tray	250.00	300.00	175.00
Cro-75	Demi-tasse	100.00	125.00	65.00
Cro-77	Egg cup, footed	75.00	100.00	50.00
Cro-80	Hot water jug	350.00	425.00	250.00
Cro-85	Jam pot with liner	175.00	225.00	135.00
Cro-90	Jug, 4″	300.00	350.00	200.00
Cro-91	Jug, 4 1/2″	325.00	400.00	225.00
Cro-92	Jug, 5″	350.00	425.00	250.00
Cro-97	Nut dish	50.00	75.00	40.00
Cro-201	Plate, 4″ sq.	50.00	75.00	40.00
Cro-202	Plate, 5″ sq.	65.00	80.00	45.00
Cro-203	Plate, 6″ sq.	75.00	90.00	50.00
Cro-204	Plate, 7″ sq.	100.00	125.00	75.00
Cro-205	Plate, 8″ sq.	135.00	165.00	95.00
Cro-206	Plate, 9″ sq.	150.00	175.00	100.00
Cro-207	Plate, 10″ sq .	165.00	200.00	115.00
Cro-112	Relish dish, small	200.00	250.00	125.00
Cro-115	Salad bowl, chrome rim	165.00	200.00	115.00
Cro-117	Salt and pepper	100.00	125.00	65.00
Cro-118	Salt and pepper on tray	175.00	225.00	125.00
Cro-120	Sandwich tray, 10″ x 6″	135.00	165.00	95.00
Cro-121	Sandwich tray, 12″ x 7″	165.00	200.00	115.00
Cro-125	Sauce boat and liner	165.00	200.00	115.00
Cro-130	Teacup and saucer	100.00	125.00	65.00
Cro-135	Teapot, 2 cup	400.00	475.00	275.00
Cro-136	Teapot, 4 cup	600.00	725.00	425.00
Cro-137	Teapot, 6 cup	700.00	850.00	500.00
Cro-140	Teapot, stacking	800.00	950.00	550.00
Cro-145	Tennis set	125.00	150.00	75.00
Cro-150	Toast rack, 4 slice	250.00	300.00	175.00
Cro-151	Toast rack, 2 slice	200.00	250.00	150.00
Cro-155	Trivet	125.00	150.00	75.00
Cro-160	Vase, bud	125.00	150.00	75.00

CROMER

The pattern number is 2078 and belongs to the "all-over" non-chintz pattern group.

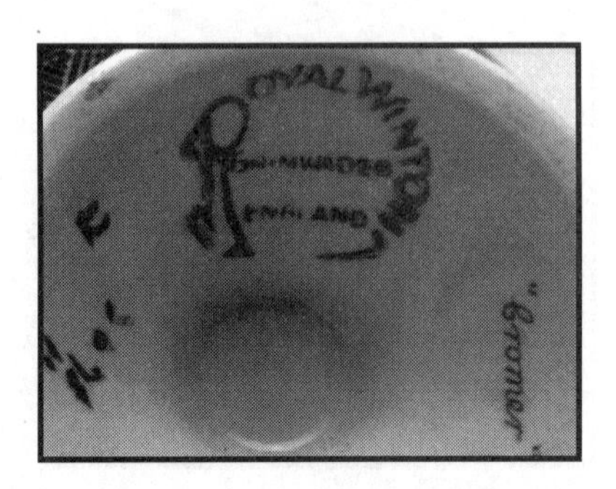

Cat.No.	Shape	U.S. $	Can. $	U.K. £
Crom-04	Bonbon dish	40.00	50.00	30.00
Crom-09	Bowl, 5"	35.00	40.00	25.00
Crom-14	Bowl, 8" soup	50.00	75.00	40.00
Crom-23	Breakfast set	550.00	650.00	375.00
Crom-28	Butter dish	125.00	150.00	75.00
Crom-30	Butter pat	35.00	40.00	25.00
Crom-35	Cake plate, open handles	150.00	175.00	100.00
Crom-36	Cake plate, tab handles	125.00	150.00	75.00
Crom-37	Cake plate, 8" sq. pedestal	150.00	175.00	100.00
Crom-40	Cake stand, 2 tier	150.00	175.00	100.00
Crom-45	Canoe-shaped dish	150.00	175.00	100.00
Crom-50	Cheese keep	150.00	175.00	100.00
Crom-52	Coaster	30.00	35.00	25.00
Crom-55	Coffee pot	450.00	550.00	325.00
Crom-60	Compote, footed	100.00	125.00	65.00
Crom-65	Condiment set on tray	135.00	165.00	85.00
Crom-70	Cream and sugar	75.00	100.00	50.00
Crom-71	Cream and sugar on tray	135.00	165.00	85.00
Crom-75	Demi-tasse	50.00	65.00	35.00
Crom-77	Egg cup, footed	45.00	50.00	35.00
Crom-80	Hot water jug	200.00	250.00	125.00
Crom-85	Jam pot with liner	100.00	125.00	75.00
Crom-90	Jug, 4"	165.00	200.00	100.00
Crom-91	Jug, 4 1/2"	175.00	225.00	125.00
Crom-92	Jug, 5"	200.00	250.00	125.00

Cat.No.	Shape	U.S. $	Can. $	U.K. £
Crom-97	Nut dish	35.00	40.00	25.00
Crom-201	Plate, 4" sq.	35.00	40.00	25.00
Crom-202	Plate, 5" sq.	40.00	50.00	30.00
Crom-203	Plate, 6" sq.	45.00	50.00	35.00
Crom-204	Plate, 7" sq.	50.00	75.00	40.00
Crom-205	Plate, 8" sq.	100.00	125.00	65.00
Crom-206	Plate, 9" sq.	100.00	125.00	65.00
Crom-207	Plate, 10" sq .	115.00	140.00	80.00
Crom-112	Relish dish, small	100.00	125.00	65.00
Crom-115	Salad bowl, chrome rim	100.00	125.00	65.00
Crom-117	Salt and pepper	55.00	70.00	40.00
Crom-118	Salt and pepper on tray	125.00	150.00	75.00
Crom-120	Sandwich tray, 10" x 6"	75.00	100.00	50.00
Crom-121	Sandwich tray, 12" x 7"	85.00	100.00	60.00
Crom-125	Sauce boat and liner	100.00	125.00	65.00
Crom-130	Teacup and saucer	50.00	65.00	35.00
Crom-135	Teapot, 2 cup	200.00	250.00	135.00
Crom-136	Teapot, 4 cup	300.00	350.00	200.00
Crom-137	Teapot, 6 cup	400.00	475.00	275.00
Crom-140	Teapot, stacking	500.00	600.00	350.00
Crom-145	Tennis set	75.00	100.00	50.00
Crom-150	Toast rack, 4 slice	165.00	195.00	115.00
Crom-151	Toast rack, 2 slice	135.00	165.00	85.00
Crom-155	Trivet	75.00	100.00	50.00
Crom-160	Vase, bud	75.00	100.00	50.00

DELPHINIUM CHINTZ

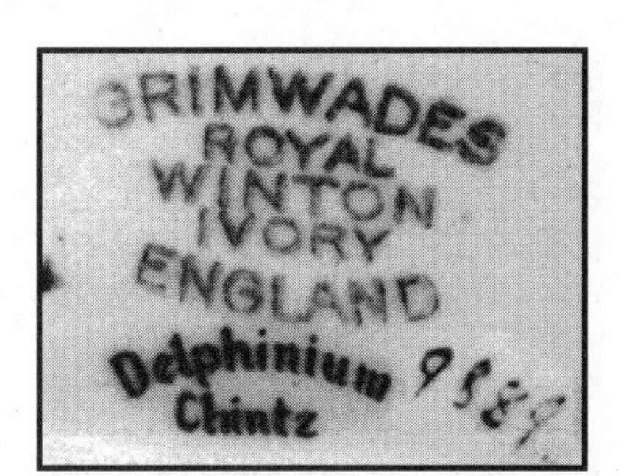

The pattern number is 9889. This pattern was introduced in 1931 in an advertisement in the *Pottery Gazette*. It first appeared a year earlier as a single spray on an ivory ground.

Cat.No.	Shape	U.S. $	Can. $	U.K. £
De-04	Bonbon dish	45.00	55.00	35.00
De-09	Bowl, 5″	40.00	50.00	30.00
De-14	Bowl, 8″ soup	75.00	100.00	50.00
De-23	Breakfast set	650.00	775.00	450.00
De-28	Butter dish	135.00	165.00	85.00
De-30	Butter pat	40.00	50.00	30.00
De-35	Cake plate, open handles	135.00	165.00	85.00
De-36	Cake plate, tab handles	125.00	150.00	75.00
De-37	Cake plate, 8″ sq. pedestal	150.00	175.00	100.00
De-40	Cake stand, 2 tier	150.00	175.00	100.00
De-45	Canoe-shaped dish	200.00	250.00	125.00
De-50	Cheese keep	175.00	200.00	125.00
De-52	Coaster	35.00	40.00	25.00
De-55	Coffee pot	525.00	650.00	375.00
De-60	Compote, footed	100.00	125.00	65.00
De-65	Condiment set on tray	150.00	175.00	100.00
De-70	Cream and sugar	85.00	100.00	60.00
De-71	Cream and sugar on tray	150.00	175.00	100.00
De-75	Demi-tasse	60.00	75.00	45.00
De-77	Egg cup, footed	50.00	65.00	35.00
De-80	Hot water jug	225.00	275.00	150.00
De-85	Jam pot with liner	125.00	150.00	75.00
De-90	Jug, 4″	200.00	250.00	135.00
De-91	Jug, 4 1/2″	200.00	250.00	135.00
De-92	Jug, 5″	225.00	275.00	150.00

Cat.No.	Shape	U.S. $	Can. $	U.K. £
De-97	Nut dish	40.00	50.00	30.00
De-201	Plate, 4″ sq.	35.00	40.00	25.00
De-202	Plate, 5″ sq.	40.00	50.00	30.00
De-203	Plate, 6″ sq.	45.00	55.00	35.00
De-204	Plate, 7″ sq.	50.00	65.00	35.00
De-205	Plate, 8″ sq.	100.00	125.00	65.00
De-206	Plate, 9″ sq.	100.00	125.00	65.00
De-207	Plate, 10″ sq.	125.00	150.00	75.00
De-112	Relish dish, small	125.00	150.00	75.00
De-115	Salad bowl, chrome rim	100.00	125.00	65.00
De-117	Salt and pepper	65.00	80.00	45.00
De-118	Salt and pepper on tray	150.00	175.00	85.00
De-120	Sandwich tray, 10″ x 6″	85.00	100.00	60.00
De-121	Sandwich tray, 12″ x 7″	100.00	125.00	65.00
De-125	Sauce boat and liner	125.00	150.00	75.00
De-130	Teacup and saucer	60.00	75.00	45.00
De-135	Teapot, 2 cup	250.00	300.00	175.00
De-136	Teapot, 4 cup	350.00	425.00	250.00
De-137	Teapot, 6 cup	450.00	550.00	325.00
De-140	Teapot, stacking	600.00	750.00	425.00
De-145	Tennis set	75.00	100.00	50.00
De-150	Toast rack, 4 slice	175.00	200.00	125.00
De-151	Toast rack, 2 slice	125.00	150.00	75.00
De-155	Trivet	75.00	100.00	50.00
De-160	Vase, bud	85.00	115.00	60.00

DORSET

The pattern number is 274, and this pattern was featured in an advertisement in Toronto, Canada, in 1949.

Cat.No.	Shape	U.S. $	Can. $	U.K. £
Do-04	Bonbon dish	40.00	50.00	30.00
Do-09	Bowl, 5″	35.00	40.00	25.00
Do-14	Bowl, 8″ soup	50.00	75.00	40.00
Do-23	Breakfast set	550.00	650.00	375.00
Do-28	Butter dish	125.00	150.00	75.00
Do-30	Butter pat	35.00	40.00	25.00
Do-35	Cake plate, open handles	150.00	175.00	100.00
Do-36	Cake plate, tab handles	125.00	150.00	75.00
Do-37	Cake plate, 8″ sq. pedestal	150.00	175.00	100.00
Do-40	Cake stand, 2 tier	150.00	175.00	100.00
Do-45	Canoe-shaped dish	150.00	175.00	100.00
Do-50	Cheese keep	150.00	175.00	100.00
Do-52	Coaster	30.00	35.00	25.00
Do-55	Coffee pot	450.00	550.00	325.00
Do-60	Compote, footed	100.00	125.00	65.00
Do-65	Condiment set on tray	135.00	165.00	85.00
Do-70	Cream and sugar	75.00	100.00	50.00
Do-71	Cream and sugar on tray	135.00	165.00	85.00
Do-75	Demi-tasse	50.00	65.00	35.00
Do-77	Egg cup, footed	45.00	55.00	35.00
Do-80	Hot water jug	200.00	250.00	150.00
Do-85	Jam pot with liner	100.00	125.00	65.00
Do-90	Jug, 4″	165.00	195.00	115.00
Do-91	Jug, 4 1/2″	175.00	225.00	125.00
Do-92	Jug, 5″	200.00	250.00	150.00

Cat.No.	Shape	U.S. $	Can. $	U.K. £
Do-97	Nut dish	35.00	40.00	25.00
Do-201	Plate, 4″ sq.	35.00	40.00	25.00
Do-202	Plate, 5″ sq.	40.00	50.00	30.00
Do-203	Plate, 6″ sq.	45.00	50.00	35.00
Do-204	Plate, 7″ sq.	50.00	75.00	40.00
Do-205	Plate, 8″ sq.	100.00	125.00	65.00
Do-206	Plate, 9″ sq.	100.00	125.00	65.00
Do-207	Plate, 10″ sq.	125.00	150.00	75.00
Do-112	Relish dish, small	100.00	125.00	65.00
Do-115	Salad bowl, chrome rim	100.00	125.00	65.00
Do-117	Salt and pepper	50.00	75.00	40.00
Do-118	Salt and pepper on tray	125.00	150.00	75.00
Do-120	Sandwich tray, 10″ x 6″	75.00	90.00	50.00
Do-121	Sandwich tray, 12″ x 7″	85.00	100.00	60.00
Do-125	Sauce boat and liner	100.00	125.00	65.00
Do-130	Teacup and saucer	50.00	65.00	35.00
Do-135	Teapot, 2 cup	200.00	250.00	150.00
Do-136	Teapot, 4 cup	300.00	350.00	200.00
Do-137	Teapot, 6 cup	400.00	475.00	275.00
Do-140	Teapot, stacking	500.00	600.00	350.00
Do-145	Tennis set	75.00	100.00	50.00
Do-150	Toast rack, 4 slice	165.00	200.00	115.00
Do-151	Toast rack, 2 slice	135.00	165.00	85.00
Do-155	Trivet	75.00	100.00	50.00
Do-160	Vase, bud	75.00	100.00	50.00

ELEANOR

The pattern number is 375, and was introduced early in the 1950s and remained in production well into the 1960s.

Cat.No.	Shape	U.S. $	Can. $	U.K. £
El-04	Bonbon dish	45.00	55.00	35.00
El-09	Bowl, 5″	40.00	50.00	30.00
El-14	Bowl, 8″ soup	75.00	10.00	50.00
El-23	Breakfast set	650.00	775.00	450.00
El-28	Butter dish	135.00	165.00	85.00
El-30	Butter pat	40.00	50.00	30.00
El-35	Cake plate, open handles	135.00	165.00	85.00
El-36	Cake plate, tab handles	125.00	150.00	75.00
El-37	Cake plate, 8″ sq. pedestal	150.00	175.00	100.00
El-40	Cake stand, 2 tier	150.00	175.00	100.00
El-45	Canoe-shaped dish	200.00	250.00	135.00
El-50	Cheese keep	175.00	200.00	125.00
El-52	Coaster	35.00	40.00	25.00
El-55	Coffee pot	525.00	625.00	350.00
El-60	Compote, footed	100.00	125.00	65.00
El-65	Condiment set on tray	150.00	175.00	100.00
El-70	Cream and sugar	85.00	100.00	60.00
El-71	Cream and sugar on tray	150.00	175.00	100.00
El-75	Demi-tasse	60.00	75.00	45.00
El-77	Egg cup, footed	50.00	65.00	35.00
El-80	Hot water jug	225.00	275.00	150.00
El-85	Jam pot with liner	125.00	150.00	75.00
El-90	Jug, 4″	200.00	250.00	135.00
El-91	Jug, 4 1/2″	200.00	250.00	135.00
El-92	Jug, 5″	225.00	275.00	150.00

Cat.No.	Shape	U.S. $	Can. $	U.K. £
El-97	Nut dish	40.00	50.00	30.00
El-201	Plate, 4″ sq.	35.00	40.00	25.00
El-202	Plate, 5″ sq.	40.00	50.00	30.00
El-203	Plate, 6″ sq.	45.00	50.00	35.00
El-204	Plate, 7″ sq.	50.00	65.00	35.00
El-205	Plate, 8″ sq.	100.00	125.00	65.00
El-206	Plate, 9″ sq.	100.00	125.00	65.00
El-207	Plate, 10″ sq.	125.00	150.00	75.00
El-112	Relish dish, small	125.00	150.00	75.00
El-115	Salad bowl, chrome rim	100.00	125.00	65.00
El-117	Salt and pepper	65.00	80.00	45.00
El-118	Salt and pepper on tray	150.00	175.00	100.00
El-120	Sandwich tray, 10″ x 6″	85.00	100.00	60.00
El-121	Sandwich tray, 12″ x 7″	100.00	125.00	65.00
El-125	Sauce boat and liner	125.00	150.00	75.00
El-130	Teacup and saucer	60.00	75.00	45.00
El-135	Teapot, 2 cup	250.00	300.00	175.00
El-136	Teapot, 4 cup	350.00	425.00	250.00
El-137	Teapot, 6 cup	450.00	550.00	325.00
El-140	Teapot, stacking	600.00	725.00	425.00
El-145	Tennis set	75.00	100.00	50.00
El-150	Toast rack, 4 slice	175.00	200.00	125.00
El-151	Toast rack, 2 slice	115.00	140.00	80.00
El-155	Trivet	75.00	100.00	50.00
El-160	Vase, bud	85.00	100.00	60.00

ENGLISH ROSE

The pattern number is 381 and the pattern was registered in Canada in 1951.

Cat.No.	Shape	U.S. $	Can. $	U.K. £
ER-04	Bonbon dish	75.00	100.00	50.00
ER-09	Bowl, 5″	50.00	75.00	40.00
ER-14	Bowl, 8″ soup	100.00	125.00	65.00
ER-23	Breakfast set	950.00	1,200.00	675.00
ER-28	Butter dish	225.00	275.00	150.00
ER-30	Butter pat	65.00	80.00	45.00
ER-35	Cake plate, open handles	225.00	275.00	150.00
ER-36	Cake plate, tab handles	200.00	250.00	150.00
ER-37	Cake plate, 8″ sq. pedestal	250.00	300.00	175.00
ER-40	Cake stand, 2 tier	250.00	300.00	175.00
ER-45	Canoe-shaped dish	350.00	400.00	225.00
ER-50	Cheese keep	300.00	375.00	200.00
ER-52	Coaster	60.00	75.00	45.00
ER-55	Coffee pot	875.00	1,100.00	600.00
ER-60	Compote, footed	175.00	225.00	135.00
ER-65	Condiment set on tray	275.00	325.00	175.00
ER-70	Cream and sugar	150.00	200.00	100.00
ER-71	Cream and sugar on tray	275.00	325.00	175.00
ER-75	Demi-tasse	100.00	125.00	65.00
ER-77	Egg cup, footed	100.00	125.00	65.00
ER-80	Hot water jug	400.00	475.00	275.00
ER-85	Jam pot with liner	200.00	250.00	150.00
ER-90	Jug, 4″	325.00	400.00	230.00
ER-91	Jug, 4 1/2″	375.00	450.00	250.00
ER-92	Jug, 5″	400.00	475.00	275.00

Cat.No.	Shape	U.S. $	Can. $	U.K. £
ER-97	Nut dish	65.00	80.00	45.00
ER-201	Plate, 4″ sq.	60.00	75.00	45.00
ER-202	Plate, 5″ sq.	65.00	80.00	45.00
ER-203	Plate, 6″ sq.	70.00	85.00	50.00
ER-204	Plate, 7″ sq.	100.00	125.00	65.00
ER-205	Plate, 8″ sq.	150.00	175.00	100.00
ER-206	Plate, 9″ sq.	150.00	175.00	100.00
ER-207	Plate, 10″ sq.	175.00	225.00	125.00
ER-112	Relish dish, small	200.00	250.00	135.00
ER-115	Salad bowl, chrome rim	175.00	225.00	125.00
ER-117	Salt and pepper	100.00	125.00	65.00
ER-118	Salt and pepper on tray	200.00	250.00	150.00
ER-120	Sandwich tray, 10″ x 6″	150.00	175.00	100.00
ER-121	Sandwich tray, 12″ x 7″	175.00	200.00	125.00
ER-125	Sauce boat and liner	175.00	200.00	125.00
ER-130	Teacup and saucer	200.00	125.00	65.00
ER-135	Teapot, 2 cup	450.00	550.00	300.00
ER-136	Teapot, 4 cup	625.00	750.00	450.00
ER-137	Teapot, 6 cup	725.00	875.00	500.00
ER-140	Teapot, stacking	825.00	1,000.00	575.00
ER-145	Tennis set	150.00	175.00	100.00
ER-150	Toast rack, 4 slice	275.00	325.00	175.00
ER-151	Toast rack, 2 slice	225.00	275.00	150.00
ER-155	Trivet	150.00	175.00	100.00
ER-160	Vase, bud	135.00	165.00	85.00

ESTELLE

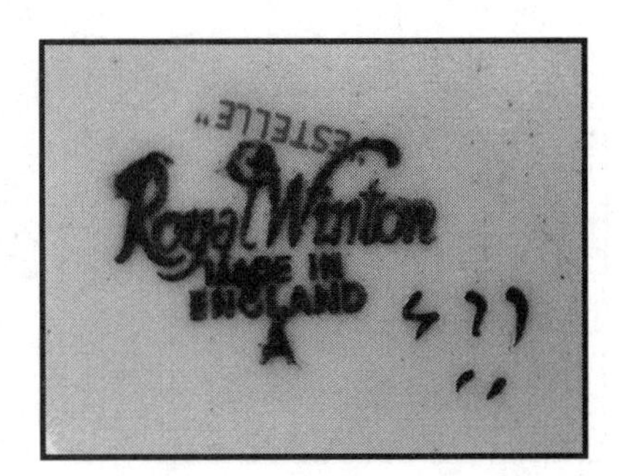

The pattern number is 423, and the pattern was introduced early in the 1950s.

Cat.No.	Shape	U.S. $	Can. $	U.K. £
Esl-04	Bonbon dish	50.00	75.00	40.00
Esl-09	Bowl, 5″	50.00	65.00	35.00
Esl-14	Bowl, 8″ soup	75.00	90.00	50.00
Esl-23	Breakfast set	800.00	975.00	550.00
Esl-28	Butter dish	150.00	200.00	100.00
Esl-30	Butter pat	45.00	55.00	35.00
Esl-35	Cake plate, open handles	150.00	200.00	100.00
Esl-36	Cake plate, tab handles	150.00	200.00	100.00
Esl-37	Cake plate, 8″ sq. pedestal	175.00	225.00	125.00
Esl-40	Cake stand, 2 tier	175.00	225.00	125.00
Esl-45	Canoe-shaped dish	235.00	275.00	165.00
Esl-50	Cheese keep	200.00	250.00	150.00
Esl-52	Coaster	40.00	50.00	30.00
Esl-55	Coffee pot	600.00	725.00	425.00
Esl-60	Compote, footed	135.00	165.00	85.00
Esl-65	Condiment set on tray	200.00	250.00	150.00
Esl-70	Cream and sugar	100.00	125.00	65.00
Esl-71	Cream and sugar on tray	200.00	250.00	150.00
Esl-75	Demi-tasse	75.00	85.00	50.00
Esl-77	Egg cup, footed	65.00	80.00	45.00
Esl-80	Hot water jug	275.00	330.00	195.00
Esl-85	Jam pot with liner	150.00	175.00	100.00
Esl-90	Jug, 4″	200.00	250.00	150.00
Esl-91	Jug, 4 1/2″	225.00	275.00	150.00
Esl-92	Jug, 5″	250.00	300.00	175.00

Cat.No.	Shape	U.S. $	Can. $	U.K. £
Esl-97	Nut dish	45.00	55.00	35.00
Esl-201	Plate, 4″ sq.	50.00	65.00	35.00
Esl-202	Plate, 5″ sq.	50.00	75.00	40.00
Esl-203	Plate, 6″ sq.	60.00	75.00	45.00
Esl-204	Plate, 7″ sq.	75.00	100.00	50.00
Esl-205	Plate, 8″ sq.	125.00	150.00	75.00
Esl-206	Plate, 9″ sq.	125.00	150.00	75.00
Esl-207	Plate, 10″ sq.	135.00	165.00	100.00
Esl-112	Relish dish, small	150.00	175.00	100.00
Esl-115	Salad bowl, chrome rim	125.00	150.00	75.00
Esl-117	Salt and pepper	75.00	90.00	50.00
Esl-118	Salt and pepper on tray	150.00	175.00	100.00
Esl-120	Sandwich tray, 10″ x 6″	100.00	125.00	65.00
Esl-121	Sandwich tray, 12″ x 7″	125.00	150.00	75.00
Esl-125	Sauce boat and liner	150.00	175.00	100.00
Esl-130	Teacup and saucer	75.00	85.00	50.00
Esl-135	Teapot, 2 cup	275.00	325.00	200.00
Esl-136	Teapot, 4 cup	450.00	550.00	325.00
Esl-137	Teapot, 6 cup	550.00	650.00	375.00
Esl-140	Teapot, stacking	650.00	675.00	450.00
Esl-145	Tennis set	100.00	125.00	65.00
Esl-150	Toast rack, 4 slice	200.00	235.00	135.00
Esl-151	Toast rack, 2 slice	135.00	165.00	85.00
Esl-155	Trivet	100.00	125.00	65.00
Esl-160	Vase, bud	100.00	125.00	65.00

ESTHER

The pattern number is 473, and the pattern was registered in Canada in 1952.

Cat.No.	Shape	U.S. $	Can. $	U.K. £
Est-04	Bonbon dish	65.00	80.00	45.00
Est-09	Bowl, 5″	50.00	75.00	40.00
Est-14	Bowl, 8″ soup	75.00	100.00	50.00
Est-23	Breakfast set	900.00	1,200.00	625.00
Est-28	Butter dish	175.00	225.00	125.00
Est-30	Butter pat	50.00	70.00	40.00
Est-35	Cake plate, open handles	175.00	225.00	125.00
Est-36	Cake plate, tab handles	75.00	100.00	50.00
Est-37	Cake plate, 8″ sq. pedestal	200.00	250.00	150.00
Est-40	Cake stand, 2 tier	200.00	250.00	150.00
Est-45	Canoe-shaped dish	275.00	325.00	200.00
Est-50	Cheese keep	250.00	300.00	175.00
Est-52	Coaster	50.00	65.00	35.00
Est-55	Coffee pot	750.00	900.00	525.00
Est-60	Compote, footed	175.00	200.00	125.00
Est-65	Condiment set on tray	225.00	275.00	150.00
Est-70	Cream and sugar	125.00	150.00	75.00
Est-71	Cream and sugar on tray	225.00	275.00	150.00
Est-75	Demi-tasse	85.00	100.00	60.00
Est-77	Egg cup, footed	75.00	90.00	50.00
Est-80	Hot water jug	325.00	400.00	225.00
Est-85	Jam pot with liner	175.00	200.00	125.00
Est-90	Jug, 4″	275.00	325.00	200.00
Est-91	Jug, 4 1/2″	300.00	350.00	200.00
Est-92	Jug, 5″	325.00	400.00	225.00
Est-97	Nut dish	50.00	75.00	40.00
Est-201	Plate, 4″ sq.	50.00	65.00	35.00
Est-202	Plate, 5″ sq.	50.00	75.00	40.00
Est-203	Plate, 6″ sq.	65.00	85.00	45.00
Est-204	Plate, 7″ sq.	85.00	100.00	60.00
Est-205	Plate, 8″ sq.	135.00	175.00	100.00
Est-206	Plate, 9″ sq.	150.00	175.00	100.00
Est-207	Plate, 10″ sq.	165.00	200.00	125.00
Est-112	Relish dish, small	175.00	225.00	125.00
Est-115	Salad bowl, chrome rim	150.00	175.00	100.00
Est-117	Salt and pepper	100.00	125.00	65.00
Est-118	Salt and pepper on tray	165.00	200.00	125.00
Est-120	Sandwich tray, 10″ x 6″	125.00	150.00	90.00
Est-121	Sandwich tray, 12″ x 7″	150.00	175.00	100.00
Est-125	Sauce boat and liner	175.00	225.00	125.00
Est-130	Teacup and saucer	85.00	100.00	60.00
Est-135	Teapot, 2 cup	450.00	550.00	325.00
Est-136	Teapot, 4 cup	550.00	650.00	375.00
Est-137	Teapot, 6 cup	650.00	775.00	450.00
Est-140	Teapot, stacking	650.00	775.00	450.00
Est-145	Tennis set	125.00	150.00	75.00
Est-150	Toast rack, 4 slice	275.00	325.00	200.00
Est-151	Toast rack, 2 slice	225.00	275.00	160.00
Est-155	Trivet	125.00	150.00	75.00
Est-160	Vase, bud	125.00	150.00	75.00

EVESHAM

The pattern number is 404, and it was registered in Canada in 1951. The pattern is thought to have been designed by Mabel Till, nee Leigh, a well-known potteries designer.

Cat.No.	Shape	U.S. $	Can. $	U.K. £
Ev-04	Bonbon dish	75.00	100.00	50.00
Ev-09	Bowl, 5″	50.00	75.00	40.00
Ev-14	Bowl, 8″ soup	100.00	125.00	65.00
Ev-23	Breakfast set	1,125.00	1,350.00	775.00
Ev-28	Butter dish	225.00	275.00	150.00
Ev-30	Butter pat	70.00	85.00	50.00
Ev-35	Cake plate, open handles	225.00	275.00	150.00
Ev-36	Cake plate, tab handles	200.00	250.00	135.00
Ev-37	Cake plate, 8″ sq. pedestal	250.00	300.00	175.00
Ev-40	Cake stand, 2 tier	250.00	300.00	175.00
Ev-45	Canoe-shaped dish	350.00	425.00	250.00
Ev-50	Cheese keep	300.00	375.00	225.00
Ev-52	Coaster	60.00	75.00	45.00
Ev-55	Coffee pot	950.00	1,150.00	650.00
Ev-60	Compote, footed	200.00	250.00	150.00
Ev-65	Condiment set on tray	275.00	350.00	200.00
Ev-70	Cream and sugar	150.00	175.00	100.00
Ev-71	Cream and sugar on tray	275.00	335.00	200.00
Ev-75	Demi-tasse	100.00	125.00	65.00
Ev-77	Egg cup, footed	100.00	125.00	65.00
Ev-80	Hot water jug	400.00	475.00	275.00
Ev-85	Jam pot with liner	225.00	250.00	150.00
Ev-90	Jug, 4″	375.00	450.00	250.00
Ev-91	Jug, 4 1/2″	400.00	475.00	275.00
Ev-92	Jug, 5″	425.00	500.00	300.00
Ev-97	Nut dish	70.00	85.00	50.00
Ev-201	Plate, 4″ sq.	65.00	80.00	45.00
Ev-202	Plate, 5″ sq.	75.00	90.00	50.00
Ev-203	Plate, 6″ sq.	100.00	125.00	65.00
Ev-204	Plate, 7″ sq.	135.00	165.00	85.00
Ev-205	Plate, 8″ sq.	175.00	225.00	125.00
Ev-206	Plate, 9″ sq.	175.00	225.00	125.00
Ev-207	Plate, 10″ sq .	200.00	250.00	150.00
Ev-112	Relish dish, small	225.00	275.00	150.00
Ev-115	Salad bowl, chrome rim	175.00	225.00	125.00
Ev-117	Salt and pepper	100.00	125.00	65.00
Ev-118	Salt and pepper on tray	200.00	250.00	150.00
Ev-120	Sandwich tray, 10″ x 6″	150.00	175.00	100.00
Ev-121	Sandwich tray, 12″ x 7″	175.00	225.00	125.00
Ev-125	Sauce boat and liner	200.00	250.00	150.00
Ev-130	Teacup and saucer	100.00	125.00	65.00
Ev-135	Teapot, 2 cup	450.00	550.00	325.00
Ev-136	Teapot, 4 cup	600.00	725.00	425.00
Ev-137	Teapot, 6 cup	800.00	975.00	550.00
Ev-140	Teapot, stacking	850.00	1,100.00	600.00
Ev-145	Tennis set	150.00	175.00	100.00
Ev-150	Toast rack, 4 slice	300.00	350.00	200.00
Ev-151	Toast rack, 2 slice	225.00	275.00	150.00
Ev-155	Trivet	150.00	175.00	100.00
Ev-160	Vase, bud	150.00	175.00	100.00

FIREGLOW BLACK

There are two totally unrelated patterns with the backstamp **Fireglow**. The black background has the pattern number 533, which is the last known chintz pattern number. See **Fireglow White.**

Cat.No.	Shape	U.S. $	Can. $	U.K. £
FiB-04	Bonbon dish	30.00	35.00	25.00
FiB-09	Bowl, 5″	30.00	35.00	25.00
FiB-14	Bowl, 8″ soup	40.00	50.00	30.00
FiB-23	Breakfast set	450.00	550.00	325.00
FiB-28	Butter dish	100.00	125.00	65.00
FiB-30	Butter pat	25.00	30.00	20.00
FiB-35	Cake plate, open handles	100.00	125.00	65.00
FiB-36	Cake plate, tab handles	85.00	100.00	60.00
FiB-37	Cake plate, 8″ sq. pedestal	100.00	125.00	65.00
FiB-40	Cake stand, 2 tier	100.00	125.00	65.00
FiB-45	Canoe-shaped dish	135.00	165.00	85.00
FiB-50	Cheese keep	125.00	150.00	75.00
FiB-52	Coaster	25.00	30.00	20.00
FiB-55	Coffee pot	375.00	450.00	250.00
FiB-60	Compote, footed	80.00	95.00	50.00
FiB-65	Condiment set on tray	100.00	125.00	65.00
FiB-70	Cream and sugar	60.00	75.00	45.00
FiB-71	Cream and sugar on tray	100.00	125.00	65.00
FiB-75	Demi-tasse	40.00	50.00	30.00
FiB-77	Egg cup, footed	35.00	40.00	25.00
FiB-80	Hot water jug	150.00	200.00	125.00
FiB-85	Jam pot with liner	75.00	100.00	50.00
FiB-90	Jug, 4″	135.00	165.00	85.00
FiB-91	Jug, 4 1/2″	150.00	175.00	100.00
FiB-92	Jug, 5″	150.00	200.00	125.00
FiB-97	Nut dish	25.00	30.00	20.00
FiB-201	Plate, 4″ sq.	30.00	35.00	25.00
FiB-202	Plate, 5″ sq.	35.00	40.00	25.00
FiB-203	Plate, 6″ sq.	40.00	50.00	30.00
FiB-204	Plate, 7″ sq.	45.00	50.00	35.00
FiB-205	Plate, 8″ sq.	65.00	80.00	45.00
FiB-206	Plate, 9″ sq.	75.00	100.00	50.00
FiB-207	Plate, 10″ sq.	85.00	100.00	60.00
FiB-112	Relish dish, small	85.00	100.00	60.00
FiB-115	Salad bowl, chrome rim	100.00	125.00	65.00
FiB-117	Salt and pepper	50.00	75.00	40.00
FiB-118	Salt and pepper on tray	115.00	150.00	75.00
FiB-120	Sandwich tray, 10″ x 6″	60.00	75.00	45.00
FiB-121	Sandwich tray, 12″ x 7″	75.00	100.00	50.00
FiB-125	Sauce boat and liner	65.00	80.00	45.00
FiB-130	Teacup and saucer	40.00	50.00	30.00
FiB-135	Teapot, 2 cup	175.00	200.00	125.00
FiB-136	Teapot, 4 cup	275.00	325.00	200.00
FiB-137	Teapot, 6 cup	325.00	400.00	225.00
FiB-140	Teapot, stacking	400.00	475.00	275.00
FiB-145	Tennis set	55.00	70.00	40.00
FiB-150	Toast rack, 4 slice	150.00	200.00	125.00
FiB-151	Toast rack, 2 slice	135.00	165.00	95.00
FiB-155	Trivet	50.00	70.00	40.00
FiB-160	Vase, bud	60.00	75.00	45.00

FIREGLOW WHITE

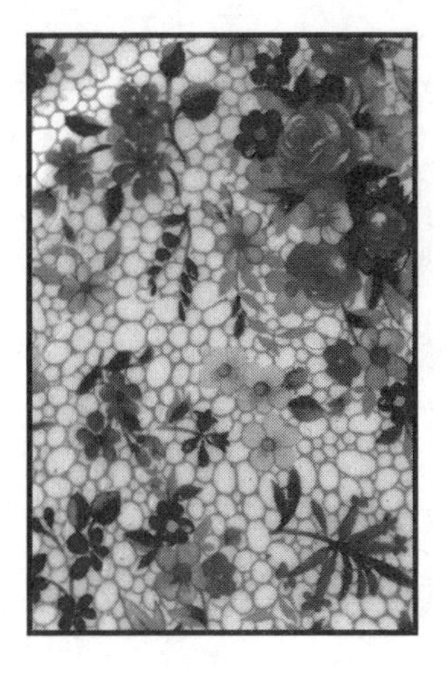

The pattern number for the white background **Fireglow** is 2510 which means it was likely introduced in 1935. It is totally unrelated to the **Black Fireglow** from the 1950s. See **Fireglow Black.**

Cat.No.	Shape	U.S. $	Can. $	U.K. £
FiW-04	Bonbon dish	50.00	65.00	35.00
FiW-09	Bowl, 5″	45.00	50.00	35.00
FiW-14	Bowl, 8″ soup	75.00	100.00	50.00
FiW-23	Breakfast set	700.00	850.00	475.00
FiW-28	Butter dish	150.00	175.00	100.00
FiW-30	Butter pat	45.00	50.00	85.00
FiW-35	Cake plate, open handles	150.00	175.00	100.00
FiW-36	Cake plate, tab handles	135.00	165.00	95.00
FiW-37	Cake plate, 8″ sq. pedestal	150.00	200.00	125.00
FiW-40	Cake stand, 2 tier	150.00	200.00	125.00
FiW-45	Canoe-shaped dish	225.00	275.00	150.00
FiW-50	Cheese keep	200.00	250.00	150.00
FiW-52	Coaster	40.00	50.00	30.00
FiW-55	Coffee pot	550.00	650.00	375.00
FiW-60	Compote, footed	135.00	165.00	85.00
FiW-65	Condiment set on tray	175.00	225.00	125.00
FiW-70	Cream and sugar	100.00	125.00	65.00
FiW-71	Cream and sugar on tray	175.00	225.00	125.00
FiW-75	Demi-tasse	70.00	85.00	50.00
FiW-77	Egg cup, footed	60.00	75.00	45.00
FiW-80	Hot water jug	250.00	325.00	175.00
FiW-85	Jam pot with liner	140.00	170.00	100.00
FiW-90	Jug, 4″	175.00	200.00	125.00
FiW-91	Jug, 4 1/2″	200.00	250.00	150.00
FiW-92	Jug, 5″	225.00	275.00	150.00

Cat.No.	Shape	U.S. $	Can. $	U.K. £
FiW-97	Nut dish	45.00	50.00	35.00
FiW-201	Plate, 4″ sq.	50.00	65.00	35.00
FiW-202	Plate, 5″ sq.	50.00	75.00	40.00
FiW-203	Plate, 6″ sq.	60.00	75.00	45.00
FiW-204	Plate, 7″ sq.	75.00	100.00	50.00
FiW-205	Plate, 8″ sq.	100.00	125.00	65.00
FiW-206	Plate, 9″ sq.	125.00	150.00	75.00
FiW-207	Plate, 10″ sq .	125.00	150.00	75.00
FiW-112	Relish dish, small	150.00	175.00	100.00
FiW-115	Salad bowl, chrome rim	125.00	150.00	75.00
FiW-117	Salt and pepper	75.00	85.00	50.00
FiW-118	Salt and pepper on tray	150.00	175.00	100.00
FiW-120	Sandwich tray, 10″ x 6″	100.00	125.00	65.00
FiW-121	Sandwich tray, 12″ x 7″	125.00	150.00	75.00
FiW-125	Sauce boat and liner	135.00	165.00	85.00
FiW-130	Teacup and saucer	75.00	85.00	50.00
FiW-135	Teapot, 2 cup	275.00	325.00	200.00
FiW-136	Teapot, 4 cup	375.00	450.00	250.00
FiW-137	Teapot, 6 cup	475.00	575.00	325.00
FiW-140	Teapot, stacking	625.00	750.00	425.00
FiW-145	Tennis set	100.00	125.00	65.00
FiW-150	Toast rack, 4 slice	200.00	250.00	150.00
FiW-151	Toast rack, 2 slice	150.00	175.00	100.00
FiW-155	Trivet	100.00	125.00	65.00
FiW-160	Vase, bud	85.00	100.00	60.00

FLORAL FEAST

The pattern number is 1394, and the pattern was probably introduced sometime in 1933. It is said to have been exported mainly to Canada.

Cat.No.	Shape	U.S. $	Can. $	U.K. £
FF-04	Bonbon dish	50.00	65.00	35.00
FF-09	Bowl, 5″	45.00	50.00	35.00
FF-14	Bowl, 8″ soup	75.00	90.00	50.00
FF-23	Breakfast set	700.00	850.00	475.00
FF-28	Butter dish	150.00	175.00	100.00
FF-30	Butter pat	45.00	50.00	35.00
FF-35	Cake plate, open handles	150.00	175.00	100.00
FF-36	Cake plate, tab handles	135.00	165.00	85.00
FF-37	Cake plate, 8″ sq. pedestal	150.00	200.00	115.00
FF-40	Cake stand, 2 tier	150.00	200.00	115.00
FF-45	Canoe-shaped dish	225.00	275.00	150.00
FF-50	Cheese keep	200.00	250.00	125.00
FF-52	Coaster	40.00	50.00	30.00
FF-55	Coffee pot	550.00	650.00	375.00
FF-60	Compote, footed	125.00	150.00	75.00
FF-65	Condiment set on tray	175.00	225.00	125.00
FF-70	Cream and sugar	100.00	125.00	65.00
FF-71	Cream and sugar on tray	175.00	225.00	125.00
FF-75	Demi-tasse	75.00	85.00	50.00
FF-77	Egg cup, footed	60.00	75.00	45.00
FF-80	Hot water jug	250.00	325.00	175.00
FF-85	Jam pot with liner	150.00	175.00	100.00
FF-90	Jug, 4″	175.00	225.00	125.00
FF-91	Jug, 4 1/2″	200.00	250.00	125.00
FF-92	Jug, 5″	225.00	275.00	150.00
FF-97	Nut dish	45.00	55.00	35.00
FF-201	Plate, 4″ sq.	50.00	65.00	35.00
FF-202	Plate, 5″ sq.	50.00	75.00	40.00
FF-203	Plate, 6″ sq.	60.00	75.00	45.00
FF-204	Plate, 7″ sq.	75.00	100.00	50.00
FF-205	Plate, 8″ sq.	100.00	125.00	65.00
FF-206	Plate, 9″ sq.	125.00	150.00	75.00
FF-207	Plate, 10″ sq .	125.00	150.00	75.00
FF-112	Relish dish, small	150.00	175.00	100.00
FF-115	Salad bowl, chrome rim	125.00	150.00	75.00
FF-117	Salt and pepper	75.00	100.00	50.00
FF-118	Salt and pepper on tray	150.00	175.00	100.00
FF-120	Sandwich tray, 10″ x 6″	100.00	125.00	65.00
FF-121	Sandwich tray, 12″ x 7″	125.00	150.00	75.00
FF-125	Sauce boat and liner	125.00	150.00	75.00
FF-130	Teacup and saucer	75.00	85.00	50.00
FF-135	Teapot, 2 cup	275.00	325.00	200.00
FF-136	Teapot, 4 cup	375.00	450.00	250.00
FF-137	Teapot, 6 cup	475.00	575.00	325.00
FF-140	Teapot, stacking	625.00	750.00	425.00
FF-145	Tennis set	100.00	125.00	65.00
FF-150	Toast rack, 4 slice	200.00	250.00	150.00
FF-151	Toast rack, 2 slice	150.00	175.00	100.00
FF-155	Trivet	85.00	110.00	60.00
FF-160	Vase, bud	85.00	110.00	60.00

FLORAL GARDEN

Photograph not available at press time

The pattern number is 4547, and there are several colourways. This green colourway has only been found in Australia with a name backstamp and probably dates to 1938.

Cat.No.	Shape	U.S. $	Can. $	U.K. £
FG-04	Bonbon dish	40.00	50.00	30.00
FG-09	Bowl, 5″	25.00	30.00	20.00
FG-14	Bowl, 8″ soup	40.00	50.00	30.00
FG-23	Breakfast set	550.00	650.00	350.00
FG-28	Butter dish	115.00	150.00	75.00
FG-30	Butter pat	30.00	35.00	25.00
FG-35	Cake plate, open handles	115.00	150.00	75.00
FG-36	Cake plate, tab handles	100.00	125.00	65.00
FG-37	Cake plate, 8″ sq. pedestal	125.00	150.00	75.00
FG-40	Cake stand, 2 tier	125.00	150.00	75.00
FG-45	Canoe-shaped dish	165.00	200.00	115.00
FG-50	Cheese keep	150.00	175.00	100.00
FG-52	Coaster	30.00	35.00	25.00
FG-55	Coffee pot	450.00	550.00	325.00
FG-60	Compote, footed	100.00	125.00	65.00
FG-65	Condiment set on tray	135.00	165.00	85.00
FG-70	Cream and sugar	75.00	90.00	50.00
FG-71	Cream and sugar on tray	135.00	165.00	85.00
FG-75	Demi-tasse	50.00	65.00	35.00
FG-77	Egg cup, footed	45.00	55.00	35.00
FG-80	Hot water jug	200.00	250.00	150.00
FG-85	Jam pot with liner	100.00	125.00	65.00
FG-90	Jug, 4″	165.00	200.00	115.00
FG-91	Jug, 4 1/2″	175.00	225.00	125.00
FG-92	Jug, 5″	200.00	250.00	150.00

Cat.No.	Shape	U.S. $	Can. $	U.K. £
FG-97	Nut dish	35.00	40.00	25.00
FG-201	Plate, 4″ sq.	25.00	30.00	20.00
FG-202	Plate, 5″ sq.	30.00	35.00	25.00
FG-203	Plate, 6″ sq.	30.00	35.00	25.00
FG-204	Plate, 7″ sq.	35.00	40.00	30.00
FG-205	Plate, 8″ sq.	50.00	65.00	35.00
FG-206	Plate, 9″ sq.	75.00	100.00	50.00
FG-207	Plate, 10″ sq.	75.00	100.00	50.00
FG-112	Relish dish, small	100.00	125.00	65.00
FG-115	Salad bowl, chrome rim	85.00	110.00	60.00
FG-117	Salt and pepper	50.00	70.00	40.00
FG-118	Salt and pepper on tray	125.00	150.00	75.00
FG-120	Sandwich tray, 10″ x 6″	75.00	90.00	50.00
FG-121	Sandwich tray, 12″ x 7″	85.00	110.00	60.00
FG-125	Sauce boat and liner	100.00	125.00	75.00
FG-130	Teacup and saucer	50.00	65.00	35.00
FG-135	Teapot, 2 cup	275.00	325.00	200.00
FG-136	Teapot, 4 cup	325.00	400.00	225.00
FG-137	Teapot, 6 cup	425.00	500.00	300.00
FG-140	Teapot, stacking	450.00	550.00	325.00
FG-145	Tennis set	75.00	85.00	50.00
FG-150	Toast rack, 4 slice	165.00	200.00	115.00
FG-151	Toast rack, 2 slice	135.00	165.00	85.00
FG-155	Trivet	75.00	85.00	50.00
FG-160	Vase, bud	75.00	90.00	50.00

FLORENCE

The pattern number is 472, which would indicate that it is one of the last chintz patterns to be produced in the 1950s. The pattern was registered in Canada in 1953. This pattern is quite rare and very sought after by collectors worldwide.

Cat.No.	Shape	U.S. $	Can. $	U.K. £
Fl-04	Bonbon dish	85.00	110.00	60.00
Fl-09	Bowl, 5″	65.00	80.00	45.00
Fl-14	Bowl, 8″ soup	85.00	110.00	60.00
Fl-23	Breakfast set	1,250.00	1,500.00	875.00
Fl-28	Butter dish	275.00	325.00	175.00
Fl-30	Butter pat	75.00	90.00	50.00
Fl-35	Cake plate, open handles	275.00	325.00	175.00
Fl-36	Cake plate, tab handles	250.00	300.00	175.00
Fl-37	Cake plate, 8″ sq. pedestal	275.00	350.00	200.00
Fl-40	Cake stand, 2 tier	275.00	350.00	200.00
Fl-45	Canoe-shaped dish	375.00	450.00	275.00
Fl-50	Cheese keep	350.00	425.00	250.00
Fl-52	Coaster	70.00	85.00	50.00
Fl-55	Coffee pot	1,100.00	1,300.00	750.00
Fl-60	Compote, footed	225.00	275.00	150.00
Fl-65	Condiment set on tray	325.00	375.00	225.00
Fl-70	Cream and sugar	175.00	200.00	125.00
Fl-71	Cream and sugar on tray	325.00	375.00	225.00
Fl-75	Demi-tasse	125.00	150.00	75.00
Fl-77	Egg cup, footed	100.00	125.00	65.00
Fl-80	Hot water jug	450.00	550.00	325.00
Fl-85	Jam pot with liner	245.00	300.00	175.00
Fl-90	Jug, 4″	400.00	475.00	275.00
Fl-91	Jug, 4 1/2″	425.00	500.00	300.00
Fl-92	Jug, 5″	450.00	550.00	325.00
Fl-97	Nut dish	75.00	90.00	50.00
Fl-201	Plate, 4″ sq.	75.00	90.00	50.00
Fl-202	Plate, 5″ sq.	100.00	125.00	65.00
Fl-203	Plate, 6″ sq.	125.00	150.00	75.00
Fl-204	Plate, 7″ sq.	135.00	165.00	85.00
Fl-205	Plate, 8″ sq.	175.00	200.00	125.00
Fl-206	Plate, 9″ sq.	175.00	225.00	125.00
Fl-207	Plate, 10″ sq .	200.00	250.00	150.00
Fl-112	Relish dish, small	250.00	300.00	175.00
Fl-115	Salad bowl, chrome rim	250.00	300.00	175.00
Fl-117	Salt and pepper	125.00	150.00	75.00
Fl-118	Salt and pepper on tray	225.00	275.00	150.00
Fl-120	Sandwich tray, 10″ x 6″	175.00	200.00	125.00
Fl-121	Sandwich tray, 12″ x 7″	200.00	250.00	150.00
Fl-125	Sauce boat and liner	225.00	275.00	150.00
Fl-130	Teacup and saucer	125.00	150.00	75.00
Fl-135	Teapot, 2 cup	550.00	650.00	375.00
Fl-136	Teapot, 4 cup	700.00	850.00	500.00
Fl-137	Teapot, 6 cup	900.00	1,100.00	625.00
Fl-140	Teapot, stacking	900.00	1,100.00	625.00
Fl-145	Tennis set	150.00	200.00	100.00
Fl-150	Toast rack, 4 slice	300.00	350.00	200.00
Fl-151	Toast rack, 2 slice	250.00	275.00	175.00
Fl-155	Trivet	150.00	200.00	100.00
Fl-160	Vase, bud	175.00	200.00	125.00

HAZEL

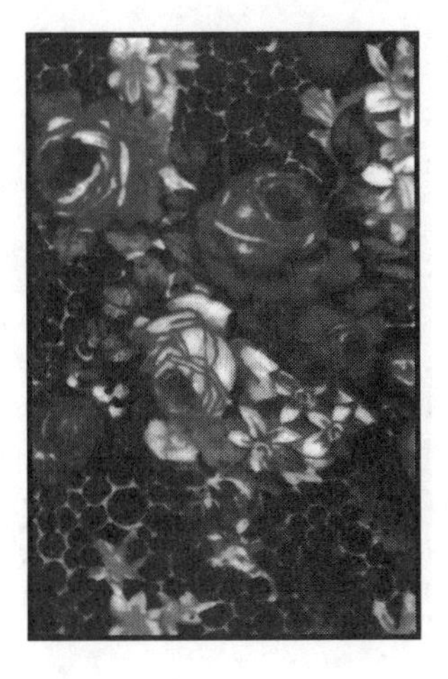

The pattern number is 2208, and the pattern was mentioned in the *Pottery Gazette* several times in 1934. **Hazel** has a black background with the alternate colourways of a white background, **Spring** 2506, and the yellow **Welbeck** 2204. This pattern was copied by the Japanese including a recent porcelain version by Fitz & Floyd called Mille Fleurs.

Cat.No.	Shape	U.S. $	Can. $	U.K. £
H-04	Bonbon dish	75.00	90.00	50.00
H-09	Bowl, 5″	50.00	65.00	35.00
H-14	Bowl, 8″ soup	85.00	100.00	60.00
H-23	Breakfast set	950.00	1,150.00	675.00
H-28	Butter dish	225.00	275.00	150.00
H-30	Butter pat	65.00	80.00	45.00
H-35	Cake plate, open handles	225.00	275.00	150.00
H-36	Cake plate, tab handles	200.00	250.00	150.00
H-37	Cake plate, 8″ sq. pedestal	225.00	275.00	150.00
H-40	Cake stand, 2 tier	225.00	275.00	150.00
H-45	Canoe-shaped dish	325.00	375.00	225.00
H-50	Cheese keep	275.00	350.00	200.00
H-52	Coaster	50.00	65.00	35.00
H-55	Coffee pot	850.00	1,050.00	600.00
H-60	Compote, footed	185.00	225.00	125.00
H-65	Condiment set on tray	250.00	300.00	175.00
H-70	Cream and sugar	150.00	175.00	100.00
H-71	Cream and sugar on tray	250.00	300.00	175.00
H-75	Demi-tasse	100.00	125.00	65.00
H-77	Egg cup, footed	85.00	100.00	60.00
H-80	Hot water jug	375.00	450.00	250.00
H-85	Jam pot with liner	200.00	250.00	150.00
H-90	Jug, 4″	325.00	375.00	225.00
H-91	Jug, 4 1/2″	350.00	475.00	250.00
H-92	Jug, 5″	375.00	450.00	250.00

Cat.No.	Shape	U.S. $	Can. $	U.K. £
H-97	Nut dish	65.00	80.00	45.00
H-201	Plate, 4″ sq.	50.00	70.00	35.00
H-202	Plate, 5″ sq.	65.00	80.00	45.00
H-203	Plate, 6″ sq.	75.00	90.00	50.00
H-204	Plate, 7″ sq.	100.00	125.00	65.00
H-205	Plate, 8″ sq.	135.00	165.00	85.00
H-206	Plate, 9″ sq.	150.00	175.00	100.00
H-207	Plate, 10″ sq.	175.00	200.00	125.00
H-112	Relish dish, small	200.00	250.00	135.00
H-115	Salad bowl, chrome rim	175.00	200.00	125.00
H-117	Salt and pepper	100.00	125.00	65.00
H-118	Salt and pepper on tray	175.00	200.00	125.00
H-120	Sandwich tray, 10″ x 6″	150.00	175.00	100.00
H-121	Sandwich tray, 12″ x 7″	175.00	225.00	125.00
H-125	Sauce boat and liner	165.00	200.00	125.00
H-130	Teacup and saucer	100.00	125.00	65.00
H-135	Teapot, 2 cup	425.00	500.00	300.00
H-136	Teapot, 4 cup	625.00	750.00	450.00
H-137	Teapot, 6 cup	725.00	875.00	500.00
H-140	Teapot, stacking	800.00	950.00	550.00
H-145	Tennis set	125.00	150.00	75.00
H-150	Toast rack, 4 slice	250.00	300.00	175.00
H-151	Toast rack, 2 slice	200.00	250.00	150.00
H-155	Trivet	125.00	150.00	75.00
H-160	Vase, bud	135.00	175.00	100.00

JOYCE-LYNN

The pattern number is 275. This pattern was probably introduced around 1950.

Cat.No.	Shape	U.S. $	Can. $	U.K. £
JL-04	Bonbon dish	50.00	65.00	35.00
JL-09	Bowl, 5″	40.00	50.00	30.00
JL-14	Bowl, 8″ soup	65.00	80.00	45.00
JL-23	Breakfast set	750.00	900.00	525.00
JL-28	Butter dish	150.00	175.00	100.00
JL-30	Butter pat	40.00	50.00	30.00
JL-35	Cake plate, open handles	175.00	225.00	125.00
JL-36	Cake plate, tab handles	150.00	175.00	100.00
JL-37	Cake plate, 8″ sq. pedestal	185.00	225.00	125.00
JL-40	Cake stand, 2 tier	150.00	175.00	100.00
JL-45	Canoe-shaped dish	200.00	250.00	150.00
JL-50	Cheese keep	175.00	225.00	125.00
JL-52	Coaster	35.00	40.00	25.00
JL-55	Coffee pot	625.00	750.00	425.00
JL-60	Compote, footed	125.00	150.00	75.00
JL-65	Condiment set on tray	165.00	200.00	115.00
JL-70	Cream and sugar	100.00	125.00	65.00
JL-71	Cream and sugar on tray	175.00	225.00	125.00
JL-75	Demi-tasse	65.00	80.00	45.00
JL-77	Egg cup, footed	50.00	75.00	40.00
JL-80	Hot water jug	250.00	300.00	175.00
JL-85	Jam pot with liner	125.00	150.00	75.00
JL-90	Jug, 4″	200.00	250.00	150.00
JL-91	Jug, 4 1/2″	225.00	275.00	150.00
JL-92	Jug, 5″	250.00	300.00	175.00
JL-97	Nut dish	40.00	50.00	30.00
JL-201	Plate, 4″ sq.	45.00	50.00	35.00
JL-202	Plate, 5″ sq.	50.00	65.00	35.00
JL-203	Plate, 6″ sq.	50.00	75.00	40.00
JL-204	Plate, 7″ sq.	65.00	80.00	45.00
JL-205	Plate, 8″ sq.	100.00	125.00	65.00
JL-206	Plate, 9″ sq.	100.00	125.00	65.00
JL-207	Plate, 10″ sq.	125.00	150.00	75.00
JL-112	Relish dish, small	130.00	175.00	100.00
JL-115	Salad bowl, chrome rim	100.00	125.00	65.00
JL-117	Salt and pepper	75.00	90.00	50.00
JL-118	Salt and pepper on tray	135.00	175.00	100.00
JL-120	Sandwich tray, 10″ x 6″	100.00	125.00	65.00
JL-121	Sandwich tray, 12″ x 7″	100.00	125.00	65.00
JL-125	Sauce boat and liner	130.00	165.00	85.00
JL-130	Teacup and saucer	65.00	80.00	45.00
JL-135	Teapot, 2 cup	300.00	375.00	225.00
JL-136	Teapot, 4 cup	400.00	500.00	275.00
JL-137	Teapot, 6 cup	500.00	600.00	350.00
JL-140	Teapot, stacking	600.00	725.00	425.00
JL-145	Tennis set	85.00	100.00	60.00
JL-150	Toast rack, 4 slice	200.00	250.00	150.00
JL-151	Toast rack, 2 slice	150.00	175.00	100.00
JL-155	Trivet	85.00	100.00	60.00
JL-160	Vase, bud	100.00	125.00	65.00

JULIA

The pattern number is 109 and probably appeared in 1939 and continued well into the 1950s. It may be the favourite chintz pattern for collectors around the world. There are great variations in the depth of this pattern, with some examples appearing quite faded.

Cat.No.	Shape	U.S. $	Can. $	U.K. £
J-04	Bonbon dish	100.00	125.00	65.00
J-09	Bowl, 5"	65.00	80.00	45.00
J-14	Bowl, 8" soup	100.00	125.00	65.00
J-23	Breakfast set	1,250.00	1,500.00	875.00
J-28	Butter dish	275.00	325.00	175.00
J-30	Butter pat	75.00	90.00	50.00
J-35	Cake plate, open handles	275.00	325.00	200.00
J-36	Cake plate, tab handles	250.00	300.00	175.00
J-37	Cake plate, 8" sq. pedestal	275.00	350.00	200.00
J-40	Cake stand, 2 tier	275.00	350.00	200.00
J-45	Canoe-shaped dish	400.00	450.00	275.00
J-50	Cheese keep	350.00	425.00	250.00
J-52	Coaster	75.00	85.00	50.00
J-55	Coffee pot	1,100.00	1,300.00	750.00
J-60	Compote, footed	225.00	275.00	150.00
J-65	Condiment set on tray	325.00	375.00	225.00
J-70	Cream and sugar	175.00	200.00	125.00
J-71	Cream and sugar on tray	325.00	375.00	225.00
J-75	Demi-tasse	125.00	150.00	75.00
J-77	Egg cup, footed	100.00	125.00	65.00
J-80	Hot water jug	450.00	550.00	325.00
J-85	Jam pot with liner	250.00	300.00	175.00
J-90	Jug, 4"	400.00	475.00	275.00
J-91	Jug, 4 1/2"	425.00	500.00	300.00
J-92	Jug, 5"	450.00	550.00	325.00

Cat.No.	Shape	U.S. $	Can. $	U.K. £
J-97	Nut dish	75.00	90.00	50.00
J-201	Plate, 4" sq.	75.00	90.00	50.00
J-202	Plate, 5" sq.	100.00	125.00	65.00
J-203	Plate, 6" sq.	115.00	150.00	75.00
J-204	Plate, 7" sq.	135.00	165.00	85.00
J-205	Plate, 8" sq.	175.00	225.00	125.00
J-206	Plate, 9" sq.	175.00	225.00	125.00
J-207	Plate, 10" sq.	200.00	250.00	150.00
J-112	Relish dish, small	250.00	300.00	175.00
J-115	Salad bowl, chrome rim	250.00	300.00	175.00
J-117	Salt and pepper	125.00	150.00	75.00
J-118	Salt and pepper on tray	225.00	275.00	150.00
J-120	Sandwich tray, 10" x 6"	175.00	225.00	125.00
J-121	Sandwich tray, 12" x 7"	200.00	250.00	150.00
J-125	Sauce boat and liner	225.00	275.00	160.00
J-130	Teacup and saucer	125.00	150.00	75.00
J-135	Teapot, 2 cup	550.00	675.00	400.00
J-136	Teapot, 4 cup	700.00	850.00	500.00
J-137	Teapot, 6 cup	900.00	1,200.00	625.00
J-140	Teapot, stacking	900.00	1,200.00	625.00
J-145	Tennis set	150.00	200.00	100.00
J-150	Toast rack, 4 slice	300.00	350.00	200.00
J-151	Toast rack, 2 slice	250.00	275.00	165.00
J-155	Trivet	165.00	200.00	125.00
J-160	Vase, bud	165.00	200.00	125.00

JUNE FESTIVAL

The pattern number is 137 and the pattern was produced with a burgundy and navy background. The navy background has been found with the pattern number 135. The black background has been found with the pattern number 139 and an actual name backstamp **May Festival**. It is very much a 1950s large-flower pattern.

Cat.No.	Shape	U.S. $	Can. $	U.K. £
JF-04	Bonbon dish	45.00	50.00	35.00
JF-09	Bowl, 5″	40.00	50.00	30.00
JF-14	Bowl, 8″ soup	70.00	85.00	50.00
JF-23	Breakfast set	650.00	775.00	450.00
JF-28	Butter dish	135.00	165.00	85.00
JF-30	Butter pat	40.00	50.00	30.00
JF-35	Cake plate, open handles	135.00	165.00	85.00
JF-36	Cake plate, tab handles	125.00	150.00	75.00
JF-37	Cake plate, 8″ sq. pedestal	150.00	175.00	100.00
JF-40	Cake stand, 2 tier	150.00	175.00	100.00
JF-45	Canoe-shaped dish	200.00	250.00	135.00
JF-50	Cheese keep	175.00	200.00	125.00
JF-52	Coaster	35.00	40.00	25.00
JF-55	Coffee pot	525.00	625.00	375.00
JF-60	Compote, footed	100.00	125.00	65.00
JF-65	Condiment set on tray	150.00	175.00	100.00
JF-70	Cream and sugar	85.00	100.00	60.00
JF-71	Cream and sugar on tray	150.00	175.00	100.00
JF-75	Demi-tasse	60.00	75.00	45.00
JF-77	Egg cup, footed	50.00	65.00	35.00
JF-80	Hot water jug	225.00	275.00	160.00
JF-85	Jam pot with liner	125.00	150.00	75.00
JF-90	Jug, 4″	200.00	225.00	125.00
JF-91	Jug, 4 1/2″	200.00	225.00	125.00
JF-92	Jug, 5″	225.00	275.00	150.00

Cat.No.	Shape	U.S. $	Can. $	U.K. £
JF-97	Nut dish	40.00	50.00	30.00
JF-201	Plate, 4″ sq.	35.00	40.00	25.00
JF-202	Plate, 5″ sq.	40.00	50.00	30.00
JF-203	Plate, 6″ sq.	45.00	50.00	35.00
JF-204	Plate, 7″ sq.	50.00	65.00	35.00
JF-205	Plate, 8″ sq.	85.00	110.00	60.00
JF-206	Plate, 9″ sq.	100.00	125.00	65.00
JF-207	Plate, 10″ sq .	125.00	150.00	65.00
JF-112	Relish dish, small	125.00	150.00	65.00
JF-115	Salad bowl, chrome rim	100.00	125.00	65.00
JF-117	Salt and pepper	65.00	80.00	45.00
JF-118	Salt and pepper on tray	150.00	175.00	100.00
JF-120	Sandwich tray, 10″ x 6″	85.00	100.00	60.00
JF-121	Sandwich tray, 12″ x 7″	100.00	125.00	65.00
JF-125	Sauce boat and liner	125.00	150.00	75.00
JF-130	Teacup and saucer	60.00	75.00	45.00
JF-135	Teapot, 2 cup	250.00	300.00	175.00
JF-136	Teapot, 4 cup	350.00	425.00	250.00
JF-137	Teapot, 6 cup	450.00	550.00	325.00
JF-140	Teapot, stacking	600.00	725.00	425.00
JF-145	Tennis set	75.00	100.00	50.00
JF-150	Toast rack, 4 slice	175.00	200.00	125.00
JF-151	Toast rack, 2 slice	135.00	165.00	85.00
JF-155	Trivet	75.00	100.00	50.00
JF-160	Vase, bud	75.00	100.00	50.00

JUNE ROSES

The pattern number is 1924 and was probably introduced in 1934.

Cat.No.	Shape	U.S. $	Can. $	U.K. £
JR-04	Bonbon dish	75.00	90.00	50.00
JR-09	Bowl, 5″	50.00	65.00	35.00
JR-14	Bowl, 8″ soup	85.00	100.00	60.00
JR-23	Breakfast set	950.00	1,140.00	675.00
JR-28	Butter dish	225.00	275.00	150.00
JR-30	Butter pat	65.00	80.00	45.00
JR-35	Cake plate, open handles	225.00	275.00	150.00
JR-36	Cake plate, tab handles	200.00	250.00	135.00
JR-37	Cake plate, 8″ sq. pedestal	225.00	275.00	150.00
JR-40	Cake stand, 2 tier	225.00	275.00	150.00
JR-45	Canoe-shaped dish	325.00	375.00	225.00
JR-50	Cheese keep	275.00	350.00	200.00
JR-52	Coaster	50.00	65.00	35.00
JR-55	Coffee pot	850.00	1,100.00	600.00
JR-60	Compote, footed	175.00	225.00	125.00
JR-65	Condiment set on tray	250.00	300.00	175.00
JR-70	Cream and sugar	150.00	175.00	100.00
JR-71	Cream and sugar on tray	250.00	300.00	175.00
JR-75	Demi-tasse	100.00	125.00	65.00
JR-77	Egg cup, footed	85.00	100.00	60.00
JR-80	Hot water jug	375.00	450.00	250.00
JR-85	Jam pot with liner	200.00	250.00	150.00
JR-90	Jug, 4″	325.00	375.00	225.00
JR-91	Jug, 4 1/2″	350.00	425.00	250.00
JR-92	Jug, 5″	375.00	450.00	250.00
JR-97	Nut dish	65.00	80.00	45.00
JR-201	Plate, 4″ sq.	50.00	70.00	40.00
JR-202	Plate, 5″ sq.	65.00	80.00	45.00
JR-203	Plate, 6″ sq.	75.00	90.00	50.00
JR-204	Plate, 7″ sq.	100.00	125.00	65.00
JR-205	Plate, 8″ sq.	135.00	165.00	85.00
JR-206	Plate, 9″ sq.	150.00	175.00	100.00
JR-207	Plate, 10″ sq .	165.00	200.00	125.00
JR-112	Relish dish, small	200.00	250.00	150.00
JR-115	Salad bowl, chrome rim	175.00	200.00	125.00
JR-117	Salt and pepper	100.00	125.00	65.00
JR-118	Salt and pepper on tray	175.00	200.00	125.00
JR-120	Sandwich tray, 10″ x 6″	150.00	175.00	100.00
JR-121	Sandwich tray, 12″ x 7″	165.00	200.00	125.00
JR-125	Sauce boat and liner	165.00	200.00	125.00
JR-130	Teacup and saucer	100.00	125.00	65.00
JR-135	Teapot, 2 cup	425.00	500.00	300.00
JR-136	Teapot, 4 cup	625.00	750.00	425.00
JR-137	Teapot, 6 cup	725.00	875.00	500.00
JR-140	Teapot, stacking	800.00	950.00	550.00
JR-145	Tennis set	125.00	150.00	75.00
JR-150	Toast rack, 4 slice	250.00	300.00	180.00
JR-151	Toast rack, 2 slice	200.00	250.00	150.00
JR-155	Trivet	125.00	150.00	75.00
JR-160	Vase, bud	125.00	150.00	75.00

KEW

The pattern number is 240 and was widely produced in the 1950s.

Cat.No.	Shape	U.S. $	Can. $	U.K. £
Ke-04	Bonbon dish	50.00	65.00	35.00
Ke-09	Bowl, 5″	45.00	50.00	35.00
Ke-14	Bowl, 8″ soup	75.00	90.00	50.00
Ke-23	Breakfast set	700.00	850.00	475.00
Ke-28	Butter dish	150.00	175.00	100.00
Ke-30	Butter pat	45.00	60.00	35.00
Ke-35	Cake plate, open handles	150.00	175.00	100.00
Ke-36	Cake plate, tab handles	135.00	165.00	85.00
Ke-37	Cake plate, 8″ sq. pedestal	165.00	200.00	115.00
Ke-40	Cake stand, 2 tier	165.00	200.00	115.00
Ke-45	Canoe-shaped dish	225.00	275.00	150.00
Ke-50	Cheese keep	200.00	250.00	150.00
Ke-52	Coaster	40.00	50.00	30.00
Ke-55	Coffee pot	550.00	650.00	375.00
Ke-60	Compote, footed	130.00	165.00	85.00
Ke-65	Condiment set on tray	175.00	225.00	125.00
Ke-70	Cream and sugar	100.00	125.00	65.00
Ke-71	Cream and sugar on tray	175.00	225.00	125.00
Ke-75	Demi-tasse	75.00	85.00	50.00
Ke-77	Egg cup, footed	60.00	75.00	45.00
Ke-80	Hot water jug	250.00	300.00	175.00
Ke-85	Jam pot with liner	150.00	175.00	100.00
Ke-90	Jug, 4″	175.00	200.00	125.00
Ke-91	Jug, 4 1/2″	200.00	250.00	150.00
Ke-92	Jug, 5″	225.00	275.00	165.00
Ke-97	Nut dish	45.00	55.00	35.00
Ke-201	Plate, 4″ sq.	50.00	65.00	35.00
Ke-202	Plate, 5″ sq.	50.00	70.00	40.00
Ke-203	Plate, 6″ sq.	60.00	75.00	45.00
Ke-204	Plate, 7″ sq.	75.00	90.00	50.00
Ke-205	Plate, 8″ sq.	100.00	125.00	65.00
Ke-206	Plate, 9″ sq.	125.00	150.00	75.00
Ke-207	Plate, 10″ sq .	125.00	150.00	75.00
Ke-112	Relish dish, small	150.00	175.00	100.00
Ke-115	Salad bowl, chrome rim	125.00	150.00	75.00
Ke-117	Salt and pepper	75.00	85.00	50.00
Ke-118	Salt and pepper on tray	150.00	175.00	100.00
Ke-120	Sandwich tray, 10″ x 6″	100.00	125.00	65.00
Ke-121	Sandwich tray, 12″ x 7″	115.00	150.00	75.00
Ke-125	Sauce boat and liner	125.00	150.00	75.00
Ke-130	Teacup and saucer	75.00	85.00	50.00
Ke-135	Teapot, 2 cup	275.00	325.00	200.00
Ke-136	Teapot, 4 cup	375.00	450.00	250.00
Ke-137	Teapot, 6 cup	475.00	575.00	300.00
Ke-140	Teapot, stacking	625.00	750.00	450.00
Ke-145	Tennis set	100.00	125.00	65.00
Ke-150	Toast rack, 4 slice	200.00	250.00	150.00
Ke-151	Toast rack, 2 slice	150.00	175.00	100.00
Ke-155	Trivet	100.00	125.00	65.00
Ke-160	Vase, bud	85.00	100.00	60.00

KINVER

The pattern number was 2254, and it was probably introduced in 1934.

Cat.No.	Shape	U.S. $	Can. $	U.K. £
Ki-04	Bonbon dish	80.00	95.00	50.00
Ki-09	Bowl, 5″	50.00	70.00	40.00
Ki-14	Bowl, 8″ soup	100.00	125.00	65.00
Ki-23	Breakfast set	950.00	1,200.00	675.00
Ki-28	Butter dish	225.00	275.00	150.00
Ki-30	Butter pat	65.00	80.00	45.00
Ki-35	Cake plate, open handles	225.00	275.00	165.00
Ki-36	Cake plate, tab handles	200.00	250.00	150.00
Ki-37	Cake plate, 8″ sq. pedestal	250.00	300.00	175.00
Ki-40	Cake stand, 2 tier	250.00	300..00	175.00
Ki-45	Canoe-shaped dish	325.00	400.00	225.00
Ki-50	Cheese keep	300.00	375.00	200.00
Ki-52	Coaster	60.00	75.00	45.00
Ki-55	Coffee pot	875.00	1,100.00	600.00
Ki-60	Compote, footed	200.00	250.00	135.00
Ki-65	Condiment set on tray	275.00	325.00	200.00
Ki-70	Cream and sugar	150.00	175.00	100.00
Ki-71	Cream and sugar on tray	275.00	325.00	200.00
Ki-75	Demi-tasse	100.00	125.00	65.00
Ki-77	Egg cup, footed	100.00	125.00	65.00
Ki-80	Hot water jug	400.00	475.00	275.00
Ki-85	Jam pot with liner	200.00	250.00	150.00
Ki-90	Jug, 4″	325.00	400.00	225.00
Ki-91	Jug, 4 1/2″	350.00	425.00	250.00
Ki-92	Jug, 5″	400.00	475.00	275.00
Ki-97	Nut dish	65.00	80.00	45.00
Ki-201	Plate, 4″ sq.	60.00	75.00	45.00
Ki-202	Plate, 5″ sq.	65.00	80.00	45.00
Ki-203	Plate, 6″ sq.	75.00	100.00	50.00
Ki-204	Plate, 7″ sq.	115.00	135.00	80.00
Ki-205	Plate, 8″ sq.	150.00	175.00	100.00
Ki-206	Plate, 9″ sq.	175.00	200.00	125.00
Ki-207	Plate, 10″ sq.	175.00	200.00	125.00
Ki-112	Relish dish, small	200.00	250.00	150.00
Ki-115	Salad bowl, chrome rim	175.00	200.00	125.00
Ki-117	Salt and pepper	100.00	125.00	75.00
Ki-118	Salt and pepper on tray	200.00	250.00	135.00
Ki-120	Sandwich tray, 10″ x 6″	150.00	175.00	100.00
Ki-121	Sandwich tray, 12″ x 7″	175.00	200.00	125.00
Ki-125	Sauce boat and liner	175.00	200.00	125.00
Ki-130	Teacup and saucer	100.00	125.00	75.00
Ki-135	Teapot, 2 cup	435.00	575.00	350.00
Ki-136	Teapot, 4 cup	625.00	750.00	425.00
Ki-137	Teapot, 6 cup	725.00	875.00	500.00
Ki-140	Teapot, stacking	825.00	1,000.00	575.00
Ki-145	Tennis set	150.00	175.00	100.00
Ki-150	Toast rack, 4 slice	275.00	325.00	200.00
Ki-151	Toast rack, 2 slice	225.00	275.00	150.00
Ki-155	Trivet	150.00	175.00	100.00
Ki-160	Vase, bud	135.00	165.00	85.00

MAJESTIC

The pattern number is 3311, this pattern with a black background was introduced in 1936 after **Royalty** 3079, the alternate colourway in yellow.

Cat.No.	Shape	U.S. $	Can. $	U.K. £
Maj-04	Bonbon dish	100.00	125.00	65.00
Maj-09	Bowl, 5″	65.00	80.00	45.00
Maj-14	Bowl, 8″ soup	100.00	125.00	65.00
Maj-23	Breakfast set	1250.00	1,500.00	875.00
Maj-28	Butter dish	275.00	325.00	175.00
Maj-30	Butter pat	75.00	90.00	50.00
Maj-35	Cake plate, open handles	275.00	325.00	175.00
Maj-36	Cake plate, tab handles	250.00	300.00	175.00
Maj-37	Cake plate, 8″ sq. pedestal	275.00	350.00	200.00
Maj-40	Cake stand, 2 tier	275.00	350.00	200.00
Maj-45	Canoe-shaped dish	375.00	450.00	275.00
Maj-50	Cheese keep	350.00	425.00	250.00
Maj-52	Coaster	75.00	85.00	50.00
Maj-55	Coffee pot	1,100.00	1,300.00	750.00
Maj-60	Compote, footed	225.00	275.00	150.00
Maj-65	Condiment set on tray	325.00	375.00	225.00
Maj-70	Cream and sugar	175.00	200.00	125.00
Maj-71	Cream and sugar on tray	325.00	375.00	225.00
Maj-75	Demi-tasse	125.00	150.00	100.00
Maj-77	Egg cup, footed	100.00	125.00	65.00
Maj-80	Hot water jug	450.00	500.00	325.00
Maj-85	Jam pot with liner	250.00	300.00	175.00
Maj-90	Jug, 4″	400.00	475.00	275.00
Maj-91	Jug, 4 1/2″	425.00	500.00	300.00
Maj-92	Jug, 5″	450.00	550.00	325.00
Maj-97	Nut dish	75.00	90.00	50.00
Maj-201	Plate, 4″ sq.	75.00	90.00	50.00
Maj-202	Plate, 5″ sq.	100.00	125.00	65.00
Maj-203	Plate, 6″ sq.	115.00	150.00	75.00
Maj-204	Plate, 7″ sq.	135.00	165.00	85.00
Maj-205	Plate, 8″ sq.	175.00	225.00	125.00
Maj-206	Plate, 9″ sq.	185.00	225.00	125.00
Maj-207	Plate, 10″ sq.	200.00	250.00	150.00
Maj-112	Relish dish, small	250.00	300.00	175.00
Maj-115	Salad bowl, chrome rim	250.00	300.00	175.00
Maj-117	Salt and pepper	125.00	150.00	75.00
Maj-118	Salt and pepper on tray	225.00	275.00	150.00
Maj-120	Sandwich tray, 10″ x 6″	175.00	225.00	125.00
Maj-121	Sandwich tray, 12″ x 7″	200.00	250.00	150.00
Maj-125	Sauce boat and liner	225.00	275.00	150.00
Maj-130	Teacup and saucer	125.00	150.00	75.00
Maj-135	Teapot, 2 cup	550.00	650.00	375.00
Maj-136	Teapot, 4 cup	700.00	850.00	500.00
Maj-137	Teapot, 6 cup	900.00	1,100.00	625.00
Maj-140	Teapot, stacking	900.00	1,100.00	625.00
Maj-145	Tennis set	165.00	200.00	100.00
Maj-150	Toast rack, 4 slice	300.00	350.00	200.00
Maj-151	Toast rack, 2 slice	225.00	275.00	165.00
Maj-155	Trivet	165.00	200.00	100.00
Maj-160	Vase, bud	165.00	200.00	100.00

MARGUERITE

Although *The Pottery Gazette* reported the pattern number as 9467, most pieces have 9432 recorded on them. **Marguerite** is considered the first "modern" Winton chintz and was produced in 1928. The design was produced in great quantity for many years with a gold, a blue and a burgundy trim. The blue trim sells for a premium over the burgundy and the gold.

Cat.No.	Shape	U.S. $	Can. $	U.K. £
Mag-04	Bonbon dish	40.00	50.00	30.00
Mag-09	Bowl, 5"	35.00	40.00	25.00
Mag-14	Bowl, 8" soup	50.00	75.00	40.00
Mag-23	Breakfast set	550.00	650.00	375.00
Mag-28	Butter dish	125.00	150.00	75.00
Mag-30	Butter pat	35.00	40.00	25.00
Mag-35	Cake plate, open handles	150.00	175.00	100.00
Mag-36	Cake plate, tab handles	125.00	150.00	75.00
Mag-37	Cake plate, 8" sq. pedestal	150.00	175.00	100.00
Mag-40	Cake stand, 2 tier	150.00	175.00	100.00
Mag-45	Canoe-shaped dish	150.00	175.00	100.00
Mag-50	Cheese keep	150.00	175.00	100.00
Mag-52	Coaster	30.00	35.00	25.00
Mag-55	Coffee pot	450.00	550.00	325.00
Mag-60	Compote, footed	100.00	125.00	65.00
Mag-65	Condiment set on tray	135.00	165.00	85.00
Mag-70	Cream and sugar	75.00	90.00	50.00
Mag-71	Cream and sugar on tray	135.00	165.00	85.00
Mag-75	Demi-tasse	50.00	65.00	35.00
Mag-77	Egg cup, footed	45.00	50.00	35.00
Mag-80	Hot water jug	200.00	225.00	150.00
Mag-85	Jam pot with liner	100.00	125.00	65.00
Mag-90	Jug, 4"	165.00	200.00	115.00
Mag-91	Jug, 4 1/2"	175.00	225.00	125.00
Mag-92	Jug, 5"	200.00	250.00	150.00
Mag-97	Nut dish	35.00	40.00	25.00
Mag-201	Plate, 4" sq.	35.00	40.00	25.00
Mag-202	Plate, 5" sq.	40.00	50.00	30.00
Mag-203	Plate, 6" sq.	45.00	50.00	35.00
Mag-204	Plate, 7" sq.	50.00	70.00	40.00
Mag-205	Plate, 8" sq.	100.00	125.00	65.00
Mag-206	Plate, 9" sq.	100.00	125.00	65.00
Mag-207	Plate, 10" sq.	115.00	150.00	75.00
Mag-112	Relish dish, small	100.00	125.00	65.00
Mag-115	Salad bowl, chrome rim	100.00	125.00	65.00
Mag-117	Salt and pepper	50.00	75.00	40.00
Mag-118	Salt and pepper on tray	125.00	150.00	75.00
Mag-120	Sandwich tray, 10" x 6"	75.00	90.00	50.00
Mag-121	Sandwich tray, 12" x 7"	85.00	100.00	60.00
Mag-125	Sauce boat and liner	105.00	125.00	65.00
Mag-130	Teacup and saucer	50.00	65.00	35.00
Mag-135	Teapot, 2 cup	200.00	250.00	150.00
Mag-136	Teapot, 4 cup	300.00	350.00	200.00
Mag-137	Teapot, 6 cup	400.00	475.00	275.00
Mag-140	Teapot, stacking	500.00	600.00	350.00
Mag-145	Tennis set	75.00	90.00	50.00
Mag-150	Toast rack, 4 slice	165.00	200.00	115.00
Mag-151	Toast rack, 2 slice	135.00	165.00	85.00
Mag-155	Trivet	75.00	90.00	50.00
Mag-160	Vase, bud	75.00	90.00	50.00

MARION

The pattern number is 324. This post-war pattern was named after the daughter of a major Canadian importer, Rudolf van der Walde of Montreal, and the pattern was controlled to him.

Cat.No.	Shape	U.S. $	Can. $	U.K. £
Mar-04	Bonbon dish	75.00	90.00	50.00
Mar-09	Bowl, 5″	50.00	65.00	35.00
Mar-14	Bowl, 8″ soup	100.00	125.00	65.00
Mar-23	Breakfast set	950.00	1,200.00	650.00
Mar-28	Butter dish	225.00	275.00	150.00
Mar-30	Butter pat	75.00	90.00	50.00
Mar-35	Cake plate, open handles	225.00	275.00	150.00
Mar-36	Cake plate, tab handles	200.00	250.00	150.00
Mar-37	Cake plate, 8″ sq. pedestal	225.00	275.00	150.00
Mar-40	Cake stand, 2 tier	225.00	275.00	150.00
Mar-45	Canoe-shaped dish	325.00	375.00	225.00
Mar-50	Cheese keep	275.00	350.00	200.00
Mar-52	Coaster	50.00	65.00	35.00
Mar-55	Coffee pot	850.00	1,100.00	600.00
Mar-60	Compote, footed	185.00	225.00	125.00
Mar-65	Condiment set on tray	250.00	300.00	175.00
Mar-70	Cream and sugar	145.00	175.00	100.00
Mar-71	Cream and sugar on tray	250.00	300.00	175.00
Mar-75	Demi-tasse	100.00	125.00	75.00
Mar-77	Egg cup, footed	85.00	100.00	60.00
Mar-80	Hot water jug	375.00	450.00	250.00
Mar-85	Jam pot with liner	200.00	250.00	150.00
Mar-90	Jug, 4″	325.00	375.00	225.00
Mar-91	Jug, 4 1/2″	350.00	400.00	250.00
Mar-92	Jug, 5″	375.00	450.00	250.00
Mar-97	Nut dish	65.00	80.00	45.00
Mar-201	Plate, 4″ sq.	50.00	75.00	40.00
Mar-202	Plate, 5″ sq.	65.00	80.00	45.00
Mar-203	Plate, 6″ sq.	75.00	90.00	55.00
Mar-204	Plate, 7″ sq.	100.00	125.00	65.00
Mar-205	Plate, 8″ sq.	135.00	165.00	85.00
Mar-206	Plate, 9″ sq.	150.00	175.00	100.00
Mar-207	Plate, 10″ sq.	165.00	200.00	115.00
Mar-112	Relish dish, small	200.00	250.00	150.00
Mar-115	Salad bowl, chrome rim	175.00	200.00	125.00
Mar-117	Salt and pepper	100.00	125.00	65.00
Mar-118	Salt and pepper on tray	175.00	200.00	125.00
Mar-120	Sandwich tray, 10″ x 6″	150.00	175.00	100.00
Mar-121	Sandwich tray, 12″ x 7″	165.00	200.00	115.00
Mar-125	Sauce boat and liner	165.00	200.00	115.00
Mar-130	Teacup and saucer	100.00	125.00	65.00
Mar-135	Teapot, 2 cup	425.00	500.00	300.00
Mar-136	Teapot, 4 cup	625.00	750.00	450.00
Mar-137	Teapot, 6 cup	725.00	875.00	500.00
Mar-140	Teapot, stacking	800.00	950.00	550.00
Mar-145	Tennis set	125.00	150.00	75.00
Mar-150	Toast rack, 4 slice	250.00	300.00	175.00
Mar-151	Toast rack, 2 slice	200.00	250.00	150.00
Mar-155	Trivet	125.00	150.00	75.00
Mar-160	Vase, bud	135.00	165.00	85.00

MAYFAIR

The pattern number is 392, and it was registered in Canada in 1951.

Cat.No.	Shape	U.S. $	Can. $	U.K. £
May-04	Bonbon dish	50.00	65.00	35.00
May-09	Bowl, 5″	45.00	50.00	35.00
May-14	Bowl, 8″ soup	75.00	90.00	50.00
May-23	Breakfast set	700.00	825.00	475.00
May-28	Butter dish	150.00	175.00	100.00
May-30	Butter pat	45.00	50.00	35.00
May-35	Cake plate, open handles	150.00	175.00	100.00
May-36	Cake plate, tab handles	135.00	165.00	100.00
May-37	Cake plate, 8″ sq. pedestal	150.00	200.00	115.00
May-40	Cake stand, 2 tier	150.00	200.00	115.00
May-45	Canoe-shaped dish	225.00	275.00	125.00
May-50	Cheese keep	200.00	250.00	150.00
May-52	Coaster	40.00	50.00	30.00
May-55	Coffee pot	550.00	650.00	375.00
May-60	Compote, footed	130.00	160.00	100.00
May-65	Condiment set on tray	175.00	225.00	125.00
May-70	Cream and sugar	100.00	125.00	65.00
May-71	Cream and sugar on tray	175.00	225.00	125.00
May-75	Demi-tasse	70.00	85.00	50.00
May-77	Egg cup, footed	60.00	75.00	45.00
May-80	Hot water jug	250.00	310.00	175.00
May-85	Jam pot with liner	150.00	175.00	100.00
May-90	Jug, 4″	175.00	200.00	125.00
May-91	Jug, 4 1/2″	225.00	250.00	150.00
May-92	Jug, 5″	225.00	275.00	150.00

Cat.No.	Shape	U.S. $	Can. $	U.K. £
May-97	Nut dish	45.00	55.00	35.00
May-201	Plate, 4″ sq.	50.00	65.00	35.00
May-202	Plate, 5″ sq.	50.00	75.00	40.00
May-203	Plate, 6″ sq.	60.00	75.00	45.00
May-204	Plate, 7″ sq.	75.00	90.00	50.00
May-205	Plate, 8″ sq.	100.00	125.00	65.00
May-206	Plate, 9″ sq.	125.00	150.00	75.00
May-207	Plate, 10″ sq.	125.00	150.00	75.00
May-112	Relish dish, small	140.00	175.00	100.00
May-115	Salad bowl, chrome rim	125.00	150.00	75.00
May-117	Salt and pepper	75.00	85.00	50.00
May-118	Salt and pepper on tray	150.00	175.00	100.00
May-120	Sandwich tray, 10″ x 6″	100.00	125.00	65.00
May-121	Sandwich tray, 12″ x 7″	125.00	150.00	75.00
May-125	Sauce boat and liner	125.00	150.00	75.00
May-130	Teacup and saucer	75.00	85.00	50.00
May-135	Teapot, 2 cup	275.00	325.00	200.00
May-136	Teapot, 4 cup	375.00	450.00	250.00
May-137	Teapot, 6 cup	475.00	575.00	325.00
May-140	Teapot, stacking	625.00	750.00	425.00
May-145	Tennis set	100.00	125.00	65.00
May-150	Toast rack, 4 slice	200.00	250.00	150.00
May-151	Toast rack, 2 slice	140.00	175.00	100.00
May-155	Trivet	100.00	125.00	65.00
May-160	Vase, bud	75.00	100.00	50.00

MAY FESTIVAL

The pattern number is 139, and it was the alternate colourway to burgundy **June Festival** 137. The navy background has no name backstamp and the pattern number is 135. **May Festival** is rarely found with a pattern name backstamp.

Cat.No.	Shape	U.S. $	Can. $	U.K. £
MF-04	Bonbon dish	45.00	50.00	35.00
MF-09	Bowl, 5″	40.00	50.00	30.00
MF-14	Bowl, 8″ soup	70.00	85.00	50.00
MF-23	Breakfast set	650.00	775.00	450.00
MF-28	Butter dish	135.00	175.00	100.00
MF-30	Butter pat	40.00	50.00	30.00
MF-35	Cake plate, open handles	135.00	165.00	85.00
MF-36	Cake plate, tab handles	125.00	150.00	75.00
MF-37	Cake plate, 8″ sq. pedestal	140.00	175.00	100.00
MF-40	Cake stand, 2 tier	140.00	175.00	100.00
MF-45	Canoe-shaped dish	190.00	225.00	135.00
MF-50	Cheese keep	175.00	200.00	125.00
MF-52	Coaster	35.00	40.00	25.00
MF-55	Coffee pot	525.00	625.00	350.00
MF-60	Compote, footed	100.00	125.00	65.00
MF-65	Condiment set on tray	150.00	175.00	100.00
MF-70	Cream and sugar	85.00	100.00	60.00
MF-71	Cream and sugar on tray	150.00	175.00	100.00
MF-75	Demi-tasse	60.00	75.00	45.00
MF-77	Egg cup, footed	50.00	65.00	35.00
MF-80	Hot water jug	225.00	275.00	150.00
MF-85	Jam pot with liner	125.00	150.00	75.00
MF-90	Jug, 4″	200.00	250.00	135.00
MF-91	Jug, 4 1/2″	200.00	250.00	135.00
MF-92	Jug, 5″	225.00	275.00	150.00

Cat.No.	Shape	U.S. $	Can. $	U.K. £
MF-97	Nut dish	40.00	50.00	30.00
MF-201	Plate, 4″ sq.	35.00	40.00	25.00
MF-202	Plate, 5″ sq.	40.00	50.00	30.00
MF-203	Plate, 6″ sq.	45.00	50.00	35.00
MF-204	Plate, 7″ sq.	50.00	65.00	35.00
MF-205	Plate, 8″ sq.	100.00	125.00	65.00
MF-206	Plate, 9″ sq.	100.00	125.00	65.00
MF-207	Plate, 10″ sq.	125.00	150.00	75.00
MF-112	Relish dish, small	125.00	150.00	75.00
MF-115	Salad bowl, chrome rim	100.00	125.00	75.00
MF-117	Salt and pepper	65.00	80.00	45.00
MF-118	Salt and pepper on tray	150.00	175.00	100.00
MF-120	Sandwich tray, 10″ x 6″	85.00	100.00	60.00
MF-121	Sandwich tray, 12″ x 7″	100.00	125.00	65.00
MF-125	Sauce boat and liner	125.00	150.00	75.00
MF-130	Teacup and saucer	60.00	75.00	45.00
MF-135	Teapot, 2 cup	250.00	300.00	175.00
MF-136	Teapot, 4 cup	350.00	425.00	250.00
MF-137	Teapot, 6 cup	450.00	550.00	325.00
MF-140	Teapot, stacking	600.00	725.00	425.00
MF-145	Tennis set	80.00	100.00	50.00
MF-150	Toast rack, 4 slice	175.00	200.00	125.00
MF-151	Toast rack, 2 slice	115.00	150.00	75.00
MF-155	Trivet	80.00	100.00	50.00
MF-160	Vase, bud	85.00	100.00	60.00

MORNING GLORY

The pattern is clearly one of the 1950s large flower chintzes and was produced with either a black or a burgundy background. The burgundy background is rarely seen in North America.

Cat.No.	Shape	U.S. $	Can. $	U.K. £
MG-04	Bonbon dish	45.00	50.00	35.00
MG-09	Bowl, 5″	40.00	50.00	30.00
MG-14	Bowl, 8″ soup	75.00	85.00	50.00
MG-23	Breakfast set	650.00	775.00	450.00
MG-28	Butter dish	135.00	165.00	85.00
MG-30	Butter pat	40.00	50.00	30.00
MG-35	Cake plate, open handles	135.00	165.00	85.00
MG-36	Cake plate, tab handles	125.00	150.00	75.00
MG-37	Cake plate,8″ sq. pedestal	140.00	175.00	100.00
MG-40	Cake stand, 2 tier	140.00	175.00	100.00
MG-45	Canoe-shaped dish	200.00	250.00	135.00
MG-50	Cheese keep	175.00	250.00	125.00
MG-52	Coaster	35.00	40.00	25.00
MG-55	Coffee pot	525.00	625.00	350.00
MG-60	Compote, footed	100.00	125.00	65.00
MG-65	Condiment set on tray	150.00	175.00	110.00
MG-70	Cream and sugar	85.00	100.00	60.00
MG-71	Cream and sugar on tray	150.00	175.00	110.00
MG-75	Demi-tasse	60.00	75.00	45.00
MG-77	Egg cup, footed	50.00	65.00	35.00
MG-80	Hot water jug	225.00	275.00	160.00
MG-85	Jam pot with liner	125.00	150.00	75.00
MG-90	Jug, 4″	200.00	250.00	125.00
MG-91	Jug, 4 1/2″	200.00	250.00	125.00
MG-92	Jug, 5″	225.00	275.00	150.00

Cat.No.	Shape	U.S. $	Can. $	U.K. £
MG-97	Nut dish	40.00	50.00	30.00
MG-201	Plate, 4″ sq.	35.00	40.00	25.00
MG-202	Plate, 5″ sq.	40.00	50.00	30.00
MG-203	Plate, 6″ sq.	45.00	50.00	35.00
MG-204	Plate, 7″ sq.	50.00	65.00	35.00
MG-205	Plate, 8″ sq.	100.00	125.00	65.00
MG-206	Plate, 9″ sq.	100.00	125.00	65.00
MG-207	Plate, 10″ sq.	125.00	150.00	75.00
MG-112	Relish dish, small	125.00	150.00	75.00
MG-115	Salad bowl, chrome rim	100.00	125.00	65.00
MG-117	Salt and pepper	65.00	80.00	45.00
MG-118	Salt and pepper on tray	150.00	175.00	100.00
MG-120	Sandwich tray, 10″ x 6″	85.00	100.00	60.00
MG-121	Sandwich tray, 12″ x 7″	100.00	125.00	65.00
MG-125	Sauce boat and liner	125.00	150.00	75.00
MG-130	Teacup and saucer	60.00	75.00	45.00
MG-135	Teapot, 2 cup	250.00	300.00	175.00
MG-136	Teapot, 4 cup	350.00	425.00	250.00
MG-137	Teapot, 6 cup	450.00	550.00	325.00
MG-140	Teapot, stacking	600.00	725.00	425.00
MG-145	Tennis set	80.00	95.00	50.00
MG-150	Toast rack, 4 slice	175.00	225.00	125.00
MG-151	Toast rack, 2 slice	125.00	150.00	75.00
MG-155	Trivet	80.00	95.00	50.00
MG-160	Vase, bud	85.00	100.00	60.00

NANTWICH

The pattern number is 291. This pattern was exported in quantity to North America in the 1950s.

Cat.No.	Shape	U.S. $	Can. $	U.K. £
N-04	Bonbon dish	65.00	80.00	45.00
N-09	Bowl, 5″	50.00	75.00	40.00
N-14	Bowl, 8″ soup	75.00	90.00	50.00
N-23	Breakfast set	900.00	1,100.00	625.00
N-28	Butter dish	200.00	250.00	125.00
N-30	Butter pat	50.00	75.00	40.00
N-35	Cake plate, open handles	200.00	250.00	125.00
N-36	Cake plate, tab handles	175.00	200.00	125.00
N-37	Cake plate, 8″ sq. pedestal	200.00	250.00	125.00
N-40	Cake stand, 2 tier	200.00	250.00	125.00
N-45	Canoe-shaped dish	275.00	325.00	200.00
N-50	Cheese keep	250.00	300.00	175.00
N-52	Coaster	50.00	65.00	35.00
N-55	Coffee pot	750.00	900.00	525.00
N-60	Compote, footed	150.00	200.00	100.00
N-65	Condiment set on tray	225.00	275.00	150.00
N-70	Cream and sugar	125.00	150.00	75.00
N-71	Cream and sugar on tray	225.00	275.00	150.00
N-75	Demi-tasse	85.00	100.00	60.00
N-77	Egg cup, footed	75.00	90.00	50.00
N-80	Hot water jug	325.00	400.00	225.00
N-85	Jam pot with liner	175.00	200.00	125.00
N-90	Jug, 4″	275.00	325.00	175.00
N-91	Jug, 4 1/2″	300.00	350.00	200.00
N-92	Jug, 5″	325.00	400.00	225.00
N-97	Nut dish	50.00	70.00	40.00
N-201	Plate, 4″ sq.	50.00	65.00	35.00
N-202	Plate, 5″ sq.	50.00	70.00	40.00
N-203	Plate, 6″ sq.	65.00	80.00	45.00
N-204	Plate, 7″ sq.	85.00	100.00	60.00
N-205	Plate, 8″ sq.	135.00	165.00	85.00
N-206	Plate, 9″ sq.	150.00	175.00	100.00
N-207	Plate, 10″ sq.	165.00	195.00	115.00
N-112	Relish dish, small	175.00	200.00	125.00
N-115	Salad bowl, chrome rim	150.00	175.00	100.00
N-117	Salt and pepper	90.00	110.00	60.00
N-118	Salt and pepper on tray	165.00	200.00	115.00
N-120	Sandwich tray, 10″ x 6″	125.00	150.00	75.00
N-121	Sandwich tray, 12″ x 7″	150.00	175.00	100.00
N-125	Sauce boat and liner	175.00	200.00	125.00
N-130	Teacup and saucer	85.00	100.00	60.00
N-135	Teapot, 2 cup	450.00	550.00	325.00
N-136	Teapot, 4 cup	550.00	650.00	375.00
N-137	Teapot, 6 cup	650.00	775.00	450.00
N-140	Teapot, stacking	650.00	775.00	450.00
N-145	Tennis set	125.00	150.00	75.00
N-150	Toast rack, 4 slice	275.00	325.00	200.00
N-151	Toast rack, 2 slice	225.00	275.00	160.00
N-155	Trivet	125.00	150.00	75.00
N-160	Vase, bud	125.00	150.00	75.00

OLD COTTAGE CHINTZ

The pattern number is 9632. The pattern was probably introduced very early in the 1930s and was produced in great quantities until the 1960s. It has been seen on an invoice as late as 1969. Be aware of the difference in the colour of the pre- and post-war transfer.

Cat.No.	Shape	U.S. $	Can. $	U.K. £
OC-04	Bonbon dish	50.00	65.00	35.00
OC-09	Bowl, 5″	45.00	50.00	35.00
OC-14	Bowl, 8″ soup	75.00	90.00	50.00
OC-23	Breakfast set	700.00	850.00	475.00
OC-28	Butter dish	150.00	200.00	100.00
OC-30	Butter pat	45.00	55.00	35.00
OC-35	Cake plate, open handles	150.00	200.00	100.00
OC-36	Cake plate, tab handles	135.00	165.00	85.00
OC-37	Cake plate,8″ sq. pedestal	150.00	200.00	100.00
OC-40	Cake stand, 2 tier	150.00	200.00	100.00
OC-45	Canoe-shaped dish	225.00	275.00	150.00
OC-50	Cheese keep	200.00	250.00	125.00
OC-52	Coaster	40.00	50.00	30.00
OC-55	Coffee pot	550.00	650.00	375.00
OC-60	Compote, footed	125.00	150.00	75.00
OC-65	Condiment set on tray	175.00	225.00	125.00
OC-70	Cream and sugar	100.00	125.00	65.00
OC-71	Cream and sugar on tray	175.00	225.00	125.00
OC-75	Demi-tasse	75.00	100.00	50.00
OC-77	Egg cup, footed	60.00	75.00	45.00
OC-80	Hot water jug	250.00	300.00	175.00
OC-85	Jam pot with liner	150.00	200.00	100.00
OC-90	Jug, 4″	175.00	200.00	125.00
OC-91	Jug, 4 1/2″	200.00	250.00	150.00
OC-92	Jug, 5″	225.00	275.00	150.00

Cat.No.	Shape	U.S. $	Can. $	U.K. £
OC-97	Nut dish	45.00	55.00	35.00
OC-201	Plate, 4″ sq.	50.00	65.00	35.00
OC-202	Plate, 5″ sq.	50.00	75.00	40.00
OC-203	Plate, 6″ sq.	60.00	75.00	45.00
OC-204	Plate, 7″ sq.	75.00	90.00	50.00
OC-205	Plate, 8″ sq.	100.00	125.00	65.00
OC-206	Plate, 9″ sq.	125.00	150.00	75.00
OC-207	Plate, 10″ sq.	125.00	150.00	75.00
OC-112	Relish dish, small	140.00	175.00	100.00
OC-115	Salad bowl, chrome rim	125.00	150.00	75.00
OC-117	Salt and pepper	75.00	100.00	50.00
OC-118	Salt and pepper on tray	150.00	175.00	85.00
OC-120	Sandwich tray, 10″ x 6″	100.00	125.00	65.00
OC-121	Sandwich tray, 12″ x 7″	125.00	150.00	75.00
OC-125	Sauce boat and liner	125.00	150.00	75.00
OC-130	Teacup and saucer	75.00	85.00	50.00
OC-135	Teapot, 2 cup	275.00	325.00	200.00
OC-136	Teapot, 4 cup	375.00	450.00	250.00
OC-137	Teapot, 6 cup	475.00	575.00	325.00
OC-140	Teapot, stacking	625.00	725.00	425.00
OC-145	Tennis set	90.00	110.00	65.00
OC-150	Toast rack, 4 slice	200.00	250.00	150.00
OC-151	Toast rack, 2 slice	150.00	200.00	100.00
OC-155	Trivet	100.00	125.00	65.00
OC-160	Vase, bud	100.00	125.00	65.00

ORIENT

The pattern number is 471, and the pattern was exclusive to Cassidy's of Canada in 1954. Jack Robertson, who was the buyer for Cassidy's, chose this pattern from a sample, but the finished product did not sell well.

Cat.No.	Shape	U.S. $	Can. $	U.K. £
O-04	Bonbon dish	40.00	50.00	30.00
O-09	Bowl, 5″	35.00	40.00	25.00
O-14	Bowl, 8″ soup	50.00	75.00	40.00
O-23	Breakfast set	550.00	650.00	375.00
O-28	Butter dish	125.00	150.00	75.00
O-30	Butter pat	35.00	40.00	25.00
O-35	Cake plate, open handles	150.00	200.00	100.00
O-36	Cake plate, tab handles	125.00	150.00	75.00
O-37	Cake plate, 8″ sq. pedestal	150.00	200.00	100.00
O-40	Cake stand, 2 tier	150.00	200.00	100.00
O-45	Canoe-shaped dish	150.00	200.00	100.00
O-50	Cheese keep	150.00	200.00	100.00
O-52	Coaster	30.00	35.00	25.00
O-55	Coffee pot	450.00	550.00	325.00
O-60	Compote, footed	100.00	125.00	65.00
O-65	Condiment set on tray	135.00	165.00	85.00
O-70	Cream and sugar	75.00	90.00	50.00
O-71	Cream and sugar on tray	135.00	165.00	85.00
O-75	Demi-tasse	50.00	65.00	35.00
O-77	Egg cup, footed	45.00	55.00	35.00
O-80	Hot water jug	200.00	250.00	150.00
O-85	Jam pot with liner	100.00	125.00	65.00
O-90	Jug, 4″	165.00	200.00	115.00
O-91	Jug, 4 1/2″	175.00	225.00	125.00
O-92	Jug, 5″	200.00	250.00	150.00

Cat.No.	Shape	U.S. $	Can. $	U.K. £
O-97	Nut dish	35.00	40.00	25.00
O-201	Plate, 4″ sq.	35.00	40.00	25.00
O-202	Plate, 5″ sq.	40.00	50.00	30.00
O-203	Plate, 6″ sq.	45.00	50.00	35.00
O-204	Plate, 7″ sq.	55.00	75.00	40.00
O-205	Plate, 8″ sq.	100.00	125.00	65.00
O-206	Plate, 9″ sq.	100.00	125.00	65.00
O-207	Plate, 10″ sq.	115.00	150.00	75.00
O-112	Relish dish, small	100.00	125.00	65.00
O-115	Salad bowl, chrome rim	90.00	110.00	60.00
O-117	Salt and pepper	50.00	75.00	40.00
O-118	Salt and pepper on tray	125.00	150.00	75.00
O-120	Sandwich tray, 10″ x 6″	75.00	90.00	50.00
O-121	Sandwich tray, 12″ x 7″	85.00	100.00	60.00
O-125	Sauce boat and liner	100.00	125.00	65.00
O-130	Teacup and saucer	50.00	65.00	35.00
O-135	Teapot, 2 cup	200.00	250.00	150.00
O-136	Teapot, 4 cup	300.00	350.00	200.00
O-137	Teapot, 6 cup	400.00	475.00	275.00
O-140	Teapot, stacking	500.00	600.00	350.00
O-145	Tennis set	75.00	85.00	50.00
O-150	Toast rack, 4 slice	165.00	200.00	100.00
O-151	Toast rack, 2 slice	135.00	165.00	75.00
O-155	Trivet	75.00	100.00	50.00
O-160	Vase, bud	75.00	100.00	50.00

PEKIN

The pattern number for the 1950s version is 320, and it was produced with black, burgundy and navy backgrounds. The pattern is seen occasionally with a cream ground. Some of the earlier versions are hand painted.

Cat.No.	Shape	U.S. $	Can. $	U.K. £
Pe-04	Bonbon dish	40.00	50.00	30.00
Pe-09	Bowl, 5″	35.00	40.00	25.00
Pe-14	Bowl, 8″ soup	50.00	75.00	40.00
Pe-23	Breakfast set	550.00	650.00	375.00
Pe-28	Butter dish	125.00	150.00	75.00
Pe-30	Butter pat	35.00	40.00	25.00
Pe-35	Cake plate, open handles	150.00	175.00	100.00
Pe-36	Cake plate, tab handles	125.00	150.00	75.00
Pe-37	Cake plate, 8″ sq. pedestal	150.00	175.00	100.00
Pe-40	Cake stand, 2 tier	150.00	175.00	100.00
Pe-45	Canoe-shaped dish	150.00	175.00	100.00
Pe-50	Cheese keep	150.00	175.00	100.00
Pe-52	Coaster	30.00	35.00	25.00
Pe-55	Coffee pot	450.00	550.00	325.00
Pe-60	Compote, footed	100.00	125.00	65.00
Pe-65	Condiment set on tray	135.00	165.00	85.00
Pe-70	Cream and sugar	75.00	95.00	50.00
Pe-71	Cream and sugar on tray	135.00	165.00	85.00
Pe-75	Demi-tasse	50.00	65.00	35.00
Pe-77	Egg cup, footed	45.00	50.00	35.00
Pe-80	Hot water jug	200.00	250.00	150.00
Pe-85	Jam pot with liner	100.00	125.00	65.00
Pe-90	Jug, 4″	165.00	200.00	100.00
Pe-91	Jug, 4 1/2″	175.00	225.00	125.00
Pe-92	Jug, 5″	100.00	250.00	150.00
Pe-97	Nut dish	35.00	40.00	25.00
Pe-201	Plate, 4″ sq.	35.00	40.00	25.00
Pe-202	Plate, 5″ sq.	40.00	50.00	30.00
Pe-203	Plate, 6″ sq.	45.00	50.00	35.00
Pe-204	Plate, 7″ sq.	50.00	75.00	40.00
Pe-205	Plate, 8″ sq.	100.00	125.00	65.00
Pe-206	Plate, 9″ sq.	100.00	125.00	65.00
Pe-207	Plate, 10″ sq.	115.00	150.00	75.00
Pe-112	Relish dish, small	100.00	125.00	65.00
Pe-115	Salad bowl, chrome rim	100.00	125.00	65.00
Pe-117	Salt and pepper	50.00	75.00	40.00
Pe-118	Salt and pepper on tray	125.00	150.00	75.00
Pe-120	Sandwich tray, 10″ x 6″	75.00	90.00	50.00
Pe-121	Sandwich tray, 12″ x 7″	85.00	100.00	60.00
Pe-125	Sauce boat and liner	100.00	125.00	65.00
Pe-130	Teacup and saucer	50.00	65.00	35.00
Pe-135	Teapot, 2 cup	200.00	250.00	150.00
Pe-136	Teapot, 4 cup	300.00	350.00	200.00
Pe-137	Teapot, 6 cup	400.00	475.00	275.00
Pe-140	Teapot, stacking	500.00	600.00	350.00
Pe-145	Tennis set	75.00	100.00	50.00
Pe-150	Toast rack, 4 slice	175.00	200.00	115.00
Pe-151	Toast rack, 2 slice	135.00	165.00	85.00
Pe-155	Trivet	75.00	100.00	50.00
Pe-160	Vase, bud	75.00	100.00	50.00

PELHAM

The pattern number is 2201, and the pattern was purchased by Queen Mary at the 1935 British Industries Fair. It came with a teal trim. This pattern is also known as **Sampler**.

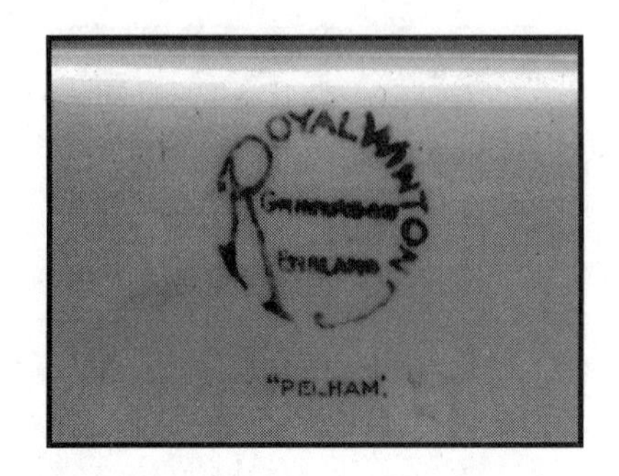

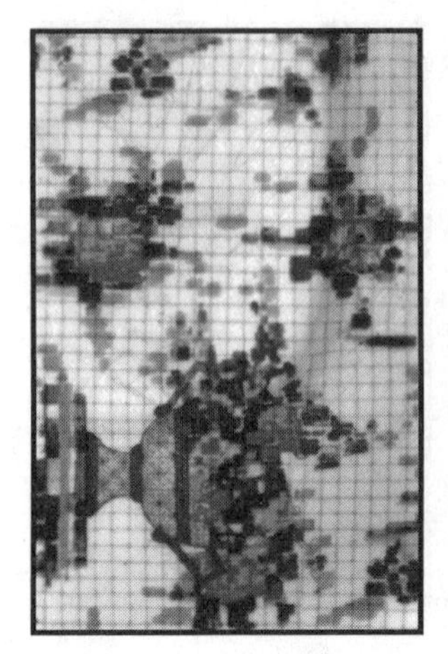

Cat.No.	Shape	U.S. $	Can. $	U.K. £
Pel-04	Bonbon dish	45.00	55.00	35.00
Pel-09	Bowl, 5″	40.00	50.00	30.00
Pel-14	Bowl, 8″ soup	50.00	75.00	40.00
Pel-23	Breakfast set	575.00	675.00	400.00
Pel-28	Butter dish	125.00	150.00	75.00
Pel-30	Butter pat	35.00	40.00	25.00
Pel-35	Cake plate, open handles	150.00	200.00	100.00
Pel-36	Cake plate, tab handles	135.00	165.00	85.00
Pel-37	Cake plate, 8″ sq. pedestal	150.00	200.00	100.00
Pel-40	Cake stand, 2 tier	150.00	200.00	100.00
Pel-45	Canoe-shaped dish	150.00	200.00	100.00
Pel-50	Cheese keep	150.00	200.00	100.00
Pel-52	Coaster	30.00	35.00	25.00
Pel-55	Coffee pot	475.00	575.00	325.00
Pel-60	Compote, footed	100.00	125.00	65.00
Pel-65	Condiment set on tray	150.00	175.00	85.00
Pel-70	Cream and sugar	75.00	100.00	50.00
Pel-71	Cream and sugar on tray	135.00	165.00	85.00
Pel-75	Demi-tasse	50.00	75.00	40.00
Pel-77	Egg cup, footed	45.00	50.00	35.00
Pel-80	Hot water jug	200.00	250.00	150.00
Pel-85	Jam pot with liner	100.00	125.00	65.00
Pel-90	Jug, 4″	175.00	225.00	125.00
Pel-91	Jug, 4 1/2″	200.00	250.00	150.00
Pel-92	Jug, 5″	200.00	250.00	150.00
Pel-97	Nut dish	35.00	40.00	25.00
Pel-201	Plate, 4″ sq.	35.00	40.00	25.00
Pel-202	Plate, 5″ sq.	40.00	50.00	30.00
Pel-203	Plate, 6″ sq.	45.00	50.00	35.00
Pel-204	Plate, 7″ sq.	50.00	75.00	40.00
Pel-205	Plate, 8″ sq.	100.00	125.00	65.00
Pel-206	Plate, 9″ sq.	100.00	125.00	65.00
Pel-207	Plate, 10″ sq.	125.00	150.00	75.00
Pel-112	Relish dish, small	125.00	150.00	75.00
Pel-115	Salad bowl, chrome rim	100.00	125.00	65.00
Pel-117	Salt and pepper	65.00	80.00	45.00
Pel-118	Salt and pepper on tray	135.00	165.00	85.00
Pel-120	Sandwich tray, 10″ x 6″	75.00	100.00	50.00
Pel-121	Sandwich tray, 12″ x 7″	100.00	125.00	65.00
Pel-125	Sauce boat and liner	125.00	150.00	75.00
Pel-130	Teacup and saucer	50.00	75.00	40.00
Pel-135	Teapot, 2 cup	300.00	350.00	200.00
Pel-136	Teapot, 4 cup	350.00	425.00	250.00
Pel-137	Teapot, 6 cup	425.00	500.00	300.00
Pel-140	Teapot, stacking	425.00	500.00	300.00
Pel-145	Tennis set	75.00	85.00	50.00
Pel-150	Toast rack, 4 slice	175.00	225.00	125.00
Pel-151	Toast rack, 2 slice	150.00	200.00	100.00
Pel-155	Trivet	75.00	85.00	50.00
Pel-160	Vase, bud	75.00	85.00	50.00

PEONY

This large flower chintz pattern is very much a 1950s chintz and was exported to North America in great quantities.

Cat.No.	Shape	U.S. $	Can. $	U.K. £
Peo-04	Bonbon dish	45.00	50.00	35.00
Peo-09	Bowl, 5″	40.00	50.00	30.00
Peo-14	Bowl, 8″ soup	50.00	75.00	40.00
Peo-23	Breakfast set	575.00	675.00	400.00
Peo-28	Butter dish	125.00	150.00	75.00
Peo-30	Butter pat	35.00	40.00	25.00
Peo-35	Cake plate, open handles	150.00	200.00	100.00
Peo-36	Cake plate, tab handles	135.00	165.00	85.00
Peo-37	Cake plate, 8″ sq. pedestal	150.00	200.00	100.00
Peo-40	Cake stand, 2 tier	150.00	200.00	100.00
Peo-45	Canoe-shaped dish	150.00	200.00	100.00
Peo-50	Cheese keep	150.00	200.00	100.00
Peo-52	Coaster	30.00	35.00	25.00
Peo-55	Coffee pot	475.00	575.00	325.00
Peo-60	Compote, footed	100.00	125.00	65.00
Peo-65	Condiment set on tray	150.00	200.00	100.00
Peo-70	Cream and sugar	80.00	100.00	50.00
Peo-71	Cream and sugar on tray	135.00	165.00	85.00
Peo-75	Demi-tasse	50.00	75.00	40.00
Peo-77	Egg cup, footed	45.00	50.00	35.00
Peo-80	Hot water jug	200.00	250.00	150.00
Peo-85	Jam pot with liner	110.00	130.00	75.00
Peo-90	Jug, 4″	175.00	225.00	125.00
Peo-91	Jug, 4 1/2″	200.00	250.00	150.00
Peo-92	Jug, 5″	200.00	250.00	150.00

Cat.No.	Shape	U.S. $	Can. $	U.K. £
Peo-97	Nut dish	35.00	40.00	25.00
Peo-201	Plate, 4″ sq.	35.00	40.00	25.00
Peo-202	Plate, 5″ sq.	40.00	50.00	30.00
Peo-203	Plate, 6″ sq.	45.00	50.00	35.00
Peo-204	Plate, 7″ sq.	50.00	75.00	40.00
Peo-205	Plate, 8″ sq.	100.00	125.00	65.00
Peo-206	Plate, 9″ sq.	100.00	125.00	65.00
Peo-207	Plate, 10″ sq.	125.00	150.00	75.00
Peo-112	Relish dish, small	125.00	150.00	75.00
Peo-115	Salad bowl, chrome rim	100.00	125.00	65.00
Peo-117	Salt and pepper	65.00	80.00	45.00
Peo-118	Salt and pepper on tray	135.00	165.00	85.00
Peo-120	Sandwich tray, 10″ x 6″	75.00	100.00	50.00
Peo-121	Sandwich tray, 12″ x 7″	100.00	125.00	65.00
Peo-125	Sauce boat and liner	125.00	150.00	75.00
Peo-130	Teacup and saucer	50.00	75.00	40.00
Peo-135	Teapot, 2 cup	300.00	350.00	205.00
Peo-136	Teapot, 4 cup	350.00	425.00	250.00
Peo-137	Teapot, 6 cup	425.00	500.00	300.00
Peo-140	Teapot, stacking	425.00	500.00	300.00
Peo-145	Tennis set	75.00	90.00	50.00
Peo-150	Toast rack, 4 slice	175.00	225.00	125.00
Peo-151	Toast rack, 2 slice	150.00	200.00	100.00
Peo-155	Trivet	75.00	100.00	50.00
Peo-160	Vase, bud	75.00	100.00	50.00

QUEEN ANNE

The pattern number is 2995 and it was introduced at the 1936 British Industries Fair. The alternate colourway is **Victorian** 3164 with a black background.

Cat.No.	Shape	U.S. $	Can. $	U.K. £
QA-04	Bonbon dish	40.00	50.00	30.00
QA-09	Bowl, 5″	35.00	40.00	25.00
QA-14	Bowl, 8″ soup	50.00	75.00	40.00
QA-23	Breakfast set	550.00	650.00	375.00
QA-28	Butter dish	125.00	150.00	75.00
QA-30	Butter pat	35.00	40.00	25.00
QA-35	Cake plate, open handles	150.00	200.00	100.00
QA-36	Cake plate, tab handles	125.00	150.00	90.00
QA-37	Cake plate, 8″ sq. pedestal	150.00	200.00	100.00
QA-40	Cake stand, 2 tier	150.00	200.00	100.00
QA-45	Canoe-shaped dish	150.00	200.00	100.00
QA-50	Cheese keep	150.00	200.00	100.00
QA-52	Coaster	30.00	35.00	25.00
QA-55	Coffee pot	450.00	550.00	325.00
QA-60	Compote, footed	100.00	125.00	65.00
QA-65	Condiment set on tray	135.00	165.00	85.00
QA-70	Cream and sugar	75.00	90.00	50.00
QA-71	Cream and sugar on tray	135.00	165.00	85.00
QA-75	Demi-tasse	50.00	65.00	35.00
QA-77	Egg cup, footed	45.00	55.00	35.00
QA-80	Hot water jug	200.00	250.00	150.00
QA-85	Jam pot with liner	100.00	125.00	65.00
QA-90	Jug, 4″	165.00	200.00	100.00
QA-91	Jug, 4 1/2″	175.00	225.00	125.00
QA-92	Jug, 5″	200.00	235.00	150.00
QA-97	Nut dish	35.00	40.00	25.00
QA-201	Plate, 4″ sq.	35.00	40.00	25.00
QA-202	Plate, 5″ sq.	40.00	50.00	30.00
QA-203	Plate, 6″ sq.	45.00	50.00	35.00
QA-204	Plate, 7″ sq.	50.00	75.00	40.00
QA-205	Plate, 8″ sq.	100.00	125.00	65.00
QA-206	Plate, 9″ sq.	100.00	125.00	65.00
QA-207	Plate, 10″ sq.	125.00	150.00	75.00
QA-112	Relish dish, small	100.00	125.00	65.00
QA-115	Salad bowl, chrome rim	90.00	110.00	65.00
QA-117	Salt and pepper	50.00	75.00	40.00
QA-118	Salt and pepper on tray	125.00	150.00	90.00
QA-120	Sandwich tray, 10″ x 6″	75.00	100.00	50.00
QA-121	Sandwich tray, 12″ x 7″	85.00	100.00	60.00
QA-125	Sauce boat and liner	100.00	125.00	75.00
QA-130	Teacup and saucer	50.00	65.00	35.00
QA-135	Teapot, 2 cup	200.00	250.00	150.00
QA-136	Teapot, 4 cup	300.00	350.00	200.00
QA-137	Teapot, 6 cup	400.00	475.00	275.00
QA-140	Teapot, stacking	500.00	600.00	350.00
QA-145	Tennis set	75.00	85.00	50.00
QA-150	Toast rack, 4 slice	175.00	225.00	125.00
QA-151	Toast rack, 2 slice	135.00	165.00	85.00
QA-155	Trivet	75.00	100.00	50.00
QA-160	Vase, bud	75.00	100.00	50.00

QUILT

The pattern number is 4515. This all-over pattern was clearly intended to be a companion pattern to **Tartans** 4514 . Both were intended to appeal to the non-chintz customer.

Cat.No.	Shape	U.S. $	Can. $	U.K. £
Q-04	Bonbon dish	45.00	50.00	35.00
Q-09	Bowl, 5″	40.00	50.00	30.00
Q-14	Bowl, 8″ soup	50.00	75.00	40.00
Q-23	Breakfast set	575.00	675.00	400.00
Q-28	Butter dish	125.00	150.00	75.00
Q-30	Butter pat	35.00	40.00	25.00
Q-35	Cake plate, open handles	150.00	185.00	110.00
Q-36	Cake plate, tab handles	135.00	165.00	85.00
Q-37	Cake plate, 8″ sq. pedestal	150.00	200.00	100.00
Q-40	Cake stand, 2 tier	150.00	200.00	100.00
Q-45	Canoe-shaped dish	150.00	200.00	100.00
Q-50	Cheese keep	150.00	200.00	100.00
Q-52	Coaster	30.00	35.00	25.00
Q-55	Coffee pot	475.00	575.00	325.00
Q-60	Compote, footed	100.00	125.00	65.00
Q-65	Condiment set on tray	150.00	175.00	100.00
Q-70	Cream and sugar	75.00	100.00	50.00
Q-71	Cream and sugar on tray	135.00	165.00	85.00
Q-75	Demi-tasse	55.00	75.00	40.00
Q-77	Egg cup, footed	45.00	50.00	35.00
Q-80	Hot water jug	200.00	250.00	150.00
Q-85	Jam pot with liner	100.00	125.00	65.00
Q-90	Jug, 4″	175.00	225.00	125.00
Q-91	Jug, 4 1/2″	200.00	250.00	150.00
Q-92	Jug, 5″	200.00	250.00	150.00

Cat.No.	Shape	U.S. $	Can. $	U.K. £
Q-97	Nut dish	35.00	40.00	25.00
Q-201	Plate, 4″ sq.	35.00	40.00	25.00
Q-202	Plate, 5″ sq.	40.00	50.00	30.00
Q-203	Plate, 6″ sq.	45.00	50.00	35.00
Q-204	Plate, 7″ sq.	50.00	75.00	40.00
Q-205	Plate, 8″ sq.	100.00	125.00	65.00
Q-206	Plate, 9″ sq.	100.00	125.00	65.00
Q-207	Plate, 10″ sq.	125.00	150.00	75.00
Q-112	Relish dish, small	125.00	150.00	75.00
Q-115	Salad bowl, chrome rim	100.00	125.00	75.00
Q-117	Salt and pepper	65.00	80.00	45.00
Q-118	Salt and pepper on tray	135.00	165.00	85.00
Q-120	Sandwich tray, 10″ x 6″	75.00	100.00	50.00
Q-121	Sandwich tray, 12″ x 7″	100.00	125.00	65.00
Q-125	Sauce boat and liner	125.00	150.00	75.00
Q-130	Teacup and saucer	50.00	70.00	40.00
Q-135	Teapot, 2 cup	300.00	350.00	200.00
Q-136	Teapot, 4 cup	350.00	425.00	250.00
Q-137	Teapot, 6 cup	425.00	500.00	300.00
Q-140	Teapot, stacking	425.00	500.00	300.00
Q-145	Tennis set	75.00	90.00	50.00
Q-150	Toast rack, 4 slice	175.00	225.00	125.00
Q-151	Toast rack, 2 slice	145.00	175.00	100.00
Q-155	Trivet	75.00	100.00	50.00
Q-160	Vase, bud	75.00	100.00	50.00

RICHMOND

The pattern number is 4249, and the pattern was registered in Canada in 1938.

Cat.No.	Shape	U.S. $	Can. $	U.K. £
Ri-04	Bonbon dish	50.00	65.00	35.00
Ri-09	Bowl, 5″	40.00	50.00	30.00
Ri-14	Bowl, 8″ soup	65.00	80.00	45.00
Ri-23	Breakfast set	700.00	850.00	475.00
Ri-28	Butter dish	150.00	175.00	85.00
Ri-30	Butter pat	40.00	50.00	30.00
Ri-35	Cake plate, open handles	175.00	225.00	125.00
Ri-36	Cake plate, tab handles	150.00	200.00	100.00
Ri-37	Cake plate, 8″ sq. pedestal	185.00	225.00	125.00
Ri-40	Cake stand, 2 tier	150.00	200.00	100.00
Ri-45	Canoe-shaped dish	200.00	250.00	150.00
Ri-50	Cheese keep	185.00	225.00	125.00
Ri-52	Coaster	35.00	40.00	25.00
Ri-55	Coffee pot	625.00	750.00	450.00
Ri-60	Compote, footed	125.00	150.00	75.00
Ri-65	Condiment set on tray	165.00	80.00	45.00
Ri-70	Cream and sugar	100.00	125.00	65.00
Ri-71	Cream and sugar on tray	175.00	225.00	125.00
Ri-75	Demi-tasse	65.00	80.00	45.00
Ri-77	Egg cup, footed	55.00	70.00	40.00
Ri-80	Hot water jug	250.00	300.00	175.00
Ri-85	Jam pot with liner	125.00	150.00	175.00
Ri-90	Jug, 4″	200.00	250.00	150.00
Ri-91	Jug, 4 1/2″	225.00	275.00	150.00
Ri-92	Jug, 5″	250.00	300.00	175.00

Cat.No.	Shape	U.S. $	Can. $	U.K. £
Ri-97	Nut dish	40.00	50.00	30.00
Ri-201	Plate, 4″ sq.	45.00	55.00	35.00
Ri-202	Plate, 5″ sq.	50.00	65.00	35.00
Ri-203	Plate, 6″ sq.	50.00	75.00	40.00
Ri-204	Plate, 7″ sq.	65.00	80.00	45.00
Ri-205	Plate, 8″ sq.	100.00	125.00	65.00
Ri-206	Plate, 9″ sq.	100.00	125.00	65.00
Ri-207	Plate, 10″ sq.	125.00	150.00	75.00
Ri-112	Relish dish, small	125.00	150.00	75.00
Ri-115	Salad bowl, chrome rim	100.00	125.00	65.00
Ri-117	Salt and pepper	75.00	100.00	50.00
Ri-118	Salt and pepper on tray	135.00	165.00	85.00
Ri-120	Sandwich tray, 10″ x 6″	100.00	125.00	65.00
Ri-121	Sandwich tray, 12″ x 7″	100.00	125.00	65.00
Ri-125	Sauce boat and liner	125.00	150.00	75.00
Ri-130	Teacup and saucer	65.00	80.00	45.00
Ri-135	Teapot, 2 cup	300.00	375.00	220.00
Ri-136	Teapot, 4 cup	400.00	500.00	275.00
Ri-137	Teapot, 6 cup	500.00	600.00	350.00
Ri-140	Teapot, stacking	600.00	725.00	425.00
Ri-145	Tennis set	85.00	100.00	60.00
Ri-150	Toast rack, 4 slice	200.00	250.00	150.00
Ri-151	Toast rack, 2 slice	150.00	175.00	100.00
Ri-155	Trivet	85.00	100.00	60.00
Ri-160	Vase, bud	100.00	125.00	65.00

ROSE DU BARRY

This pattern has a **Rose Du Barry** backstamp in North America, but in Australia the backstamp is **Chelsea Rose**. James Kent also used the same litho and the backstamp is James Kent **Chelsea Rose**. Most of the Winton pieces found in North America have "Henry Morgan & Co. Ltd." as well as the pattern name in the backstamp. This may have been an exclusive name for Morgan's. In 1938 a **Rose Du Barry** breakfast set was advertised in a Montreal newspaper by Morgan's for sale at $2.50.

Cat.No.	Shape	U.S. $	Can. $	U.K. £
RD-04	Bonbon dish	45.00	50.00	35.00
RD-09	Bowl, 5″	40.00	50.00	30.00
RD-14	Bowl, 8″ soup	75.00	100.00	50.00
RD-23	Breakfast set	650.00	775.00	450.00
RD-28	Butter dish	135.00	165.00	85.00
RD-30	Butter pat	40.00	50.00	30.00
RD-35	Cake plate, open handles	135.00	165.00	85.00
RD-36	Cake plate, tab handles	125.00	150.00	75.00
RD-37	Cake plate, 8″ sq. pedestal	150.00	200.00	100.00
RD-40	Cake stand, 2 tier	150.00	200.00	100.00
RD-45	Canoe-shaped dish	200.00	250.00	125.00
RD-50	Cheese keep	175.00	250.00	125.00
RD-52	Coaster	35.00	40.00	25.00
RD-55	Coffee pot	525.00	625.00	375.00
RD-60	Compote, footed	100.00	125.00	65.00
RD-65	Condiment set on tray	150.00	200.00	100.00
RD-70	Cream and sugar	85.00	100.00	60.00
RD-71	Cream and sugar on tray	150.00	200.00	100.00
RD-75	Demi-tasse	60.00	75.00	45.00
RD-77	Egg cup, footed	50.00	65.00	35.00
RD-80	Hot water jug	225.00	275.00	150.00
RD-85	Jam pot with liner	125.00	150.00	75.00
RD-90	Jug, 4″	200.00	250.00	150.00
RD-91	Jug, 4 1/2″	200.00	250.00	150.00
RD-92	Jug, 5″	225.00	275.00	150.00
RD-97	Nut dish	40.00	50.00	30.00
RD-201	Plate, 4″ sq.	35.00	40.00	25.00
RD-202	Plate, 5″ sq.	40.00	50.00	30.00
RD-203	Plate, 6″ sq.	45.00	50.00	35.00
RD-204	Plate, 7″ sq.	50.00	65.00	35.00
RD-205	Plate, 8″ sq.	85.00	110.00	60.00
RD-206	Plate, 9″ sq.	100.00	125.00	65.00
RD-207	Plate, 10″ sq.	125.00	150.00	75.00
RD-112	Relish dish, small	125.00	150.00	75.00
RD-115	Salad bowl, chrome rim	100.00	125.00	65.00
RD-117	Salt and pepper	65.00	80.00	45.00
RD-118	Salt and pepper on tray	150.00	200.00	100.00
RD-120	Sandwich tray, 10″ x 6″	85.00	100.00	60.00
RD-121	Sandwich tray, 12″ x 7″	100.00	125.00	65.00
RD-125	Sauce boat and liner	125.00	150.00	75.00
RD-130	Teacup and saucer	60.00	75.00	45.00
RD-135	Teapot, 2 cup	250.00	300.00	175.00
RD-136	Teapot, 4 cup	350.00	425.00	250.00
RD-137	Teapot, 6 cup	450.00	550.00	325.00
RD-140	Teapot, stacking	600.00	725.00	425.00
RD-145	Tennis set	80.00	95.00	50.00
RD-150	Toast rack, 4 slice	175.00	200.00	125.00
RD-151	Toast rack, 2 slice	135.00	165.00	85.00
RD-155	Trivet	80.00	95.00	50.00
RD-160	Vase, bud	85.00	100.00	60.00

ROYALTY

The pattern number is 3079. The pattern was introduced at the 1936 British Industries Fair. The alternate colourway is **Majestic** 3311 with a black background.

Cat.No.	Shape	U.S. $	Can. $	U.K. £
Ro-04	Bonbon dish	80.00	100.00	50.00
Ro-09	Bowl, 5"	50.00	75.00	40.00
Ro-14	Bowl, 8" soup	100.00	125.00	65.00
Ro-23	Breakfast set	1,100.00	1,350.00	800.00
Ro-28	Butter dish	225.00	275.00	165.00
Ro-30	Butter pat	75.00	100.00	50.00
Ro-35	Cake plate, open handles	225.00	275.00	165.00
Ro-36	Cake plate, tab handles	200.00	250.00	150.00
Ro-37	Cake plate, 8" sq. pedestal	250.00	300.00	175.00
Ro-40	Cake stand, 2 tier	250.00	300.00	175.00
Ro-45	Canoe-shaped dish	350.00	425.00	250.00
Ro-50	Cheese keep	300.00	375.00	225.00
Ro-52	Coaster	60.00	75.00	45.00
Ro-55	Coffee pot	925.00	1,150.00	650.00
Ro-60	Compote, footed	200.00	250.00	125.00
Ro-65	Condiment set on tray	275.00	325.00	200.00
Ro-70	Cream and sugar	150.00	175.00	100.00
Ro-71	Cream and sugar on tray	275.00	350.00	200.00
Ro-75	Demi-tasse	100.00	125.00	65.00
Ro-77	Egg cup, footed	100.00	125.00	65.00
Ro-80	Hot water jug	400.00	475.00	275.00
Ro-85	Jam pot with liner	225.00	275.00	150.00
Ro-90	Jug, 4"	375.00	450.00	250.00
Ro-91	Jug, 4 1/2"	400.00	475.00	275.00
Ro-92	Jug, 5"	425.00	500.00	300.00
Ro-97	Nut dish	70.00	85.00	50.00
Ro-201	Plate, 4" sq.	65.00	80.00	45.00
Ro-202	Plate, 5" sq.	75.00	100.00	50.00
Ro-203	Plate, 6" sq.	100.00	125.00	65.00
Ro-204	Plate, 7" sq.	135.00	165.00	100.00
Ro-205	Plate, 8" sq.	175.00	225.00	125.00
Ro-206	Plate, 9" sq.	175.00	225.00	125.00
Ro-207	Plate, 10" sq.	200.00	250.00	150.00
Ro-112	Relish dish, small	225.00	275.00	150.00
Ro-115	Salad bowl, chrome rim	100.00	125.00	65.00
Ro-117	Salt and pepper	100.00	125.00	65.00
Ro-118	Salt and pepper on tray	200.00	250.00	150.00
Ro-120	Sandwich tray, 10" x 6"	150.00	185.00	100.00
Ro-121	Sandwich tray, 12" x 7"	175.00	225.00	125.00
Ro-125	Sauce boat and liner	200.00	250.00	150.00
Ro-130	Teacup and saucer	100.00	125.00	65.00
Ro-135	Teapot, 2 cup	450.00	550.00	325.00
Ro-136	Teapot, 4 cup	600.00	725.00	425.00
Ro-137	Teapot, 6 cup	800.00	950.00	550.00
Ro-140	Teapot, stacking	850.00	1,100.00	600.00
Ro-145	Tennis set	150.00	200.00	100.00
Ro-150	Toast rack, 4 slice	300.00	350.00	200.00
Ro-151	Toast rack, 2 slice	225.00	275.00	165.00
Ro-155	Trivet	150.00	200.00	100.00
Ro-160	Vase, bud	150.00	200.00	100.00

RUTLAND

The pattern number is 1470, and the pattern was probably introduced in 1933. Many pieces come with green trim.

Cat.No.	Shape	U.S. $	Can. $	U.K. £
Ru-04	Bonbon dish	50.00	65.00	35.00
Ru-09	Bowl, 5″	40.00	50.00	30.00
Ru-14	Bowl, 8″ soup	65.00	80.00	45.00
Ru-23	Breakfast set	700.00	850.00	475.00
Ru-28	Butter dish	150.00	200.00	100.00
Ru-30	Butter pat	40.00	50.00	30.00
Ru-35	Cake plate, open handles	175.00	225.00	125.00
Ru-36	Cake plate, tab handles	150.00	200.00	100.00
Ru-37	Cake plate, 8″ sq. pedestal	175.00	225.00	125.00
Ru-40	Cake stand, 2 tier	150.00	200.00	100.00
Ru-45	Canoe-shaped dish	200.00	250.00	150.00
Ru-50	Cheese keep	175.00	225.00	125.00
Ru-52	Coaster	35.00	40.00	25.00
Ru-55	Coffee pot	625.00	750.00	425.00
Ru-60	Compote, footed	120.00	150.00	75.00
Ru-65	Condiment set on tray	165.00	200.00	100.00
Ru-70	Cream and sugar	100.00	125.00	65.00
Ru-71	Cream and sugar on tray	175.00	225.00	125.00
Ru-75	Demi-tasse	65.00	80.00	45.00
Ru-77	Egg cup, footed	50.00	75.00	40.00
Ru-80	Hot water jug	250.00	300.00	175.00
Ru-85	Jam pot with liner	125.00	150.00	75.00
Ru-90	Jug, 4″	200.00	250.00	150.00
Ru-91	Jug, 4 1/2″	225.00	275.00	150.00
Ru-92	Jug, 5″	250.00	300.00	175.00
Ru-97	Nut dish	40.00	50.00	30.00
Ru-201	Plate, 4″ sq.	45.00	50.00	35.00
Ru-202	Plate, 5″ sq.	50.00	65.00	35.00
Ru-203	Plate, 6″ sq.	50.00	75.00	40.00
Ru-204	Plate, 7″ sq.	65.00	80.00	45.00
Ru-205	Plate, 8″ sq.	100.00	125.00	65.00
Ru-206	Plate, 9″ sq.	100.00	125.00	65.00
Ru-207	Plate, 10″ sq.	125.00	150.00	75.00
Ru-112	Relish dish, small	135.00	165.00	100.00
Ru-115	Salad bowl, chrome rim	100.00	125.00	65.00
Ru-117	Salt and pepper	75.00	100.00	50.00
Ru-118	Salt and pepper on tray	135.00	165.00	85.00
Ru-120	Sandwich tray, 10″ x 6″	100.00	125.00	65.00
Ru-121	Sandwich tray, 12″ x 7″	100.00	125.00	65.00
Ru-125	Sauce boat and liner	125.00	150.00	75.00
Ru-130	Teacup and saucer	65.00	80.00	45.00
Ru-135	Teapot, 2 cup	300.00	375.00	225.00
Ru-136	Teapot, 4 cup	400.00	500.00	275.00
Ru-137	Teapot, 6 cup	500.00	600.00	350.00
Ru-140	Teapot, stacking	600.00	700.00	425.00
Ru-145	Tennis set	75.00	100.00	60.00
Ru-150	Toast rack, 4 slice	200.00	250.00	150.00
Ru-151	Toast rack, 2 slice	150.00	200.00	100.00
Ru-155	Trivet	75.00	100.00	60.00
Ru-160	Vase, bud	100.00	125.00	65.00

SHREWSBURY

The pattern number is 418. This post-war pattern was one of the Royal Winton patterns produced by Howard Potteries after the takeover in 1964.

Cat.No.	Shape	U.S.$	Can. $	U.K. £
Sh-04	Bonbon dish	50.00	65.00	35.00
Sh-09	Bowl, 5″	45.00	50.00	35.00
Sh-14	Bowl, 8″ soup	75.00	100.00	50.00
Sh-23	Breakfast set	700.00	825.00	475.00
Sh-28	Butter dish	150.00	200.00	100.00
Sh-30	Butter pat	45.00	50.00	35.00
Sh-35	Cake plate, open handles	150.00	200.00	100.00
Sh-36	Cake plate, tab handles	135.00	165.00	85.00
Sh-37	Cake plate, 8″ sq. pedestal	160.00	150.00	100.00
Sh-40	Cake stand, 2 tier	160.00	150.00	100.00
Sh-45	Canoe-shaped dish	225.00	275.00	150.00
Sh-50	Cheese keep	200.00	250.00	150.00
Sh-52	Coaster	40.00	50.00	30.00
Sh-55	Coffee pot	550.00	650.00	475.00
Sh-60	Compote, footed	125.00	150.00	75.00
Sh-65	Condiment set on tray	175.00	225.00	125.00
Sh-70	Cream and sugar	100.00	125.00	65.00
Sh-71	Cream and sugar on tray	175.00	225.00	125.00
Sh-75	Demi-tasse	75.00	100.00	50.00
Sh-77	Egg cup, footed	60.00	75.00	45.00
Sh-80	Hot water jug	250.00	300.00	175.00
Sh-85	Jam pot with liner	150.00	200.00	100.00
Sh-90	Jug, 4″	175.00	225.00	125.00
Sh-91	Jug, 4 1/2″	200.00	250.00	150.00
Sh-92	Jug, 5″	225.00	275.00	150.00

Cat.No.	Shape	U.S. $	Can. $	U.K. £
Sh-97	Nut dish	45.00	50.00	35.00
Sh-201	Plate, 4″ sq.	50.00	65.00	35.00
Sh-202	Plate, 5″ sq.	50.00	75.00	40.00
Sh-203	Plate, 6″ sq.	60.00	75.00	45.00
Sh-204	Plate, 7″ sq.	75.00	90.00	50.00
Sh-205	Plate, 8″ sq.	100.00	125.00	65.00
Sh-206	Plate, 9″ sq.	125.00	150.00	75.00
Sh-207	Plate, 10″ sq.	125.00	150.00	75.00
Sh-112	Relish dish, small	150.00	200.00	100.00
Sh-115	Salad bowl, chrome rim	125.00	150.00	75.00
Sh-117	Salt and pepper	75.00	100.00	50.00
Sh-118	Salt and pepper on tray	150.00	200.00	100.00
Sh-120	Sandwich tray, 10″ x 6″	100.00	125.00	65.00
Sh-121	Sandwich tray, 12″ x 7″	125.00	150.00	75.00
Sh-125	Sauce boat and liner	125.00	150.00	75.00
Sh-130	Teacup and saucer	70.00	85.00	50.00
Sh-135	Teapot, 2 cup	275.00	350.00	200.00
Sh-136	Teapot, 4 cup	375.00	450.00	250.00
Sh-137	Teapot, 6 cup	475.00	575.00	325.00
Sh-140	Teapot, stacking	625.00	725.00	425.00
Sh-145	Tennis set	100.00	125.00	65.00
Sh-150	Toast rack, 4 slice	200.00	250.00	150.00
Sh-151	Toast rack, 2 slice	150.00	200.00	100.00
Sh-155	Trivet	90.00	110.00	65.00
Sh-160	Vase, bud	85.00	100.00	60.00

SOMERSET

The pattern number is 1420, and it was probably introduced late in 1932 or early 1933. This pattern came with both a gold and a blue trim.

Cat.No.	Shape	U.S. $	Can. $	U.K. £
So-04	Bonbon dish	75.00	90.00	50.00
So-09	Bowl, 5″	50.00	65.00	35.00
So-14	Bowl, 8″ soup	85.00	100.00	60.00
So-23	Breakfast set	950.00	1,200.00	675.00
So-28	Butter dish	225.00	275.00	150.00
So-30	Butter pat	65.00	80.00	45.00
So-35	Cake plate, open handles	225.00	275.00	150.00
So-36	Cake plate, tab handles	200.00	250.00	125.00
So-37	Cake plate, 8″ sq. pedestal	225.00	275.00	150.00
So-40	Cake stand, 2 tier	225.00	275.00	150.00
So-45	Canoe-shaped dish	325.00	375.00	225.00
So-50	Cheese keep	275.00	350.00	200.00
So-52	Coaster	50.00	65.00	35.00
So-55	Coffee pot	850.00	1,100.00	600.00
So-60	Compote, footed	175.00	225.00	125.00
So-65	Condiment set on tray	250.00	300.00	175.00
So-70	Cream and sugar	150.00	200.00	100.00
So-71	Cream and sugar on tray	250.00	300.00	175.00
So-75	Demi-tasse	100.00	125.00	65.00
So-77	Egg cup, footed	85.00	100.00	60.00
So-80	Hot water jug	375.00	450.00	250.00
So-85	Jam pot with liner	200.00	250.00	150.00
So-90	Jug, 4″	325.00	375.00	225.00
So-91	Jug, 4 1/2″	350.00	475.00	250.00
So-92	Jug, 5″	375.00	450.00	275.00
So-97	Nut dish	65.00	80.00	45.00
So-201	Plate, 4″ sq.	50.00	75.00	40.00
So-202	Plate, 5″ sq.	65.00	80.00	45.00
So-203	Plate, 6″ sq.	75.00	100.00	50.00
So-204	Plate, 7″ sq.	100.00	125.00	65.00
So-205	Plate, 8″ sq.	135.00	165.00	85.00
So-206	Plate, 9″ sq.	150.00	200.00	100.00
So-207	Plate, 10″ sq.	175.00	200.00	125.00
So-112	Relish dish, small	200.00	250.00	150.00
So-115	Salad bowl, chrome rim	175.00	225.00	125.00
So-117	Salt and pepper	100.00	125.00	65.00
So-118	Salt and pepper on tray	175.00	225.00	125.00
So-120	Sandwich tray, 10″ x 6″	150.00	200.00	100.00
So-121	Sandwich tray, 12″ x 7″	175.00	225.00	125.00
So-125	Sauce boat and liner	150.00	200.00	100.00
So-130	Teacup and saucer	100.00	125.00	65.00
So-135	Teapot, 2 cup	425.00	500.00	300.00
So-136	Teapot, 4 cup	625.00	750.00	425.00
So-137	Teapot, 6 cup	725.00	875.00	500.00
So-140	Teapot, stacking	795.00	950.00	550.00
So-145	Tennis set	125.00	150.00	75.00
So-150	Toast rack, 4 slice	250.00	300.00	175.00
So-151	Toast rack, 2 slice	200.00	250.00	150.00
So-155	Trivet	125.00	150.00	75.00
So-160	Vase, bud	135.00	175.00	85.00

SPRING

The pattern number is 2506, and it was introduced some months after the alternate colourways **Hazel** 2208 and **Welbeck** 2204. This pattern was copied by the Japanese.

Cat.No.	Shape	U.S. $	Can. $	U.K. £
Sp-04	Bonbon dish	75.00	100.00	50.00
Sp-09	Bowl, 5″	50.00	65.00	35.00
Sp-14	Bowl, 8″ soup	85.00	100.00	60.00
Sp-23	Breakfast set	950.00	1,200.00	675.00
Sp-28	Butter dish	225.00	275.00	150.00
Sp-30	Butter pat	65.00	80.00	45.00
Sp-35	Cake plate, open handles	225.00	275.00	150.00
Sp-36	Cake plate, tab handles	200.00	225.00	125.00
Sp-37	Cake plate, 8″ sq. pedestal	225.00	275.00	150.00
Sp-40	Cake stand, 2 tier	225.00	275.00	150.00
Sp-45	Canoe-shaped dish	325.00	375.00	225.00
Sp-50	Cheese keep	275.00	350.00	200.00
Sp-52	Coaster	50.00	65.00	35.00
Sp-55	Coffee pot	850.00	1,100.00	600.00
Sp-60	Compote, footed	175.00	225.00	125.00
Sp-65	Condiment set on tray	250.00	300.00	175.00
Sp-70	Cream and sugar	150.00	200.00	100.00
Sp-71	Cream and sugar on tray	250.00	300.00	175.00
Sp-75	Demi-tasse	100.00	125.00	65.00
Sp-77	Egg cup, footed	85.00	100.00	60.00
Sp-80	Hot water jug	375.00	450.00	250.00
Sp-85	Jam pot with liner	200.00	250.00	150.00
Sp-90	Jug, 4″	325.00	375.00	225.00
Sp-91	Jug, 4 1/2″	350.00	425.00	250.00
Sp-92	Jug, 5″	375.00	450.00	275.00

Cat.No.	Shape	U.S. $	Can. $	U.K. £
Sp-97	Nut dish	65.00	80.00	45.00
Sp-201	Plate, 4″ sq.	50.00	75.00	40.00
Sp-202	Plate, 5″ sq.	65.00	80.00	45.00
Sp-203	Plate, 6″ sq.	75.00	90.00	50.00
Sp-204	Plate, 7″ sq.	100.00	125.00	65.00
Sp-205	Plate, 8″ sq.	135.00	165.00	85.00
Sp-206	Plate, 9″ sq.	150.00	200.00	100.00
Sp-207	Plate, 10″ sq.	175.00	225.00	125.00
Sp-112	Relish dish, small	200.00	250.00	150.00
Sp-115	Salad bowl, chrome rim	175.00	200.00	125.00
Sp-117	Salt and pepper	100.00	125.00	65.00
Sp-118	Salt and pepper on tray	175.00	225.00	125.00
Sp-120	Sandwich tray, 10″ x 6″	150.00	200.00	100.00
Sp-121	Sandwich tray, 12″ x 7″	175.00	225.00	125.00
Sp-125	Sauce boat and liner	150.00	200.00	100.00
Sp-130	Teacup and saucer	100.00	125.00	75.00
Sp-135	Teapot, 2 cup	425.00	500.00	300.00
Sp-136	Teapot, 4 cup	625.00	750.00	450.00
Sp-137	Teapot, 6 cup	725.00	875.00	500.00
Sp-140	Teapot, stacking	800.00	950.00	550.00
Sp-145	Tennis set	125.00	150.00	75.00
Sp-150	Toast rack, 4 slice	250.00	325.00	175.00
Sp-151	Toast rack, 2 slice	200.00	250.00	150.00
Sp-155	Trivet	125.00	150.00	75.00
Sp-160	Vase, bud	125.00	150.00	75.00

SPRING GLORY

The pattern number is 402, and it is one of the series of 1950s large-flower open chintz patterns. This pattern is rarely seen in North America.

Cat.No.	Shape	U.S. $	Can. $	U.K. £
SG-04	Bonbon dish	45.00	50.00	35.00
SG-09	Bowl, 5″	40.00	50.00	30.00
SG-14	Bowl, 8″ soup	75.00	100.00	50.00
SG-23	Breakfast set	650.00	775.00	450.00
SG-28	Butter dish	135.00	165.00	85.00
SG-30	Butter pat	40.00	50.00	30.00
SG-35	Cake plate, open handles	135.00	165.00	85.00
SG-36	Cake plate, tab handles	125.00	150.00	75.00
SG-37	Cake plate, 8″ sq. pedestal	150.00	200.00	100.00
SG-40	Cake stand, 2 tier	150.00	200.00	100.00
SG-45	Canoe-shaped dish	200.00	250.00	125.00
SG-50	Cheese keep	175.00	225.00	125.00
SG-52	Coaster	35.00	40.00	25.00
SG-55	Coffee pot	525.00	625.00	375.00
SG-60	Compote, footed	100.00	125.00	65.00
SG-65	Condiment set on tray	150.00	200.00	100.00
SG-70	Cream and sugar	85.00	100.00	60.00
SG-71	Cream and sugar on tray	150.00	200.00	100.00
SG-75	Demi-tasse	60.00	75.00	45.00
SG-77	Egg cup, footed	50.00	65.00	35.00
SG-80	Hot water jug	225.00	275.00	150.00
SG-85	Jam pot with liner	125.00	150.00	75.00
SG-90	Jug, 4″	200.00	250.00	135.00
SG-91	Jug, 4 1/2″	200.00	250.00	125.00
SG-92	Jug, 5″	225.00	275.00	150.00

Cat.No.	Shape	U.S. $	Can. $	U.K. £
SG-97	Nut dish	40.00	50.00	30.00
SG-201	Plate, 4″ sq.	35.00	40.00	25.00
SG-202	Plate, 5″ sq.	40.00	50.00	30.00
SG-203	Plate, 6″ sq.	45.00	50.00	35.00
SG-204	Plate, 7″ sq.	50.00	65.00	35.00
SG-205	Plate, 8″ sq.	85.00	100.00	60.00
SG-206	Plate, 9″ sq.	100.00	125.00	65.00
SG-207	Plate, 10″ sq.	125.00	150.00	75.00
SG-112	Relish dish, small	125.00	150.00	75.00
SG-115	Salad bowl, chrome rim	100.00	125.00	65.00
SG-117	Salt and pepper	65.00	80.00	45.00
SG-118	Salt and pepper on tray	150.00	200.00	100.00
SG-120	Sandwich tray, 10″ x 6″	85.00	100.00	60.00
SG-121	Sandwich tray, 12″ x 7″	100.00	125.00	65.00
SG-125	Sauce boat and liner	125.00	150.00	75.00
SG-130	Teacup and saucer	60.00	75.00	45.00
SG-135	Teapot, 2 cup	250.00	300.00	175.00
SG-136	Teapot, 4 cup	350.00	425.00	250.00
SG-137	Teapot, 6 cup	450.00	550.00	325.00
SG-140	Teapot, stacking	600.00	725.00	425.00
SG-145	Tennis set	75.00	100.00	50.00
SG-150	Toast rack, 4 slice	175.00	200.00	125.00
SG-151	Toast rack, 2 slice	135.00	165.00	85.00
SG-155	Trivet	75.00	100.00	50.00
SG-160	Vase, bud	85.00	100.00	60.00

SPRINGTIME

This pattern, number 10017, was introduced in 1932 and was much in demand at the British Industries Fair that year. This pattern is difficult to find in North America.

Cat.No.	Shape	U.S. $	Can. $	U.K. £
Spt-04	Bonbon dish	50.00	65.00	35.00
Spt-09	Bowl, 5″	35.00	40.00	25.00
Spt-14	Bowl, 8″ soup	50.00	65.00	35.00
Spt-23	Breakfast set	675.00	800.00	475.00
Spt-28	Butter dish	150.00	175.00	100.00
Spt-30	Butter pat	40.00	50.00	30.00
Spt-35	Cake plate, open handles	150.00	175.00	100.00
Spt-36	Cake plate, tab handles	125.00	150.00	75.00
Spt-37	Cake plate, 8″ sq. pedestal	150.00	175.00	100.00
Spt-40	Cake stand, 2 tier	150.00	175.00	100.00
Spt-45	Canoe-shaped dish	200.00	250.00	150.00
Spt-50	Cheese keep	200.00	250.00	150.00
Spt-52	Coaster	40.00	50.00	30.00
Spt-55	Coffee pot	550.00	675.00	400.00
Spt-60	Compote, footed	125.00	150.00	75.00
Spt-65	Condiment set on tray	175.00	225.00	125.00
Spt-70	Cream and sugar	100.00	125.00	65.00
Spt-71	Cream and sugar on tray	175.00	225.00	125.00
Spt-75	Demi-tasse	65.00	80.00	45.00
Spt-77	Egg cup, footed	50.00	75.00	40.00
Spt-80	Hot water jug	250.00	300.00	175.00
Spt-85	Jam pot with liner	125.00	150.00	75.00
Spt-90	Jug, 4″	200.00	250.00	150.00
Spt-91	Jug, 4 1/2″	225.00	275.00	160.00
Spt-92	Jug, 5″	250.00	300.00	175.00
Spt-97	Nut dish	40.00	50.00	30.00
Spt-201	Plate, 4″ sq.	30.00	35.00	25.00
Spt-202	Plate, 5″ sq.	35.00	40.00	25.00
Spt-203	Plate, 6″ sq.	40.00	50.00	30.00
Spt-204	Plate, 7″ sq.	45.00	50.00	35.00
Spt-205	Plate, 8″ sq.	65.00	80.00	45.00
Spt-206	Plate, 9″ sq.	100.00	125.00	65.00
Spt-207	Plate, 10″ sq.	100.00	125.00	65.00
Spt-112	Relish dish, small	125.00	150.00	75.00
Spt-115	Salad bowl, chrome rim	100.00	125.00	65.00
Spt-117	Salt and pepper	65.00	80.00	45.00
Spt-118	Salt and pepper on tray	125.00	150.00	75.00
Spt-120	Sandwich tray, 10″ x 6″	100.00	125.00	65.00
Spt-121	Sandwich tray, 12″ x 7″	100.00	125.00	65.00
Spt-125	Sauce boat and liner	125.00	150.00	75.00
Spt-130	Teacup and saucer	65.00	80.00	45.00
Spt-135	Teapot, 2 cup	350.00	400.00	250.00
Spt-136	Teapot, 4 cup	400.00	500.00	275.00
Spt-137	Teapot, 6 cup	500.00	600.00	350.00
Spt-140	Teapot, stacking	500.00	600.00	350.00
Spt-145	Tennis set	85.00	100.00	60.00
Spt-150	Toast rack, 4 slice	200.00	250.00	150.00
Spt-151	Toast rack, 2 slice	175.00	225.00	125.00
Spt-155	Trivet	85.00	100.00	60.00
Spt-160	Vase, bud	100.00	125.00	65.00

STRATFORD

The pattern number is 493 and it was registered in Canada in 1953. One of the last of the Royal Winton chintz patterns it is very popular in the United States.

Cat.No.	Shape	U.S. $	Can. $	U.K. £
St-04	Bonbon dish	100.00	125.00	65.00
St-09	Bowl, 5″	65.00	80.00	45.00
St-14	Bowl, 8″ soup	100.00	125.00	65.00
St-23	Breakfast set	1,250.00	1,500.00	875.00
St-28	Butter dish	275.00	325.00	175.00
St-30	Butter pat	75.00	100.00	50.00
St-35	Cake plate, open handles	275.00	325.00	175.00
St-36	Cake plate, tab handles	250.00	300.00	150.00
St-37	Cake plate, 8″ sq. pedestal	275.00	325.00	175.00
St-40	Cake stand, 2 tier	275.00	325.00	175.00
St-45	Canoe-shaped dish	375.00	450.00	275.00
St-50	Cheese keep	350.00	420.00	250.00
St-52	Coaster	75.00	100.00	50.00
St-55	Coffee pot	1,100.00	1,300.00	725.00
St-60	Compote, footed	225.00	275.00	150.00
St-65	Condiment set on tray	325.00	375.00	225.00
St-70	Cream and sugar	175.00	200.00	125.00
St-71	Cream and sugar on tray	325.00	375.00	225.00
St-75	Demi-tasse	125.00	150.00	75.00
St-77	Egg cup, footed	100.00	125.00	65.00
St-80	Hot water jug	450.00	550.00	325.00
St-85	Jam pot with liner	250.00	300.00	175.00
St-90	Jug, 4″	400.00	475.00	275.00
St-91	Jug, 4 1/2″	425.00	500.00	300.00
St-92	Jug, 5″	450.00	550.00	325.00
St-97	Nut dish	75.00	100.00	50.00
St-201	Plate, 4″ sq.	75.00	100.00	50.00
St-202	Plate, 5″ sq.	100.00	125.00	65.00
St-203	Plate, 6″ sq.	125.00	150.00	75.00
St-204	Plate, 7″ sq.	135.00	165.00	85.00
St-205	Plate, 8″ sq.	175.00	200.00	125.00
St-206	Plate, 9″ sq.	185.00	225.00	135.00
St-207	Plate, 10″ sq.	200.00	250.00	125.00
St-112	Relish dish, small	250.00	300.00	175.00
St-115	Salad bowl, chrome rim	250.00	300.00	175.00
St-117	Salt and pepper	125.00	150.00	75.00
St-118	Salt and pepper on tray	225.00	275.00	150.00
St-120	Sandwich tray, 10″ x 6″	175.00	200.00	125.00
St-121	Sandwich tray, 12″ x 7″	200.00	250.00	150.00
St-125	Sauce boat and liner	225.00	275.00	165.00
St-130	Teacup and saucer	125.00	150.00	75.00
St-135	Teapot, 2 cup	550.00	650.00	375.00
St-136	Teapot, 4 cup	700.00	850.00	500.00
St-137	Teapot, 6 cup	900.00	1,200.00	625.00
St-140	Teapot, stacking	900.00	1,200.00	625.00
St-145	Tennis set	160.00	200.00	115.00
St-150	Toast rack, 4 slice	300.00	350.00	200.00
St-151	Toast rack, 2 slice	225.00	275.00	165.00
St-155	Trivet	165.00	200.00	115.00
St-160	Vase, bud	165.00	200.00	115.00

SUMMERTIME

The pattern number is 775, and this pattern was introduced in 1932. The alternate colourway is **Bedale** 1703. **Summertime** was perhaps the most popular and most widely produced Winton pattern until production ceased well into the 1960s. Complete dinner services were sold in this pattern and still turn up regularly in North America. The pattern came with both a gold and a green trim. Be aware of the difference in the colour of the pre- and post-war transfer.

Cat.No.	Shape	U.S. $	Can. $	U.K. £
Su-04	Bonbon dish	65.00	80.00	45.00
Su-09	Bowl, 5"	50.00	75.00	40.00
Su-14	Bowl, 8" soup	75.00	100.00	50.00
Su-23	Breakfast set	900.00	1,200.00	625.00
Su-28	Butter dish	190.00	225.00	135.00
Su-30	Butter pat	55.00	70.00	40.00
Su-35	Cake plate, open handles	190.00	225.00	135.00
Su-36	Cake plate, tab handles	175.00	200.00	125.00
Su-37	Cake plate, 8" sq. pedestal	200.00	250.00	150.00
Su-40	Cake stand, 2 tier	200.00	250.00	150.00
Su-45	Canoe-shaped dish	275.00	325.00	175.00
Su-50	Cheese keep	250.00	300.00	175.00
Su-52	Coaster	50.00	65.00	35.00
Su-55	Coffee pot	750.00	900.00	525.00
Su-60	Compote, footed	160.00	200.00	115.00
Su-65	Condiment set on tray	225.00	275.00	150.00
Su-70	Cream and sugar	125.00	150.00	75.00
Su-71	Cream and sugar on tray	225.00	275.00	160.00
Su-75	Demi-tasse	85.00	100.00	60.00
Su-77	Egg cup, footed	75.00	100.00	50.00
Su-80	Hot water jug	325.00	400.00	225.00
Su-85	Jam pot with liner	175.00	200.00	125.00
Su-90	Jug, 4"	275.00	325.00	200.00
Su-91	Jug, 4 1/2"	300.00	350.00	200.00
Su-92	Jug, 5"	325.00	400.00	225.00

Cat.No.	Shape	U.S. $	Can. $	U.K. £
Su-97	Nut dish	50.00	75.00	40.00
Su-201	Plate, 4" sq.	50.00	65.00	35.00
Su-202	Plate, 5" sq.	50.00	75.00	40.00
Su-203	Plate, 6" sq.	65.00	80.00	45.00
Su-204	Plate, 7" sq.	85.00	100.00	60.00
Su-205	Plate, 8" sq.	135.00	165.00	85.00
Su-206	Plate, 9" sq.	150.00	175.00	100.00
Su-207	Plate, 10" sq.	165.00	200.00	115.00
Su-112	Relish dish, small	175.00	200.00	125.00
Su-115	Salad bowl, chrome rim	150.00	175.00	100.00
Su-117	Salt and pepper	100.00	125.00	65.00
Su-118	Salt and pepper on tray	165.00	200.00	115.00
Su-120	Sandwich tray, 10" x 6"	125.00	150.00	75.00
Su-121	Sandwich tray, 12" x 7"	150.00	175.00	100.00
Su-125	Sauce boat and liner	175.00	200.00	125.00
Su-130	Teacup and saucer	85.00	100.00	60.00
Su-135	Teapot, 2 cup	450.00	550.00	325.00
Su-136	Teapot, 4 cup	550.00	650.00	375.00
Su-137	Teapot, 6 cup	650.00	775.00	450.00
Su-140	Teapot, stacking	650.00	775.00	450.00
Su-145	Tennis set	115.00	150.00	75.00
Su-150	Toast rack, 4 slice	275.00	325.00	200.00
Su-151	Toast rack, 2 slice	225.00	275.00	160.00
Su-155	Trivet	115.00	150.00	75.00
Su-160	Vase, bud	125.00	150.00	75.00

SUNSHINE

The pattern number is 4030, and the pattern was probably introduced in 1937.

Cat.No.	Shape	U.S. $	Can. $	U.K. £
Sun-04	Bonbon dish	60.00	75.00	45.00
Sun-09	Bowl, 5″	40.00	50.00	30.00
Sun-14	Bowl, 8″ soup	60.00	75.00	45.00
Sun-23	Breakfast set	800.00	950.00	550.00
Sun-28	Butter dish	175.00	200.00	125.00
Sun-30	Butter pat	50.00	65.00	35.00
Sun-35	Cake plate, open handles	175.00	200.00	125.00
Sun-36	Cake plate, tab handles	150.00	175.00	115.00
Sun-37	Cake plate, 8″ sq. pedestal	175.00	225.00	125.00
Sun-40	Cake stand, 2 tier	175.00	225.00	125.00
Sun-45	Canoe-shaped dish	250.00	300.00	175.00
Sun-50	Cheese keep	225.00	275.00	160.00
Sun-52	Coaster	45.00	55.00	35.00
Sun-55	Coffee pot	675.00	800.00	475.00
Sun-60	Compote, footed	150.00	175.00	100.00
Sun-65	Condiment set on tray	200.00	250.00	150.00
Sun-70	Cream and sugar	100.00	125.00	65.00
Sun-71	Cream and sugar on tray	200.00	250.00	150.00
Sun-75	Demi-tasse	75.00	90.00	50.00
Sun-77	Egg cup, footed	65.00	80.00	45.00
Sun-80	Hot water jug	300.00	350.00	200.00
Sun-85	Jam pot with liner	150.00	175.00	85.00
Sun-90	Jug, 4″	250.00	300.00	175.00
Sun-91	Jug, 4 1/2″	275.00	325.00	200.00
Sun-92	Jug, 5″	300.00	350.00	200.00
Sun-97	Nut dish	50.00	65.00	35.00
Sun-201	Plate, 4″ sq.	35.00	40.00	25.00
Sun-202	Plate, 5″ sq.	40.00	50.00	30.00
Sun-203	Plate, 6″ sq.	45.00	50.00	35.00
Sun-204	Plate, 7″ sq.	50.00	75.00	40.00
Sun-205	Plate, 8″ sq.	75.00	90.00	50.00
Sun-206	Plate, 9″ sq.	100.00	125.00	65.00
Sun-207	Plate, 10″ sq.	125.00	150.00	75.00
Sun-112	Relish dish, small	150.00	185.00	100.00
Sun-115	Salad bowl, chrome rim	135.00	165.00	85.00
Sun-117	Salt and pepper	80.00	100.00	50.00
Sun-118	Salt and pepper on tray	150.00	175.00	100.00
Sun-120	Sandwich tray, 10″ x 6″	125.00	150.00	75.00
Sun-121	Sandwich tray, 12″ x 7″	125.00	150.00	75.00
Sun-125	Sauce boat and liner	150.00	175.00	100.00
Sun-130	Teacup and saucer	75.00	90.00	50.00
Sun-135	Teapot, 2 cup	400.00	475.00	275.00
Sun-136	Teapot, 4 cup	500.00	600.00	350.00
Sun-137	Teapot, 6 cup	575.00	700.00	400.00
Sun-140	Teapot, stacking	575.00	700.00	400.00
Sun-145	Tennis set	100.00	125.00	65.00
Sun-150	Toast rack, 4 slice	250.00	300.00	175.00
Sun-151	Toast rack, 2 slice	200.00	250.00	150.00
Sun-155	Trivet	100.00	125.00	65.00
Sun-160	Vase, bud	110.00	135.00	75.00

SWEET NANCY

The pattern number is 5828, and it was probably introduced in 1939.

Cat.No.	Shape	U.S. $	Can. $	U.K. £
SN-04	Bonbon dish	45.00	50.00	35.00
SN-09	Bowl, 5″	40.00	50.00	30.00
SN-14	Bowl, 8″ soup	70.00	85.00	50.00
SN-23	Breakfast set	650.00	775.00	450.00
SN-28	Butter dish	135.00	165.00	85.00
SN-30	Butter pat	40.00	50.00	30.00
SN-35	Cake plate, open handles	135.00	165.00	85.00
SN-36	Cake plate, tab handles	125.00	150.00	75.00
SN-37	Cake plate, 8″ sq. pedestal	150.00	175.00	100.00
SN-40	Cake stand, 2 tier	150.00	175.00	100.00
SN-45	Canoe-shaped dish	190.00	230.00	135.00
SN-50	Cheese keep	175.00	200.00	125.00
SN-52	Coaster	35.00	40.00	25.00
SN-55	Coffee pot	525.00	625.00	375.00
SN-60	Compote, footed	100.00	125.00	65.00
SN-65	Condiment set on tray	150.00	175.00	110.00
SN-70	Cream and sugar	85.00	100.00	60.00
SN-71	Cream and sugar on tray	150.00	185.00	100.00
SN-75	Demi-tasse	60.00	75.00	45.00
SN-77	Egg cup, footed	50.00	65.00	35.00
SN-80	Hot water jug	225.00	275.00	150.00
SN-85	Jam pot with liner	125.00	150.00	85.00
SN-90	Jug, 4″	200.00	250.00	125.00
SN-91	Jug, 4 1/2″	200.00	250.00	150.00
SN-92	Jug, 5″	225.00	275.00	160.00
SN-97	Nut dish	40.00	50.00	30.00
SN-201	Plate, 4″ sq.	35.00	40.00	25.00
SN-202	Plate, 5″ sq.	40.00	50.00	30.00
SN-203	Plate, 6″ sq.	45.00	50.00	35.00
SN-204	Plate, 7″ sq.	50.00	65.00	35.00
SN-205	Plate, 8″ sq.	100.00	125.00	65.00
SN-206	Plate, 9″ sq.	100.00	125.00	65.00
SN-207	Plate, 10″ sq.	125.00	150.00	75.00
SN-112	Relish dish, small	125.00	150.00	75.00
SN-115	Salad bowl, chrome rim	100.00	125.00	65.00
SN-117	Salt and pepper	65.00	80.00	45.00
SN-118	Salt and pepper on tray	150.00	175.00	100.00
SN-120	Sandwich tray, 10″ x 6″	85.00	100.00	60.00
SN-121	Sandwich tray, 12″ x 7″	100.00	125.00	65.00
SN-125	Sauce boat and liner	125.00	150.00	75.00
SN-130	Teacup and saucer	60.00	75.00	45.00
SN-135	Teapot, 2 cup	250.00	300.00	175.00
SN-136	Teapot, 4 cup	350.00	425.00	250.00
SN-137	Teapot, 6 cup	450.00	550.00	325.00
SN-140	Teapot, stacking	600.00	725.00	425.00
SN-145	Tennis set	75.00	100.00	50.00
SN-150	Toast rack, 4 slice	175.00	200.00	125.00
SN-151	Toast rack, 2 slice	135.00	165.00	85.00
SN-155	Trivet	75.00	100.00	50.00
SN-160	Vase, bud	85.00	100.00	60.00

SWEET PEA

The pattern number is 3030, and the pattern was introduced in 1936 with great success. It is still a favorite with English collectors and recently has become very popular in Australia. There are great variations in the depth of colour in examples of this pattern, with some pieces appearing very faded.

Cat.No.	Shape	U.S. $	Can. $	U.K. £
SP-04	Bonbon dish	80.00	95.00	50.00
SP-09	Bowl, 5"	50.00	75.00	40.00
SP-14	Bowl, 8" soup	100.00	125.00	65.00
SP-23	Breakfast set	950.00	1,200.00	650.00
SP-28	Butter dish	225.00	275.00	150.00
SP-30	Butter pat	65.00	80.00	45.00
SP-35	Cake plate, open handles	225.00	275.00	150.00
SP-36	Cake plate, tab handles	200.00	250.00	135.00
SP-37	Cake plate, 8" sq. pedestal	250.00	300.00	150.00
SP-40	Cake stand, 2 tier	250.00	300.00	150.00
SP-45	Canoe-shaped dish	325.00	400.00	225.00
SP-50	Cheese keep	300.00	350.00	200.00
SP-52	Coaster	60.00	75.00	45.00
SP-55	Coffee pot	875.00	1,050.00	600.00
SP-60	Compote, footed	200.00	225.00	125.00
SP-65	Condiment set on tray	275.00	325.00	200.00
SP-70	Cream and sugar	150.00	175.00	100.00
SP-71	Cream and sugar on tray	275.00	325.00	200.00
SP-75	Demi-tasse	100.00	125.00	65.00
SP-77	Egg cup, footed	100.00	125.00	65.00
SP-80	Hot water jug	400.00	475.00	275.00
SP-85	Jam pot with liner	200.00	250.00	150.00
SP-90	Jug, 4"	325.00	400.00	225.00
SP-91	Jug, 4 1/2"	350.00	425.00	250.00
SP-92	Jug, 5"	400.00	475.00	275.00

Cat.No.	Shape	U.S. $	Can. $	U.K. £
SP-97	Nut dish	65.00	80.00	45.00
SP-201	Plate, 4" sq.	60.00	75.00	45.00
SP-202	Plate, 5" sq.	65.00	80.00	45.00
SP-203	Plate, 6" sq.	75.00	85.00	50.00
SP-204	Plate, 7" sq.	100.00	125.00	65.00
SP-205	Plate, 8" sq.	150.00	175.00	100.00
SP-206	Plate, 9" sq.	160.00	200.00	115.00
SP-207	Plate, 10" sq.	175.00	225.00	125.00
SP-112	Relish dish, small	200.00	250.00	150.00
SP-115	Salad bowl, chrome rim	175.00	225.00	125.00
SP-117	Salt and pepper	100.00	125.00	65.00
SP-118	Salt and pepper on tray	200.00	250.00	150.00
SP-120	Sandwich tray, 10" x 6"	150.00	175.00	100.00
SP-121	Sandwich tray, 12" x 7"	175.00	200.00	125.00
SP-125	Sauce boat and liner	175.00	200.00	125.00
SP-130	Teacup and saucer	100.00	125.00	65.00
SP-135	Teapot, 2 cup	425.00	525.00	300.00
SP-136	Teapot, 4 cup	625.00	750.00	450.00
SP-137	Teapot, 6 cup	725.00	875.00	500.00
SP-140	Teapot, stacking	825.00	1,000.00	575.00
SP-145	Tennis set	150.00	175.00	100.00
SP-150	Toast rack, 4 slice	275.00	325.00	200.00
SP-151	Toast rack, 2 slice	225.00	250.00	150.00
SP-155	Trivet	150.00	175.00	100.00
SP-160	Vase, bud	135.00	165.00	100.00

TARTANS

The pattern number is 4514. The pattern is clearly a companion to **Quilt** 4515, both patterns are intended for a non-chintz customer.

Cat.No.	Shape	U.S. $	Can. $	U.K. £
T-04	Bonbon dish	40.00	50.00	30.00
T-09	Bowl, 5"	35.00	40.00	25.00
T-14	Bowl, 8" soup	50.00	75.00	40.00
T-23	Breakfast set	550.00	650.00	375.00
T-28	Butter dish	125.00	150.00	75.00
T-30	Butter pat	35.00	40.00	25.00
T-35	Cake plate, open handles	150.00	175.00	100.00
T-36	Cake plate, tab handles	125.00	150.00	75.00
T-37	Cake plate, 8" sq. pedestal	150.00	175.00	100.00
T-40	Cake stand, 2 tier	150.00	175.00	100.00
T-45	Canoe-shaped dish	150.00	175.00	100.00
T-50	Cheese keep	150.00	175.00	100.00
T-52	Coaster	30.00	35.00	25.00
T-55	Coffee pot	450.00	550.00	300.00
T-60	Compote, footed	95.00	115.00	60.00
T-65	Condiment set on tray	135.00	165.00	85.00
T-70	Cream and sugar	75.00	100.00	50.00
T-71	Cream and sugar on tray	135.00	165.00	85.00
T-75	Demi-tasse	50.00	65.00	35.00
T-77	Egg cup, footed	45.00	50.00	35.00
T-80	Hot water jug	200.00	250.00	150.00
T-85	Jam pot with liner	100.00	125.00	65.00
T-90	Jug, 4"	165.00	80.00	45.00
T-91	Jug, 4 1/2"	175.00	225.00	125.00
T-92	Jug, 5"	200.00	250.00	150.00

Cat.No.	Shape	U.S. $	Can. $	U.K. £
T-97	Nut dish	35.00	40.00	25.00
T-201	Plate, 4" sq.	35.00	40.00	25.00
T-202	Plate, 5" sq.	40.00	50.00	30.00
T-203	Plate, 6" sq.	45.00	50.00	35.00
T-204	Plate, 7" sq.	55.00	75.00	40.00
T-205	Plate, 8" sq.	95.00	115.00	60.00
T-206	Plate, 9" sq.	100.00	125.00	65.00
T-207	Plate, 10" sq.	115.00	150.00	75.00
T-112	Relish dish, small	100.00	125.00	65.00
T-115	Salad bowl, chrome rim	90.00	110.00	60.00
T-117	Salt and pepper	50.00	75.00	40.00
T-118	Salt and pepper on tray	125.00	150.00	75.00
T-120	Sandwich tray, 10" x 6"	75.00	100.00	50.00
T-121	Sandwich tray, 12" x 7"	85.00	100.00	60.00
T-125	Sauce boat and liner	100.00	125.00	65.00
T-130	Teacup and saucer	50.00	65.00	35.00
T-135	Teapot, 2 cup	200.00	250.00	150.00
T-136	Teapot, 4 cup	300.00	350.00	200.00
T-137	Teapot, 6 cup	400.00	475.00	275.00
T-140	Teapot, stacking	500.00	600.00	350.00
T-145	Tennis set	75.00	85.00	50.00
T-150	Toast rack, 4 slice	165.00	200.00	115.00
T-151	Toast rack, 2 slice	135.00	165.00	100.00
T-155	Trivet	75.00	85.00	50.00
T-160	Vase, bud	75.00	100.00	50.00

VICTORIAN

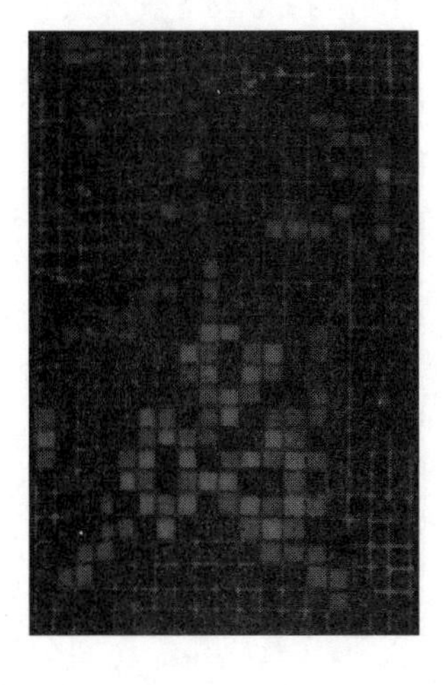

The pattern number is 3164 and it was introduced in 1936 shortly after the alternate colourway **Queen Anne** 2995. The pattern was very popular at the time and sold in quantity.

Cat.No.	Shape	U.S. $	Can. $	U.K. £
V-04	Bonbon dish	45.00	50.00	35.00
V-09	Bowl, 5″	40.00	50.00	30.00
V-14	Bowl, 8″ soup	50.00	75.00	40.00
V-23	Breakfast set	575.00	675.00	400.00
V-28	Butter dish	125.00	150.00	75.00
V-30	Butter pat	35.00	40.00	25.00
V-35	Cake plate, open handles	150.00	175.00	100.00
V-36	Cake plate, tab handles	135.00	165.00	85.00
V-37	Cake plate,8″ sq. pedestal	150.00	175.00	100.00
V-40	Cake stand, 2 tier	150.00	175.00	100.00
V-45	Canoe-shaped dish	165.00	200.00	115.00
V-50	Cheese keep	165.00	200.00	115.00
V-52	Coaster	30.00	35.00	25.00
V-55	Coffee pot	475.00	575.00	325.00
V-60	Compote, footed	100.00	125.00	65.00
V-65	Condiment set on tray	150.00	175.00	75.00
V-70	Cream and sugar	75.00	100.00	50.00
V-71	Cream and sugar on tray	135.00	165.00	85.00
V-75	Demi-tasse	50.00	75.00	40.00
V-77	Egg cup, footed	45.00	50.00	35.00
V-80	Hot water jug	200.00	250.00	150.00
V-85	Jam pot with liner	100.00	125.00	65.00
V-90	Jug, 4″	175.00	225.00	125.00
V-91	Jug, 4 1/2″	200.00	250.00	150.00
V-92	Jug, 5″	200.00	250.00	150.00

Cat.No.	Shape	U.S. $	Can. $	U.K. £
V-97	Nut dish	35.00	40.00	25.00
V-201	Plate, 4″ sq.	35.00	40.00	25.00
V-202	Plate, 5″ sq.	40.00	50.00	30.00
V-203	Plate, 6″ sq.	45.00	50.00	35.00
V-204	Plate, 7″ sq.	50.00	75.00	40.00
V-205	Plate, 8″ sq.	100.00	125.00	65.00
V-206	Plate, 9″ sq.	100.00	125.00	65.00
V-207	Plate, 10″ sq.	125.00	150.00	75.00
V-112	Relish dish, small	125.00	150.00	75.00
V-115	Salad bowl, chrome rim	100.00	125.00	65.00
V-117	Salt and pepper	65.00	80.00	45.00
V-118	Salt and pepper on tray	135.00	165.00	85.00
V-120	Sandwich tray, 10″ x 6″	80.00	100.00	50.00
V-121	Sandwich tray, 12″ x 7″	100.00	125.00	65.00
V-125	Sauce boat and liner	125.00	150.00	75.00
V-130	Teacup and saucer	50.00	75.00	40.00
V-135	Teapot, 2 cup	300.00	350.00	200.00
V-136	Teapot, 4 cup	350.00	425.00	250.00
V-137	Teapot, 6 cup	425.00	500.00	300.00
V-140	Teapot, stacking	425.00	500.00	300.00
V-145	Tennis set	75.00	100.00	50.00
V-150	Toast rack, 4 slice	175.00	225.00	125.00
V-151	Toast rack, 2 slice	150.00	175.00	100.00
V-155	Trivet	75.00	100.00	50.00
V-160	Vase, bud	75.00	100.00	50.00

VICTORIAN ROSE

The pattern number is 440, and was registered in Canada in 1953. It was one of the patterns produced by Howard Potteries after the takeover in 1964. This pattern is mentioned on a factory invoice dated 1969.

Cat.No.	Shape	U.S. $	Can. $	U.K. £
VR-04	Bonbon dish	50.00	75.00	40.00
VR-09	Bowl, 5″	50.00	65.00	35.00
VR-14	Bowl, 8″ soup	75.00	100.00	50.00
VR-23	Breakfast set	775.00	925.00	550.00
VR-28	Butter dish	150.00	200.00	100.00
VR-30	Butter pat	45.00	55.00	35.00
VR-35	Cake plate, open handles	150.00	200.00	100.00
VR-36	Cake plate, tab handles	150.00	175.00	100.00
VR-37	Cake plate,8″ sq. pedestal	175.00	200.00	125.00
VR-40	Cake stand, 2 tier	175.00	200.00	125.00
VR-45	Canoe-shaped dish	250.00	275.00	175.00
VR-50	Cheese keep	200.00	250.00	150.00
VR-52	Coaster	40.00	50.00	30.00
VR-55	Coffee pot	600.00	725.00	425.00
VR-60	Compote, footed	135.00	165.00	100.00
VR-65	Condiment set on tray	200.00	230.00	135.00
VR-70	Cream and sugar	100.00	125.00	65.00
VR-71	Cream and sugar on tray	200.00	250.00	135.00
VR-75	Demi-tasse	75.00	100.00	50.00
VR-77	Egg cup, footed	65.00	80.00	45.00
VR-80	Hot water jug	275.00	325.00	200.00
VR-85	Jam pot with liner	150.00	185.00	100.00
VR-90	Jug, 4″	200.00	250.00	150.00
VR-91	Jug, 4 1/2″	225.00	275.00	165.00
VR-92	Jug, 5″	250.00	300.00	175.00
VR-97	Nut dish	45.00	50.00	35.00
VR-201	Plate, 4″ sq.	50.00	65.00	35.00
VR-202	Plate, 5″ sq.	50.00	75.00	40.00
VR-203	Plate, 6″ sq.	60.00	75.00	45.00
VR-204	Plate, 7″ sq.	75.00	100.00	50.00
VR-205	Plate, 8″ sq.	115.00	150.00	75.00
VR-206	Plate, 9″ sq.	125.00	150.00	75.00
VR-207	Plate, 10″ sq.	135.00	165.00	85.00
VR-112	Relish dish, small	150.00	175.00	100.00
VR-115	Salad bowl, chrome rim	125.00	150.00	75.00
VR-117	Salt and pepper	75.00	90.00	50.00
VR-118	Salt and pepper on tray	150.00	175.00	100.00
VR-120	Sandwich tray, 10″ x 6″	100.00	125.00	65.00
VR-121	Sandwich tray, 12″ x 7″	125.00	150.00	100.00
VR-125	Sauce boat and liner	150.00	175.00	75.00
VR-130	Teacup and saucer	70.00	85.00	50.00
VR-135	Teapot, 2 cup	275.00	325.00	200.00
VR-136	Teapot, 4 cup	450.00	550.00	325.00
VR-137	Teapot, 6 cup	550.00	650.00	375.00
VR-140	Teapot, stacking	650.00	775.00	450.00
VR-145	Tennis set	100.00	125.00	65.00
VR-150	Toast rack, 4 slice	200.00	225.00	150.00
VR-151	Toast rack, 2 slice	135.00	175.00	100.00
VR-155	Trivet	100.00	125.00	65.00
VR-160	Vase, bud	100.00	125.00	65.00

WELBECK

The pattern number is 2204, and it was probably introduced in 1934 along with **Hazel** 2208. **Hazel** and **Spring** 2506 are the alternate colourways to **Welbeck**. This pattern was much copied by the Japanese.

Cat.No.	Shape	U.S. $	Can. $	U.K. £
W-04	Bonbon dish	90.00	110.00	60.00
W-09	Bowl, 5″	65.00	80.00	45.00
W-14	Bowl, 8″ soup	90.00	110.00	60.00
W-23	Breakfast set	1,250.00	1,500.00	875.00
W-28	Butter dish	275.00	325.00	175.00
W-30	Butter pat	75.00	100.00	50.00
W-35	Cake plate, open handles	275.00	325.00	175.00
W-36	Cake plate, tab handles	250.00	275.00	165.00
W-37	Cake plate,8″ sq. pedestal	275.00	325.00	200.00
W-40	Cake stand, 2 tier	275.00	325.00	200.00
W-45	Canoe-shaped dish	375.00	450.00	275.00
W-50	Cheese keep	350.00	425.00	250.00
W-52	Coaster	75.00	100.00	50.00
W-55	Coffee pot	1,100.00	1,300.00	725.00
W-60	Compote, footed	225.00	275.00	150.00
W-65	Condiment set on tray	325.00	350.00	225.00
W-70	Cream and sugar	175.00	200.00	125.00
W-71	Cream and sugar on tray	325.00	350.00	225.00
W-75	Demi-tasse	125.00	150.00	75.00
W-77	Egg cup, footed	100.00	125.00	65.00
W-80	Hot water jug	450.00	550.00	325.00
W-85	Jam pot with liner	250.00	300.00	175.00
W-90	Jug, 4″	400.00	480.00	275.00
W-91	Jug, 4 1/2″	425.00	500.00	300.00
W-92	Jug, 5″	450.00	550.00	325.00

Cat.No.	Shape	U.S. $	Can. $	U.K. £
W-97	Nut dish	75.00	100.00	50.00
W-201	Plate, 4″ sq.	75.00	100.00	50.00
W-202	Plate, 5″ sq.	100.00	125.00	65.00
W-203	Plate, 6″ sq.	115.00	150.00	80.00
W-204	Plate, 7″ sq.	135.00	165.00	100.00
W-205	Plate, 8″ sq.	175.00	200.00	125.00
W-206	Plate, 9″ sq.	185.00	225.00	125.00
W-207	Plate, 10″ sq.	200.00	250.00	150.00
W-112	Relish dish, small	250.00	300.00	175.00
W-115	Salad bowl, chrome rim	250.00	300.00	175.00
W-117	Salt and pepper	125.00	150.00	90.00
W-118	Salt and pepper on tray	275.00	275.00	150.00
W-120	Sandwich tray, 10″ x 6″	175.00	225.00	125.00
W-121	Sandwich tray, 12″ x 7″	200.00	250.00	150.00
W-125	Sauce boat and liner	225.00	275.00	160.00
W-130	Teacup and saucer	125.00	150.00	75.00
W-135	Teapot, 2 cup	550.00	650.00	375.00
W-136	Teapot, 4 cup	700.00	850.00	500.00
W-137	Teapot, 6 cup	900.00	1,200.00	625.00
W-140	Teapot, stacking	900.00	1,200.00	625.00
W-145	Tennis set	150.00	200.00	115.00
W-150	Toast rack, 4 slice	300.00	375.00	200.00
W-151	Toast rack, 2 slice	225.00	275.00	150.00
W-155	Trivet	150.00	200.00	115.00
W-160	Vase, bud	165.00	200.00	115.00

WILD FLOWERS

The pattern number is 3149, and it was probably introduced in 1936.

Cat.No.	Shape	U.S. $	Can. $	U.K. £
WF-04	Bonbon dish	50.00	75.00	40.00
WF-09	Bowl, 5"	50.00	65.00	35.00
WF-14	Bowl, 8" soup	75.00	100.00	50.00
WF-23	Breakfast set	800.00	950.00	550.00
WF-28	Butter dish	165.00	200.00	115.00
WF-30	Butter pat	45.00	55.00	35.00
WF-35	Cake plate, open handles	165.00	200.00	115.00
WF-36	Cake plate, tab handles	150.00	175.00	100.00
WF-37	Cake plate,8" sq. pedestal	175.00	225.00	125.00
WF-40	Cake stand, 2 tier	175.00	225.00	125.00
WF-45	Canoe-shaped dish	225.00	275.00	165.00
WF-50	Cheese keep	200.00	250.00	150.00
WF-52	Coaster	40.00	50.00	30.00
WF-55	Coffee pot	600.00	725.00	425.00
WF-60	Compote, footed	135.00	165.00	100.00
WF-65	Condiment set on tray	200.00	250.00	135.00
WF-70	Cream and sugar	100.00	125.00	75.00
WF-71	Cream and sugar on tray	190.00	225.00	135.00
WF-75	Demi-tasse	70.00	85.00	50.00
WF-77	Egg cup, footed	65.00	80.00	45.00
WF-80	Hot water jug	275.00	325.00	175.00
WF-85	Jam pot with liner	150.00	175.00	100.00
WF-90	Jug, 4"	200.00	250.00	125.00
WF-91	Jug, 4 1/2"	225.00	275.00	150.00
WF-92	Jug, 5"	250.00	300.00	175.00
WF-97	Nut dish	45.00	55.00	35.00
WF-201	Plate, 4" sq.	50.00	65.00	35.00
WF-202	Plate, 5" sq.	50.00	75.00	40.00
WF-203	Plate, 6" sq.	60.00	75.00	45.00
WF-204	Plate, 7" sq.	75.00	100.00	50.00
WF-205	Plate, 8" sq.	125.00	150.00	75.00
WF-206	Plate, 9" sq.	125.00	150.00	75.00
WF-207	Plate, 10" sq.	135.00	165.00	85.00
WF-112	Relish dish, small	150.00	175.00	85.00
WF-115	Salad bowl, chrome rim	125.00	150.00	75.00
WF-117	Salt and pepper	75.00	100.00	50.00
WF-118	Salt and pepper on tray	150.00	175.00	100.00
WF-120	Sandwich tray, 10" x 6"	100.00	125.00	65.00
WF-121	Sandwich tray, 12" x 7"	125.00	150.00	75.00
WF-125	Sauce boat and liner	150.00	175.00	100.00
WF-130	Teacup and saucer	75.00	100.00	50.00
WF-135	Teapot, 2 cup	275.00	325.00	200.00
WF-136	Teapot, 4 cup	450.00	540.00	325.00
WF-137	Teapot, 6 cup	550.00	660.00	375.00
WF-140	Teapot, stacking	650.00	780.00	450.00
WF-145	Tennis set	100.00	125.00	65.00
WF-150	Toast rack, 4 slice	200.00	250.00	150.00
WF-151	Toast rack, 2 slice	135.00	165.00	100.00
WF-155	Trivet	100.00	125.00	65.00
WF-160	Vase, bud	100.00	125.00	65.00

WINIFRED

Unfortunately we have no information on this pattern at this time.

Cat.No.	Shape	U.S. $	Can. $	U.K. £
Wi-04	Bonbon dish	30.00	35.00	25.00
Wi-09	Bowl, 5″	30.00	35.00	25.00
Wi-14	Bowl, 8″ soup	40.00	50.00	30.00
Wi-23	Breakfast set	450.00	550.00	325.00
Wi-28	Butter dish	100.00	125.00	65.00
Wi-30	Butter pat	25.00	30.00	20.00
Wi-35	Cake plate, open handles	100.00	125.00	65.00
Wi-36	Cake plate, tab handles	85.00	100.00	60.00
Wi-37	Cake plate, 8″ sq. pedestal	100.00	125.00	65.00
Wi-40	Cake stand, 2 tier	100.00	125.00	65.00
Wi-45	Canoe-shaped dish	135.00	165.00	85.00
Wi-50	Cheese keep	125.00	150.00	75.00
Wi-52	Coaster	25.00	30.00	20.00
Wi-55	Coffee pot	375.00	450.00	250.00
Wi-60	Compote, footed	75.00	100.00	50.00
Wi-65	Condiment set on tray	100.00	125.00	65.00
Wi-70	Cream and sugar	60.00	75.00	45.00
Wi-71	Cream and sugar on tray	100.00	125.00	65.00
Wi-75	Demi-tasse	40.00	50.00	30.00
Wi-77	Egg cup, footed	35.00	40.00	25.00
Wi-80	Hot water jug	150.00	200.00	115.00
Wi-85	Jam pot with liner	85.00	100.00	60.00
Wi-90	Jug, 4″	135.00	165.00	85.00
Wi-91	Jug, 4 1/2″	150.00	200.00	115.00
Wi-92	Jug, 5″	150.00	200.00	115.00

Cat.No.	Shape	U.S. $	Can. $	U.K. £
Wi-97	Nut dish	25.00	30.00	20.00
Wi-201	Plate, 4″ sq.	30.00	35.00	25.00
Wi-202	Plate, 5″ sq.	35.00	40.00	25.00
Wi-203	Plate, 6″ sq.	40.00	50.00	30.00
Wi-204	Plate, 7″ sq.	45.00	50.00	35.00
Wi-205	Plate, 8″ sq.	65.00	75.00	45.00
Wi-206	Plate, 9″ sq.	75.00	100.00	50.00
Wi-207	Plate, 10″ sq.	85.00	100.00	60.00
Wi-112	Relish dish, small	85.00	100.00	60.00
Wi-115	Salad bowl, chrome rim	100.00	125.00	65.00
Wi-117	Salt and pepper	50.00	75.00	40.00
Wi-118	Salt and pepper on tray	125.00	150.00	75.00
Wi-120	Sandwich tray, 10″ x 6″	60.00	75.00	45.00
Wi-121	Sandwich tray, 12″ x 7″	70.00	85.00	50.00
Wi-125	Sauce boat and liner	65.00	80.00	45.00
Wi-130	Teacup and saucer	40.00	50.00	30.00
Wi-135	Teapot, 2 cup	175.00	200.00	125.00
Wi-136	Teapot, 4 cup	275.00	325.00	200.00
Wi-137	Teapot, 6 cup	325.00	400.00	225.00
Wi-140	Teapot, stacking	400.00	475.00	275.00
Wi-145	Tennis set	50.00	75.00	40.00
Wi-150	Toast rack, 4 slice	150.00	200.00	115.00
Wi-151	Toast rack, 2 slice	135.00	165.00	100.00
Wi-155	Trivet	50.00	75.00	40.00
Wi-160	Vase, bud	60.00	80.00	45.00

9/1121
4-Pc. Cruet Set
Nantwich FANCIES
by ROYAL WINTON
An appealing chintz decoration of multi-colored floral sprays in soft tones of blue, yellow, pink and green on a black background. Heavy gold trim.
9/1101
Cup and Saucer
9/1110
Comport 6½''
9/1114
Covered Butter 6''
9/1103
Plate, Square, 10''
9/1102
Plate, Square, 9''
9/1118
Sandwich tray 12''
9/1115
Cheese dish 6''
9/1107 – Tray, Peebles 9''
9/1112
Celery Tray 11''
9/1104
Sugar and Cream
9/1124
23-Pc. Tea Set
9/1123
16-Pc. Coffee Set
9/1108
Tray, Malta 10''
9/1119
Fruit bowl 8''
B 44
Cassidy's Ltd.

9/1710
3-Pc. Condiment Set

9/1706
Tea Pot
5 cup

ORIENT FANCIES
by ROYAL WINTON

An oriental motif including pink cherry blossoms, lotus buds and butterflies in rich yellow, pink and green on a black background. Trimmed with heavy gold.

9/1709
4-Pc. Cruet Set

9/1721
Butter Dish, 6''

9/1702
Plate, sq. 8''

9/1704
Plate, sq. 10''

9/1714
Candy Box, rectangle, 5½''

9/1707
3-Pc. Tea Set,
Delaware

9/1703
Plate, sq. 9''

9/1719
Tray, Humber, 9½''

9/1715
Bon Bon, 3½''

9/1712
Tennis Set

B 42

Cassidy's Ltd.

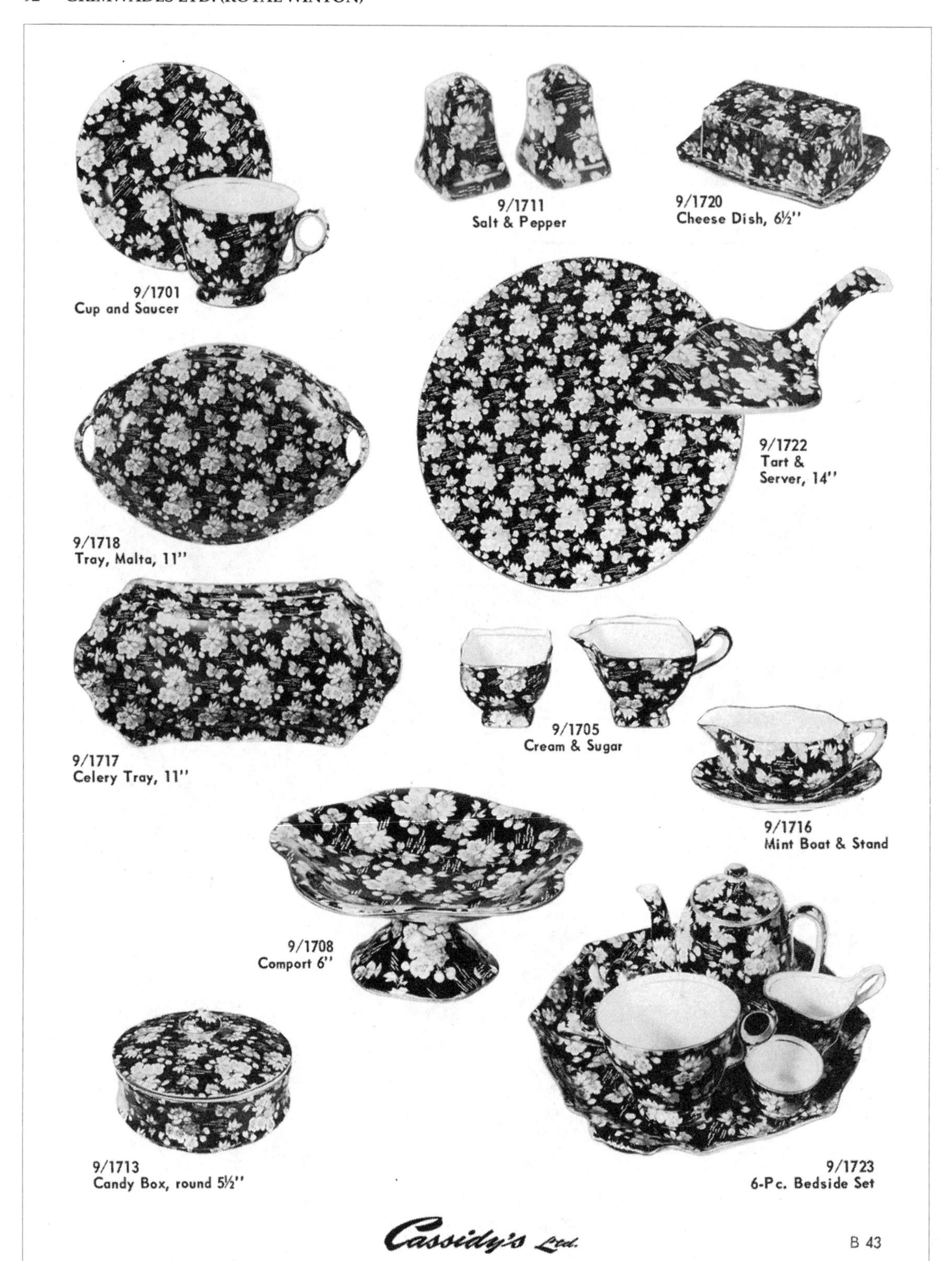
9/1701
Cup and Saucer
9/1711
Salt & Pepper
9/1720
Cheese Dish, 6½''
9/1722
Tart &
Server, 14''
9/1718
Tray, Malta, 11''
9/1717
Celery Tray, 11''
9/1705
Cream & Sugar
9/1716
Mint Boat & Stand
9/1708
Comport 6''
9/1713
Candy Box, round 5½''
9/1723
6-Pc. Bedside Set
Cassidy's Ltd.
B 43

JAMES KENT, LTD.

James Kent, Ltd. was another of those Staffordshire factories that tried to serve as many mid- or low-priced markets as they could identify. As reported in the 1935 *Pottery Gazette*, Old Foley Pottery at Longton was one of the oldest factories in the potteries. John Wesley preached from the steps of the old house that was incorporated into the James Kent factory on his visit to the potteries in 1790. James Kent took over the factory in 1897 and for more than forty years continued to produce earthenwares which "catered for expressed needs." His three sons helped him to keep in touch with modern movements and the *Gazette* reported the Kent range to be thoroughly up to date.

After this extended report there is remarkably little reference to James Kent in any of the trade publications. In 1939 there is a report of **Dubarry** being presented in the London showrooms. In 1941 Goodwin Johnson Inc. of New York City advertised for sale the following James Kent chintzes: **Harmony, Apple Blossom, Capri, Hydrangea, Dubarry, Pearl Delight, Mille Fleurs,** and **Rosalynde.** Ebeling & Reuss Co., with headquarters in Philadelphia, were the American distributors for Royal Winton and they also appear to have taken on James Kent in 1942. In April 1942 they advertised the six Kent chintz patterns in four place settings to the trade at $17.95. In 1949 they offered open stock in dinnerware and gift items in **Apple Blossom**; cups and saucers were $10.00 per dozen and luncheon plates $12.00 per dozen wholesale. In a Birk's catalogue the same year an Aynsley bone china cup and saucer retailed for $1.95. By 1950 Ebeling & Reuss were urging retailers to stock up on assorted **Rosalynde,** offering coffee pots at $33.00 a dozen and small teapots at $24.00 a dozen. The next report we came across about the factory came in the 1958 *Gazette* and mentioned four new James Kent chintzes, including **Tapestry**, on display at the Blackpool Gift Fair.

We were fortunate to be able to spend a morning with one of Jimmy Kent's workers. Mrs. Doreen Donegan worked at James Kent in the 1930s, which she described as "hard work for small wages." She joined the factory in 1935 at the age of 16 and was paid 5 shillings and 9 pence a week. She remembers the women who worked on chintz were considered a little above the others. Two slightly stand-offish sisters called Ada and Maude Kent (no relation) did nearly all of the chintzware for many years. "Since you went onto piece work after a training period and chintz was much harder to do everyone wanted to be paid more for doing chintz. I was never able to do teapots . . . they were beyond me." Doreen described cutting out all the little notches for the ruffled sweet dishes and how often the girls cut their fingers while they were working. She said that employees were allowed to buy "thirds" not "seconds" — the difference being that the thirds had obvious chips or cracks. When we asked about day after day of applying transfers, Doreen looked surprised and explained, "I couldn't grumble because I was working." After Jimmy Kent the factory was run by his son Peter and then by Peter's sister, Ruth Kent. By all accounts, Ruth Kent, who had never expected to be running the factory, did a splendid job and was well regarded throughout the potteries.

After being bought and sold several times through the 1980s, the firm went into receivership in 1989 and was bought by M.R. Hadida Ltd., a bathroom furnishings company and owner of Hadida Fine Bone China Ltd. For a brief time in 1985 James Kent made **Dubarry** once again, but the backstamp is very clear: "MIKASA Semi Porcelain Dubarry James Kent England."

APPLE BLOSSOM

This pattern was introduced in the 1930s and exported in quantity to North America before and after the war. Complete dinner services still turn up occasionally in North America.

JAMES KENT LTD.
LONGTON
MADE IN ENGLAND
"Apple Blossom"

Cat.No.	Shape	U.S $	Can. $	U.K. £
AB-04	Bonbon dish	50.00	75.00	35.00
AB-10	Bowl, 6″	50.00	75.00	35.00
AB-15	Bowl, 9″	150.00	175.00	85.00
AB-23	Breakfast set	750.00	900.00	450.00
AB-28	Butter dish	150.00	175.00	100.00
AB-36	Cake plate, square, 11″	125.00	150.00	75.00
AB-55	Coffee pot	600.00	725.00	350.00
AB-60	Compote, footed	115.00	150.00	75.00
AB-65	Condiment set on tray	200.00	250.00	115.00
AB-70	Cream and sugar	125.00	150.00	75.00
AB-71	Cream and sugar on tray	175.00	225.00	125.00
AB-75	Demi-tasse	65.00	80.00	40.00
AB-85	Jam pot	125.00	150.00	75.00

Cat.No.	Shape	U.S. $	Can. $	U.K. £
AB-97	Nut dish	50.00	65.00	30.00
AB-103	Plate, 6 1/2″	60.00	75.00	35.00
AB-106	Plate, 9″	100.00	125.00	65.00
AB-112	Relish dish	125.00	150.00	75.00
AB-117	Salt and pepper	75.00	90.00	45.00
AB-118	Salt and pepper on tray	150.00	175.00	90.00
AB-120	Sandwich tray	100.00	125.00	65.00
AB-130	Teacup and saucer	75.00	90.00	45.00
AB-136	Teapot, 4 cup	550.00	650.00	325.00
AB-137	Teapot, 6 cup	650.00	775.00	400.00
AB-150	Toast rack, 4 slice	200.00	250.00	125.00
AB-160	Vase, bud	85.00	100.00	50.00

CRAZY PAVING

The pattern number is 2839.

Cat.No.	Shape	U.S $	Can. $	U.K. £
CP-04	Bonbon dish	45.00	50.00	30.00
CP-10	Bowl, 6 1/2"	45.00	50.00	30.00
CP-15	Bowl, 9"	125.00	150.00	75.00
CP-23	Breakfast set	650.00	775.00	400.00
CP-28	Butter dish	125.00	150.00	75.00
CP-36	Cake plate, square, 11"	100.00	125.00	60.00
CP-55	Coffee pot	500.00	600.00	300.00
CP-60	Compote, footed	100.00	125.00	65.00
CP-65	Condiment set on tray	165.00	200.00	100.00
CP-70	Cream and sugar	100.00	125.00	65.00
CP-71	Cream and sugar on tray	150.00	175.00	90.00
CP-75	Demi-tasse	55.00	70.00	35.00
CP-85	Jam pot	100.00	125.00	65.00

Cat.No.	Shape	U.S. $	Can. $	U.K. £
CP-97	Nut dish	40.00	50.00	25.00
CP-103	Plate, 6 1/2"	45.00	50.00	30.00
CP-106	Plate, 9"	75.00	100.00	50.00
CP-112	Relish dish	100.00	125.00	65.00
CP-117	Salt and pepper	65.00	80.00	40.00
CP-118	Salt and pepper on tray	135.00	165.00	85.00
CP-120	Sandwich tray	85.00	100.00	50.00
CP-130	Teacup and saucer	65.00	80.00	40.00
CP-136	Teapot, 4 cup	450.00	550.00	275.00
CP-137	Teapot, 6 cup	550.00	650.00	325.00
CP-150	Toast rack, 4 slice	200.00	250.00	125.00
CP-160	Vase, bud	75.00	90.00	45.00

DU BARRY

This pattern was in the London showrooms in 1938 and exported in quantity to North America before and after the war. Complete dinner services still turn up occasionally in North America. It was reproduced briefly in 1985, but clearly marked MIKASA.

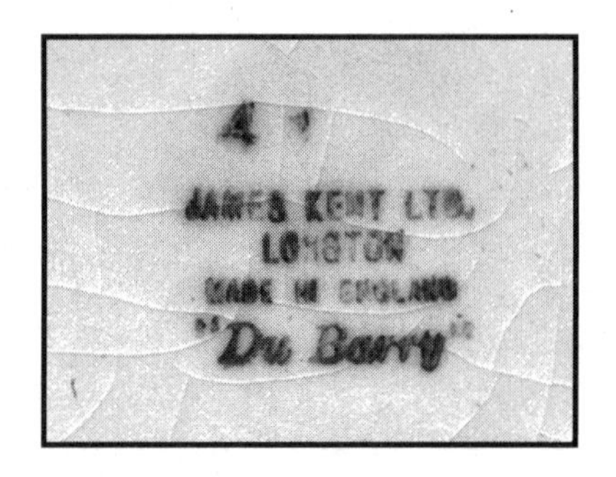

Cat.No.	Shape	U.S $	Can. $	U.K. £
D-04	Bonbon dish	50.00	75.00	35.00
D-10	Bowl, 6″	50.00	75.00	35.00
D-15	Bowl, 9″	150.00	175.00	85.00
D-23	Breakfast set	750.00	900.00	475.00
D-28	Butter dish	150.00	175.00	100.00
D-36	Cake plate, square, 11″	125.00	150.00	75.00
D-55	Coffee pot	700.00	850.00	450.00
D-60	Compote, footed	115.00	150.00	75.00
D-65	Condiment set on tray	200.00	250.00	115.00
D-70	Cream and sugar	100.00	125.00	65.00
D-71	Cream and sugar on tray	175.00	225.00	100.00
D-75	Demi-tasse	65.00	80.00	40.00
D-85	Jam pot	125.00	150.00	75.00

Cat.No.	Shape	U.S. $	Can. $	U.K. £
D-97	Nut dish	50.00	65.00	30.00
D-103	Plate, 6 1/2″	60.00	75.00	35.00
D-106	Plate, 9″	100.00	125.00	65.00
D-112	Relish dish	125.00	150.00	75.00
D-117	Salt and pepper	75.00	90.00	45.00
D-118	Salt and pepper on tray	150.00	175.00	85.00
D-120	Sandwich tray	100.00	125.00	60.00
D-130	Teacup and saucer	75.00	90.00	45.00
D-136	Teapot, 4 cup	550.00	650.00	325.00
D-137	Teapot, 6 cup	650.00	775.00	400.00
D-150	Toast rack, 4 slice	225.00	250.00	125.00
D-160	Vase, bud	85.00	100.00	50.00

FLORITA

The pattern number is 5008, and the pattern was probably introduced in early 1958. It is very popular with North American collectors.

Cat.No.	Shape	U.S $	Can. $	U.K. £
F-04	Bonbon dish	60.00	75.00	35.00
F-10	Bowl, 6″	60.00	75.00	35.00
F-15	Bowl, 9″	165.00	200.00	100.00
F-23	Breakfast set	800.00	950.00	475.00
F-28	Butter dish	165.00	200.00	100.00
F-36	Cake plate, square, 11″	150.00	175.00	85.00
F-55	Coffee pot	750.00	900.00	450.00
F-60	Compote, footed	125.00	150.00	75.00
F-65	Condiment set on tray	225.00	275.00	125.00
F-70	Cream and sugar	125.00	150.00	75.00
F-71	Cream and sugar on tray	200.00	250.00	115.00
F-75	Demi-tasse	75.00	90.00	45.00
F-85	Jam Pot	150.00	175.00	100.00

Cat.No.	Shape	U.S. $	Can. $	U.K. £
F-97	Nut dish	50.00	75.00	35.00
F-103	Plate, 6 1/2″	65.00	75.00	40.00
F-106	Plate, 9″	100.00	125.00	65.00
F-112	Relish dish	150.00	175.00	85.00
F-117	Salt and pepper	75.00	100.00	50.00
F-118	Salt and pepper on tray	165.00	200.00	100.00
F-120	Sandwich tray	115.00	150.00	75.00
F-130	Teacup and saucer	75.00	100.00	50.00
F-136	Teapot, 4 cup	600.00	725.00	375.00
F-137	Teapot, 6 cup	700.00	850.00	425.00
F-150	Toast rack, 4 slice	225.00	275.00	135.00
F-160	Vase, bud	75.00	100.00	50.00

HARMONY

This chintz pattern was an uncontrolled pattern and was used by a number of companies, including A.G. Richardson, and Hollinshead & Kirkham.

Cat.No.	Shape	U.S $	Can. $	U.K. £
Ha-04	Bonbon dish	40.00	50.00	25.00
Ha-10	Bowl, 6″	45.00	50.00	30.00
Ha-15	Bowl, 9″	100.00	125.00	65.00
Ha-23	Breakfast set	550.00	650.00	325.00
Ha-28	Butter dish	100.00	125.00	65.00
Ha-36	Cake plate, square, 11″	100.00	125.00	65.00
Ha-55	Coffee pot	450.00	550.00	300.00
Ha-60	Compote, footed	75.00	100.00	50.00
Ha-65	Condiment set on tray	135.00	165.00	80.00
Ha-70	Cream and sugar	75.00	100.00	45.00
Ha-71	Cream and sugar on tray	125.00	150.00	75.00
Ha-75	Demi-tasse	45.00	55.00	30.00
Ha-85	Jam pot	100.00	125.00	60.00

Cat.No.	Shape	U.S. $	Can. $	U.K. £
Ha-97	Nut dish	45.00	55.00	30.00
Ha-103	Plate, 6 1/2″	40.00	50.00	25.00
Ha-106	Plate, 9″	65.00	75.00	40.00
Ha-112	Relish dish	75.00	100.00	50.00
Ha-117	Salt and pepper	60.00	75.00	35.00
Ha-118	Salt and pepper on tray	115.00	150.00	75.00
Ha-120	Sandwich tray	75.00	100.00	45.00
Ha-130	Teacup and saucer	50.00	65.00	30.00
Ha-136	Teapot, 4 cup	375.00	450.00	250.00
Ha-137	Teapot, 6 cup	450.00	550.00	300.00
Ha-150	Toast rack, 4 slice	150.00	175.00	90.00
Ha-160	Vase, bud	65.00	80.00	40.00

HYDRANGEA (White)

This pattern is the most sought after James Kent pattern in North America. The pattern was also available with a black background, but this version is much preferred.

Cat.No.	Shape	U.S $	Can. $	U.K. £
Hy-04	Bonbon dish	65.00	80.00	40.00
Hy-10	Bowl, 6″	75.00	90.00	45.00
Hy-15	Bowl, 9″	175.00	225.00	100.00
Hy-23	Breakfast set	850.00	1,020.00	500.00
Hy-28	Butter dish	175.00	200.00	100.00
Hy-36	Cake plate, square, 11″	150.00	175.00	85.00
Hy-55	Coffee pot	750.00	900.00	450.00
Hy-60	Compote, footed	135.00	165.00	85.00
Hy-65	Condiment set on tray	225.00	275.00	135.00
Hy-70	Cream and sugar	125.00	150.00	75.00
Hy-71	Cream and sugar on tray	200.00	250.00	125.00
Hy-75	Demi-tasse	75.00	90.00	45.00
Hy-85	Jam pot	150.00	180.00	90.00
Hy-97	Nut dish	50.00	75.00	35.00
Hy-103	Plate, 6 1/2″	75.00	90.00	45.00
Hy-106	Plate, 9″	125.00	150.00	75.00
Hy-112	Relish dish	150.00	175.00	85.00
Hy-117	Salt and pepper	100.00	125.00	60.00
Hy-118	Salt and pepper on tray	175.00	225.00	100.00
Hy-120	Sandwich tray	125.00	150.00	75.00
Hy-130	Teacup and saucer	85.00	100.00	50.00
Hy-136	Teapot, 4 cup	650.00	775.00	400.00
Hy-137	Teapot, 6 cup	750.00	900.00	450.00
Hy-150	Toast rack, 4 slice	250.00	300.00	150.00
Hy-160	Vase, bud	100.00	125.00	65.00

HYDRANGEA (BLACK)

This pattern is the alternate colourway to **Hydrangea** but it is not as popular with collectors.

Cat.No.	Shape	U.S $	Can. $	U.K. £
HyB-04	Bonbon dish	40.00	50.00	25.00
HyB-10	Bowl, 6″	45.00	50.00	30.00
HyB-15	Bowl, 9″	100.00	125.00	65.00
HyB-23	Breakfast set	550.00	650.00	350.00
HyB-28	Butter dish	100.00	125.00	65.00
HyB-36	Cake plate, square, 11″	90.00	110.00	50.00
HyB-55	Coffee pot	450.00	550.00	300.00
HyB-60	Compote, footed	80.00	100.00	50.00
HyB-65	Condiment set on tray	135.00	165.00	85.00
HyB-70	Cream and sugar	75.00	90.00	45.00
HyB-71	Cream and sugar on tray	125.00	150.00	75.00
HyB-75	Demi-tasse	45.00	55.00	30.00
HyB-85	Jam pot	100.00	125.00	65.00
HyB-97	Nut dish	45.00	50.00	30.00
HyB-103	Plate, 6 1/2″	40.00	50.00	25.00
HyB-106	Plate, 9″	65.00	75.00	40.00
HyB-112	Relish dish	85.00	100.00	50.00
HyB-117	Salt and pepper	60.00	75.00	35.00
HyB-118	Salt and pepper on tray	115.00	150.00	75.00
HyB-120	Sandwich tray	75.00	90.00	45.00
HyB-130	Teacup and saucer	50.00	65.00	30.00
HyB-136	Teapot, 4 cup	375.00	450.00	250.00
HyB-137	Teapot, 6 cup	450.00	550.00	300.00
HyB-150	Toast rack, 4 slice	150.00	175.00	85.00
HyB-160	Vase, bud	65.00	80.00	40.00

MARIGOLD

We currently have no information available on this pattern.

Cat.No.	Shape	U.S $	Can. $	U.K. £
Mg-04	Bonbon dish	40.00	50.00	25.00
Mg-10	Bowl, 6″	45.00	50.00	30.00
Mg-15	Bowl, 9″	100.00	125.00	65.00
Mg-23	Breakfast set	550.00	650.00	350.00
Mg-28	Butter dish	100.00	125.00	65.00
Mg-36	Cake plate, square, 11″	90.00	110.00	50.00
Mg-55	Coffee pot	450.00	550.00	300.00
Mg-60	Compote, footed	80.00	95.00	50.00
Mg-65	Condiment set on tray	135.00	165.00	85.00
Mg-70	Cream and sugar	75.00	90.00	45.00
Mg-71	Cream and sugar on tray	125.00	150.00	75.00
Mg-75	Demi-tasse	45.00	55.00	30.00
Mg-85	Jam pot	100.00	125.00	65.00

Cat.No.	Shape	U.S. $	Can. $	U.K. £
Mg-97	Nut dish	45.00	50.00	30.00
Mg-103	Plate, 6 1/2″	40.00	50.00	25.00
Mg-106	Plate, 9″	65.00	80.00	40.00
Mg-112	Relish dish	85.00	100.00	50.00
Mg-117	Salt and pepper	60.00	75.00	35.00
Mg-118	Salt and pepper on tray	115.00	150.00	75.00
Mg-120	Sandwich tray	75.00	90.00	45.00
Mg-130	Teacup and saucer	50.00	65.00	30.00
Mg-136	Teapot, 4 cup	375.00	450.00	250.00
Mg-137	Teapot, 6 cup	450.00	550.00	300.00
Mg-150	Toast rack, 4 slice	150.00	175.00	90.00
Mg-160	Vase, bud	65.00	75.00	40.00

MILLE FLEURS

This pattern was an uncontrolled pattern and was used by a number of companies, including A.G. Richardson and Elijah Cotton, who called it **Marigold**. It was also produced in Czechoslovakia. The James Kent version was featured in a 1941 American advertisement.

Cat.No.	Shape	U.S $	Can. $	U.K. £
MF-04	Bonbon dish	50.00	65.00	30.00
MF-10	Bowl, 6″	50.00	65.00	30.00
MF-15	Bowl, 9″	115.00	150.00	75.00
MF-23	Breakfast set	650.00	775.00	400.00
MF-28	Butter dish	125.00	150.00	75.00
MF-36	Cake plate, square, 11″	125.00	150.00	75.00
MF-55	Coffee pot	550.00	650.00	350.00
MF-60	Compote, footed	100.00	125.00	65.00
MF-65	Condiment set on tray	175.00	225.00	100.00
MF-70	Cream and sugar	85.00	100.00	50.00
MF-71	Cream and sugar on tray	150.00	175.00	85.00
MF-75	Demi-tasse	60.00	75.00	35.00
MF-85	Jam pot	110.00	125.00	65.00

Cat.No.	Shape	U.S. $	Can. $	U.K. £
MF-97	Nut dish	45.00	55.00	30.00
MF-103	Plate, 6 1/2″	50.00	65.00	30.00
MF-106	Plate, 9″	85.00	100.00	50.00
MF-112	Relish dish	100.00	125.00	65.00
MF-117	Salt and pepper	75.00	90.00	45.00
MF-118	Salt and pepper on tray	135.00	165.00	80.00
MF-120	Sandwich tray	85.00	100.00	50.00
MF-130	Teacup and saucer	65.00	80.00	40.00
MF-136	Teapot, 4 cup	450.00	550.00	300.00
MF-137	Teapot, 6 cup	550.00	650.00	350.00
MF-150	Toast rack, 4 slice	200.00	250.00	115.00
MF-160	Vase, bud	70.00	85.00	45.00

PRIMULA

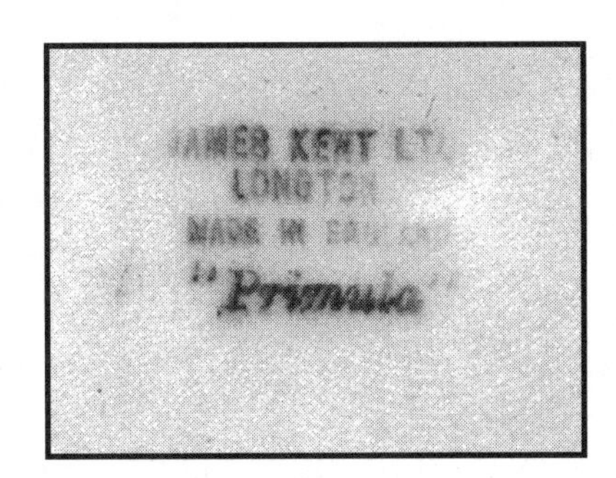

We currently have no information available on this pattern.

Cat.No.	Shape	U.S $	Can. $	U.K. £
Pr-04	Bonbon dish	50.00	65.00	30.00
Pr-10	Bowl, 6″	50.00	65.00	30.00
Pr-15	Bowl, 9″	115.00	150.00	75.00
Pr-23	Breakfast set	650.00	775.00	400.00
Pr-28	Butter dish	125.00	150.00	75.00
Pr-36	Cake plate, square, 11″	120.00	150.00	75.00
Pr-55	Coffee pot	550.00	650.00	350.00
Pr-60	Compote, footed	100.00	125.00	65.00
Pr-65	Condiment set on tray	175.00	200.00	100.00
Pr-70	Cream and sugar	100.00	125.00	65.00
Pr-71	Cream and sugar on tray	150.00	175.00	85.00
Pr-75	Demi-tasse	60.00	75.00	35.00
Pr-85	Jam pot	110.00	125.00	65.00

Cat.No.	Shape	U.S. $	Can. $	U.K. £
Pr-97	Nut dish	45.00	50.00	30.00
Pr-103	Plate, 6 1/2″	50.00	65.00	30.00
Pr-106	Plate, 9″	85.00	100.00	50.00
Pr-112	Relish dish	105.00	125.00	65.00
Pr-117	Salt and pepper	75.00	100.00	45.00
Pr-118	Salt and pepper on tray	135.00	165.00	85.00
Pr-120	Sandwich tray	85.00	115.00	50.00
Pr-130	Teacup and saucer	65.00	80.00	40.00
Pr-136	Teapot, 4 cup	450.00	550.00	300.00
Pr-137	Teapot, 6 cup	550.00	650.00	350.00
Pr-150	Toast rack, 4 slice	200.00	250.00	115.00
Pr-160	Vase, bud	75.00	100.00	45.00

RAPTURE

The pattern number is 3007.

Cat.No.	Shape	U.S $	Can. $	U.K. £
Ra-04	Bonbon dish	40.00	50.00	25.00
Ra-10	Bowl, 6″	45.00	50.00	30.00
Ra-15	Bowl, 9″	100.00	125.00	65.00
Ra-23	Breakfast set	550.00	650.00	350.00
Ra-28	Butter dish	100.00	125.00	65.00
Ra-36	Cake plate, square, 11″	100.00	125.00	65.00
Ra-55	Coffee pot	450.00	550.00	300.00
Ra-60	Compote, footed	80.00	100.00	50.00
Ra-65	Condiment set on tray	135.00	165.00	85.00
Ra-70	Cream and sugar	75.00	90.00	45.00
Ra-71	Cream and sugar on tray	125.00	150.00	75.00
Ra-75	Demi-tasse	45.00	50.00	30.00
Ra-85	Jam pot	100.00	125.00	65.00

Cat.No.	Shape	U.S. $	Can. $	U.K. £
Ra-97	Nut dish	45.00	50.00	30.00
Ra-103	Plate, 6 1/2″	40.00	50.00	25.00
Ra-106	Plate, 9″	65.00	80.00	40.00
Ra-112	Relish dish	85.00	100.00	50.00
Ra-117	Salt and pepper	60.00	75.00	35.00
Ra-118	Salt and pepper on tray	115.00	150.00	75.00
Ra-120	Sandwich tray	75.00	90.00	45.00
Ra-140	Stacking Teapot		Rare	
Ra-130	Teacup and saucer	50.00	65.00	30.00
Ra-136	Teapot, 4 cup	375.00	450.00	250.00
Ra-137	Teapot, 6 cup	450.00	550.00	300.00
Ra-150	Toast rack, 4 slice	150.00	175.00	85.00
Ra-160	Vase, bud	65.00	80.00	40.00

ROSALYNDE

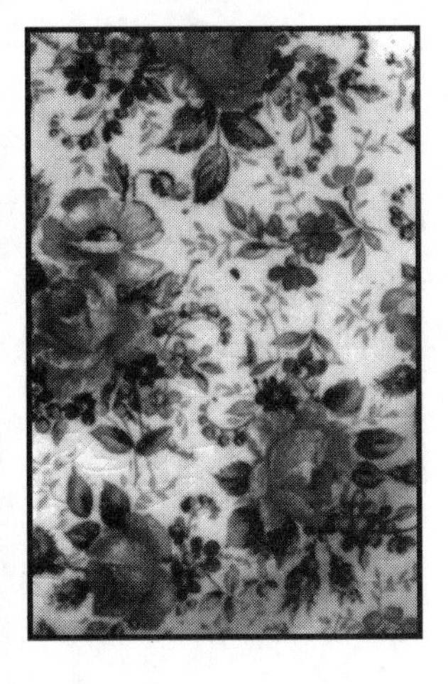

This pattern was introduced in the 1930s and exported in quantity to North America before and after the war. Complete dinner services still turn up occasionally in North America. The pattern number is 2662.

Cat.No.	Shape	U.S $	Can. $	U.K. £
Ro-04	Bonbon dish	60.00	75.00	35.00
Ro-10	Bowl, 6″	60.00	75.00	35.00
Ro-15	Bowl, 9″	165.00	195.00	100.00
Ro-23	Breakfast set	800.00	950.00	500.00
Ro-28	Butter dish	165.00	200.00	100.00
Ro-36	Cake plate, square, 11″	150.00	175.00	85.00
Ro-55	Coffee pot	750.00	900.00	475.00
Ro-60	Compote, footed	125.00	150.00	75.00
Ro-65	Condiment set on tray	225.00	275.00	150.00
Ro-70	Cream and sugar	125.00	150.00	75.00
Ro-71	Cream and sugar on tray	200.00	225.00	115.00
Ro-75	Demi-tasse	75.00	90.00	45.00
Ro-85	Jam pot	150.00	175.00	85.00

Cat.No.	Shape	U.S. $	Can. $	U.K. £
Ro-97	Nut dish	50.00	70.00	35.00
Ro-103	Plate, 6 1/2″	65.00	80.00	40.00
Ro-106	Plate, 9″	110.00	125.00	65.00
Ro-112	Relish dish	150.00	175.00	85.00
Ro-117	Salt and pepper	80.00	100.00	50.00
Ro-118	Salt and pepper on tray	165.00	200.00	100.00
Ro-120	Sandwich tray	110.00	125.00	65.00
Ro-130	Teacup and saucer	80.00	100.00	50.00
Ro-136	Teapot, 4 cup	600.00	725.00	375.00
Ro-137	Teapot, 6 cup	700.00	850.00	450.00
Ro-150	Toast rack, 4 slice	225.00	275.00	135.00
Ro-160	Vase, bud	90.00	110.00	50.00

SILVERDALE

The James Kent pattern number is 1097, but this pattern has also been found with a Royal Winton backstamp.

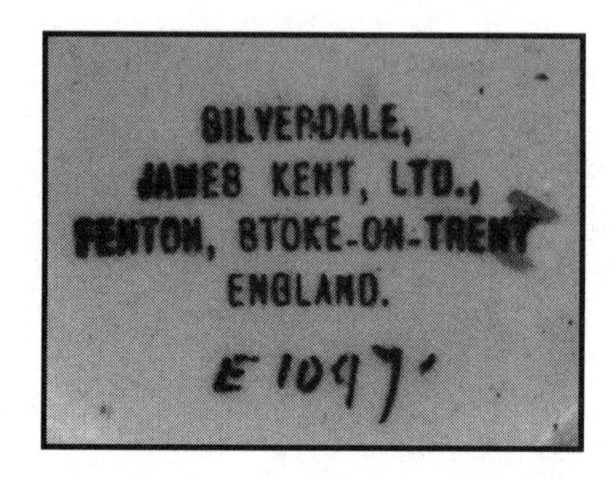

Cat.No.	Shape	U.S $	Can. $	U.K. £
S-04	Bonbon dish	30.00	35.00	20.00
S-10	Bowl, 6″	35.00	40.00	20.00
S-15	Bowl, 9″	75.00	90.00	45.00
S-23	Breakfast set	450.00	550.00	300.00
S-28	Butter dish	100.00	125.00	60.00
S-36	Cake plate, square, 11″	75.00	90.00	45.00
S-55	Coffee pot	400.00	475.00	250.00
S-60	Compote, footed	75.00	90.00	45.00
S-65	Condiment set on tray	135.00	165.00	85.00
S-70	Cream and sugar	65.00	80.00	40.00
S-71	Cream and sugar on tray	115.00	150.00	75.00
S-75	Demi-tasse	40.00	50.00	25.00
S-85	Jam pot	85.00	100.00	50.00

Cat.No.	Shape	U.S. $	Can. $	U.K. £
S-97	Nut dish	35.00	40.00	20.00
S-103	Plate, 6 1/2″	35.00	40.00	20.00
S-106	Plate, 9″	75.00	85.00	45.00
S-112	Relish dish	75.00	90.00	45.00
S-117	Salt and pepper	50.00	75.00	35.00
S-118	Salt and pepper on tray	110.00	125.00	65.00
S-120	Sandwich tray	60.00	75.00	35.00
S-130	Teacup and saucer	45.00	50.00	30.00
S-136	Teapot, 4 cup	325.00	400.00	200.00
S-137	Teapot, 6 cup	395.00	475.00	225.00
S-150	Toast rack, 4 slice	125.00	150.00	75.00
S-160	Vase, bud	65.00	80.00	40.00

TAPESTRY

The pattern number is 5615, and the pattern was introduced at the gift show in Blackpool in 1958.

Cat.No.	Shape	U.S $	Can. $	U.K. £
Tp-04	Bonbon dish	50.00	65.00	30.00
Tp-10	Bowl, 6″	50.00	65.00	30.00
Tp-15	Bowl, 9″	115.00	150.00	75.00
Tp-23	Breakfast set	650.00	775.00	400.00
Tp-28	Butter dish	125.00	150.00	75.00
Tp-36	Cake plate, square, 11″	125.00	150.00	75.00
Tp-55	Coffee pot	550.00	650.00	350.00
Tp-60	Compote, footed	100.00	125.00	65.00
Tp-65	Condiment set on tray	175.00	225.00	100.00
Tp-70	Cream and sugar	100.00	125.00	65.00
Tp-71	Cream and sugar on tray	150.00	175.00	85.00
Tp-75	Demi-tasse	60.00	75.00	35.00
Tp-85	Jam pot	110.00	130.00	65.00

Cat.No.	Shape	U.S. $	Can. $	U.K. £
Tp-97	Nut dish	45.00	50.00	30.00
Tp-103	Plate, 6 1/2″	50.00	65.00	30.00
Tp-106	Plate, 9″	85.00	100.00	50.00
Tp-112	Relish dish	100.00	125.00	65.00
Tp-117	Salt and pepper	75.00	90.00	45.00
Tp-118	Salt and pepper on tray	135.00	165.00	85.00
Tp-120	Sandwich tray	85.00	100.00	50.00
Tp-130	Teacup and saucer	65.00	80.00	40.00
Tp-136	Teapot, 4 cup	450.00	550.00	300.00
Tp-137	Teapot, 6 cup	550.00	650.00	350.00
Tp-150	Toast rack, 4 slice	200.00	225.00	115.00
Tp-160	Vase, bud	75.00	100.00	50.00

35/1117 Bon Bon, Oval
35/1115 – Bon Bon, Rd.
35/1116 – Bon Bon, Sq.
35/1104
Tray 8", Kendall
35/1114
Celery Tray 12" Oct.
GOLDEN ROSA FANCIES
by James Kent of England
A bright golden chintz decoration highlighting attractive full-bloom roses and sprays. White body. Sold as open stock or in suggested packages.
35/1105
Bon Bon Sq. 5"
35/1108
Tray 10", Oct.
35/1102
Plate 9", Granville
35/1113
Sweet 6", Diamond
35/1119
4-Pc. Cosy set
35/1106
Tray 8½", York
35/1109
Sweet 7", Round
35/1107
Tray, Oxford
35/1103
Cream & Sugar, Kendall
35/1111
Cheese S/S York
B 40
Cassidy's Ltd.

W.R. MIDWINTER LTD.

William Robinson Midwinter spent 18 years working for the head of Royal Doulton and selling "seconds" at night and on weekends. By 1910 he had saved 50 pounds and was ready to set up his own business at Bournes Bank Pottery in Burslem. The factory turned out very much the same product lines as every other small pottery in Staffordshire, and it prospered. After buying up the Albion Pottery and Stewart Maddock Ltd., Midwinter increased production and began to produce tablewares in addition to teawares and toiletwares. For the most part the patterns were the traditional florals produced by the other factories.

According to Allan Peat, author of *Midwinter: A Collectors' Guide,* the Midwinter factory worked on the basis of one new pattern a week and Roy Midwinter, William's son, set off for North America in 1952 with a number of recent designs. Colonel Keene, the legendary buyer for Eaton's of Canada, is reported to have said, "Get that...stuff out of here," and his colleague at Robert Simpson of Canada, Maurice Pickles, concurred. Asked for advice, Colonel Keene directed Roy Midwinter to the American West Coast and designers like Eva Zeisal. Roy shipped samples home from California and helped to change the design direction not only of Midwinter but of the Potteries as well.

Midwinter became renowned for their risk taking in leading the way in modern design in Staffordshire. Their designs by Jessie Tait, Terence Conran, Sir Hugh Casson and David Queensberry have found their way into most museums of modern design. Roy Midwinter never lost sight of the traditional markets, however, and he was careful to continue to cater for them. The Midwinter chintzes are part of this traditional market and they warrant exactly one line in Allan Peat's book on Midwinter.

Although the whole factory was modernized and a decorating department opened, the printing shop was still used principally for traditional printed patterns such as **Springtime.** Several Midwinter advertisements from the mid 1940s feature **Springtime** as a controlled Midwinter chintz. The only other reference to **Springtime** is in the pattern information from *The Midwinter Trade Price Book,* which states that the pattern was discontinued in 1974 on the Fine shape. Since this shape is chunky and seemingly unsuited to chintz, one wonders if **Springtime** was now a different pattern. This could account for chintz pieces with the name **Brama** clearly marked on **Springtime** chintz and for backstamps which date to the late 1940s and the 1950s.

An advertisement appeared in May 1949 for a "new Wilkinson production of superb colour and charm . . ." and the pattern was called **Lorna Doone**. This identical pattern appears frequently with the Midwinter Stylecraft backstamp. In fact, Midwinter bought Wilkinson from Clarice Cliff in 1964 and presumably took over the pattern. It is an excellent example of a transitional period in design. The Midwinter **Lorna Doone** range is a strange amalgam of traditional decoration and modern styling. Most of the line was in some way fitted with chrome handles or chrome bases. Neither the shapes nor the fittings were particularly well-suited to chintz. Some pieces have a Midwinter backstamp with the name **Bird Chintz** underneath so perhaps at some point the factory renamed their patterns.

In 1968 Midwinter merged with J & G Meakin Ltd., and in 1970 the combined company was taken over by the Wedgwood Group.

BRAMA

This was a pattern controlled to Midwinter as **Springtime** and advertised as such before and after the second world war. It is unclear when and why the name was changed to **Brama**.

Cat.No.	Shape	U.S. $	Can. $	U.K. £
Br-170	Biscuit barrel	400.00	475.00	250.00
Br-04	Bonbon dish	60.00	75.00	35.00
Br-40	Cake plate, 2 tier	125.00	150.00	75.00
Br-41	Cake plate, 3 tier	175.00	225.00	125.00
Br-42	Cake plate, with server	175.00	225.00	125.00
Br-43	Cake stand, chrome handle	100.00	125.00	65.00
Br-44	Cake stand, chrome base	100.00	125.00	65.00

Cat.No.	Shape	U.S. $	Can. $	U.K. £
Br-65	Condiment set on tray	200.00	250.00	125.00
Br-85	Jam pot with liner	125.00	150.00	75.00
Br-103	Plate, 6″	75.00	90.00	45.00
Br-106	Plate, 9″	125.00	150.00	75.00
Br-120	Sandwich tray	150.00	175.00	85.00
Br-169	Sugar shaker	250.00	300.00	150.00
Br-130	Teacup and saucer	85.00	100.00	50.00

CORAL

We currently have no information available on this pattern.

Cat.No.	Shape	U.S. $	Can. $	U.K. £
C-170	Biscuit barrel	400.00	475.00	250.00
C-04	Bonbon dish	50.00	65.00	30.00
C-40	Cake plate, 2 tier	125.00	150.00	75.00
C-41	Cake plate, 3 tier	175.00	225.00	125.00
C-42	Cake plate, with server	175.00	225.00	125.00
C-43	Cake stand, chrome handle	100.00	125.00	50.00
C-44	Cake stand, chrome base	85.00	100.00	50.00

Cat.No.	Shape	U.S. $	Can. $	U.K. £
C-65	Condiment set on tray	175.00	225.00	125.00
C-85	Jam pot with liner	100.00	125.00	65.00
C-103	Plate, 6"	60.00	75.00	35.00
C-106	Plate, 9"	115.00	150.00	75.00
C-120	Sandwich tray	125.00	150.00	75.00
C-169	Sugar shaker	225.00	275.00	150.00
C-130	Teacup and saucer	85.00	100.00	50.00

LORNA DOONE

This pattern can be found in the A.J. Wilkinson Clarice Cliff archive from the late 1940s. Any piece of **Lorna Doone** with a Midwinter backstamp must have been produced after the 1964 takeover of Wilkinsons.

At some point Midwinter changed the name and pieces appear with the backstamp pattern name **Bird Chintz**. This pattern was also produced by Barker Brothers.

Cat.No.	Shape	U.S. $	Can. $	U.K. £
LD-170	Biscuit barrel	350.00	425.00	225.00
LD-04	Bonbon dish	40.00	50.00	25.00
LD-40	Cake plate, 2 tier	110.00	135.00	65.00
LD-41	Cake plate, 3 tier	150.00	175.00	100.00
LD-42	Cake plate, with server	150.00	175.00	100.00
LD-43	Cake stand, chrome handle	85.00	100.00	50.00
LD-44	Cake stand, chrome base	75.00	90.00	45.00
LD-65	Condiment set on tray	150.00	175.00	100.00
LD-85	Jam pot with liner	95.00	115.00	60.00
LD-103	Plate, 6"	50.00	65.00	30.00
LD-106	Plate, 9"	100.00	125.00	65.00
LD-120	Sandwich tray	100.00	125.00	65.00
LD-169	Sugar shaker	200.00	250.00	150.00
LD-130	Teacup and saucer	75.00	90.00	45.00

MYOTT SON & COMPANY

Although the original pottery was established in the early nineteenth century, when Ashley Myott inherited the chairmanship at 19 years of age, he and his brother Sydney built up the business into a worldwide concern. The factory tried to produce a little of everything in earthenware. They produced some extreme shapes with vivid handpainting during the 1920s and 1930s in competition with Newport Pottery. They produced art pottery in the Carlton ware mould but not of the same quality. They used a wide variety of prints and enamels on their tablewares during the 1930s, and the company registered almost 500 different patterns between the years 1933 and 1935. Myott were not known for their chintzes, but obviously did not want to let a potential market go completely unaddressed. A couple of Myott chintzes have come to light, but there may well be others. The **Summer Flower** pattern seems to date from the 1930s.

The factory passed out of family hands some years after the war and eventually amalgamated with Alfred Meakin Pottery. There was a dreadful fire in 1949 and all the records and pattern books from the Myott factory were destroyed. The Churchill Group took over the combined company in 1991.

"SPRING FLOWER"

The pattern number is 3005. This pattern appears to have been used for complete dinner services. The handles of the teapots and coffee pots are painted bright orange and black.

Photograph not available
at
press time.

Cat.No.	Shape	U.S. $	Can. $	U.K. £
SF-55	Coffee pot, 6 cup	500.00	600.00	350.00
SF-70	Cream and sugar	135.00	165.00	85.00
SF-95	Jug, 7" straight-sided	300.00	350.00	200.00
SF-103	Plate, 6"	60.00	75.00	35.00
SF-104	Plate, 7"	75.00	90.00	45.00
SF-106	Plate, 9"	125.00	150.00	75.00
SF-130	Teacup and saucer	75.00	90.00	45.00
SF-137	Teapot, 6 cup	450.00	550.00	300.00

SUMMER FLOWER

We currently have no information available on this pattern.

Cat.No.	Shape	U.S. $	Can. $	U.K. £
SuF-55	Coffee pot, 6 cup	500.00	600.00	350.00
SuF-70	Cream and sugar	135.00	165.00	85.00
SuF-95	Jug, 7″ straight-sided	300.00	350.00	200.00
SuF-103	Plate, 6″	60.00	75.00	35.00
SuF-104	Plate, 7″	75.00	90.00	45.00
SuF-106	Plate, 9″	125.00	150.00	75.00
SuF-130	Teacup and saucer	75.00	90.00	45.00
SuF-137	Teapot, 6 cup	450.00	550.00	300.00

The Ware with Appeal
Royal Winton
FAMOUS FOR
CHINTZ
London : J. H. Service & Sons, 21, Charterhouse Street, E.C.1.
Australia : Reslaw Green & Scott Pty., Ltd., P.O. Box 471, FF. Danks
Buildings, 324, Pitt Street, Sydney, N.S.W. Distributors
for U.S.A. : The Hambro Trading Co. of America (Incorporated), 832, Baronne
Street, New Orleans, Louisiana. Canada : G. O. Coales, 32,
Front Street West, Toronto. South Africa : W. P. M. Kellam &
Co., P.O. Box 1664, Johannesburg. P.O. Box 362, Durban. P.O. Box 1111,
Capetown. New Zealand : W. G. Douglas, Paykel's
Buildings, Anzac Avenue, Auckland.
GRIMWADES LTD ROYAL WINTON POTTERIES · STOKE-ON-TRENT

A.G. RICHARDSON & CO. LTD. (CROWN DUCAL)

In 1915 at the Gordon Pottery, Tunstall, Albert Goodwin Richardson formed A.G. Richardson & Co. Ltd. with the stated intention of producing good quality earthenware under the trade name "Crown Ducal." The early production included Victorian silver luster ware and black groundlay decoration. The first chintz pattern produced by Richardson was in 1918 and was numbered A500. The pattern book started at A1 and by 1931 had reached A2000, when the "A" was dropped. In 1919 *The Pottery and Glass Record* noted two new Ducal chintzes, **Rose and Motifs** A601 and **Delhi** A617. According to this report, vases were made from 4 1/2 inches up to 12 inches and the flower pots came in four sizes.

In 1919 Albert Richardson left Richardsons, and Harry Taylor, owner of Universal Transfer Company, Burslem, bought a major interest in the company. Universal, Rataud, and the Chromo Transfer Company supplied most of Richardson's lithographs.

Maddock & Miller, the New York importers, agreed to represent Richardsons in the United States and sales grew rapidly. Crown Ducal is mentioned in *The Pottery Glass & Brass Salesman* in June 1920 and frequently thereafter. Chintzware was particularly popular with the American public, and Richardson's expanded the line to include teaware in 1921. Again with the urging of America, Richardson's expanded their line in 1925 to include dinnerware for the first time. All-over patterns like **Blue Chintz** A1885 and **Florida** A1257 (known to many American collectors as **Mauve CD**) were advertised in 1926 and much admired.

By 1929 the *Brass Salesman* had published a two-page story on the success of A.G. Richardson in America. They said the thrifty American housewife loved Crown Ducal, which duplicated bone china in terms of quality but cost $100 compared to $500 for a china service of equal charm. Richardson's led the way in adapting designs which had previously been reserved for fine china to earthenware. "The great success of the Crown Ducal ware surely proves that people of moderate means as well as the wealthier class prefer to have good-looking belongings in table service, even if the price is necessarily slightly higher than that of uninspired thick potteries." They were praised in English publications as well. The 1932 *Pottery Gazette* commented that they were reliable without being high-priced and exclusive and noted their ability to lead rather than follow the other potteries.

The company purchased a second potbank, Britannia Pottery at Cobridge to cope with increased production. Although Harold Holdcroft joined the design staff in 1928 and is said to be responsible for many of the firm's lithographic patterns, most of the exotic chintzes were already in production by that time and he was gone by 1934. Charlotte Rhead joined them as a designer in 1931 and stayed for the next eleven years. Many wonderful designs were produced over the next few years but there seems to be a gap of close to ten years before the next group of chintz designs were produced at Richardson. **Primrose**, **Peony**, **Pansy**, and **Priscilla** were all designed late in the 1930s, but none achieved the popularity of the earlier chintzes. The deep ivory glaze base colour which was developed at Richardsons in 1931 was used for all the later chintzes. Richardson's were still producing chintzes in 1940 but wartime restrictions drastically reduced the output of decorated ware.

Although there is no mention of Crown Ducal chintzes in the American trade magazines after the war, a reporter for *The Pottery and Glass Record*, on a visit to the works at Cobridge in 1955 commended the earthenware as being "of very fine quality...an all-over engraving of a conventionalized bird and flowers in blue, mauve or pink is a magnificent reminder of Victorian plenitude." This would suggest that Crown Ducal chintzes were still being produced in the 1950s.

Like all too many potteries during these years, A.G. Richardson could not survive alone and they were acquired by Enoch Wedgwood (Tunstall) Ltd. in 1974 which in turn were taken over by the Wedgwood Group in 1980 and renamed the Unicorn Pottery.

ASCOT

This pattern was introduced in the United States in 1926.

Cat.No.	Shape	U.S. $	Can. $	U.K. £
As-17	Bowl, lily 12″	100.00	125.00	65.00
As-22	Bowl, octagonal, 7″	255.00	300.00	175.00
As-24	Bowl, octagonal, 8″	300.00	350.00	200.00
As-53	Coffee pot, 3 cup	550.00	650.00	350.00
As-65	Condiment set	165.00	200.00	100.00
As-70	Cream and sugar	115.00	150.00	75.00
As-75	Demi-tasse	65.00	80.00	40.00
As-85	Jam pot	100.00	125.00	65.00
As-95	Jug, 5″	200.00	250.00	150.00
As-96	Jug, 7″	225.00	275.00	175.00

Cat.No.	Shape	U.S. $	Can. $	U.K. £
As-402	Plate, octagonal, 5″	65.00	80.00	40.00
As-406	Plate, octagonal, 9″	100.00	125.00	65.00
As-407	Plate, octagonal, 10″	125.00	150.00	75.00
As-130	Teacup and saucer	75.00	100.00	45.00
As-135	Teapot, 2 cup	375.00	450.00	250.00
As-136	Teapot, 4 cup	475.00	575.00	300.00
As-160	Vase, bud	100.00	125.00	65.00
As-163	Vase, spill, 8″	165.00	200.00	100.00
As-162	Vase, trumpet 6″	135.00	165.00	80.00
As-165	Vase, 9″	225.00	275.00	150.00

BLUE CHINTZ

This chintz pattern was introduced in the United States in 1926 and continued in production for many years.

Cat.No.	Shape	U.S. $	Can. $	U.K. £
BC-17	Bowl, lily 12″	125.00	150.00	75.00
BC-22	Bowl, octagonal, 7″	300.00	350.00	200.00
BC-24	Bowl, octagonal, 8″	350.00	425.00	250.00
BC-53	Coffee pot, 3 cup	650.00	775.00	400.00
BC-65	Condiment set	200.00	250.00	115.00
BC-70	Cream and sugar	135.00	165.00	85.00
BC-75	Demi-tasse	75.00	90.00	45.00
BC-85	Jam pot	125.00	150.00	75.00
BC-95	Jug, 5″	225.00	275.00	150.00
BC-96	Jug, 7″	250.00	300.00	175.00

Cat.No.	Shape	U.S. $	Can. $	U.K. £
BC-402	Plate, octagonal, 5″	75.00	90.00	45.00
BC-406	Plate, octagonal, 9″	125.00	150.00	75.00
BC-407	Plate, octagonal, 10″	150.00	175.00	90.00
BC-130	Teacup and saucer	85.00	100.00	50.00
BC-135	Teapot, 2 cup	450.00	550.00	300.00
BC-136	Teapot, 4 cup	550.00	650.00	350.00
BC-160	Vase, bud	125.00	150.00	75.00
BC-163	Vase, spill, 8″	200.00	250.00	115.00
BC-162	Vase, trumpet 6″	165.00	200.00	100.00
BC-165	Vase, 9″	275.00	325.00	175.00

CANTON

This chintz-like pattern was produced by a number of companies.

Cat.No.	Shape	U.S. $	Can. $	U.K. £
C-17	Bowl, lily 12″	100.00	125.00	65.00
C-22	Bowl, octagonal, 7″	225.00	275.00	150.00
C-24	Bowl, octagonal, 8″	250.00	325.00	175.00
C-53	Coffee pot, 3 cup	475.00	575.00	300.00
C-65	Condiment set	150.00	175.00	90.00
C-70	Cream and sugar	100.00	125.00	60.00
C-75	Demi-tasse	50.00	75.00	35.00
C-85	Jam pot	100.00	125.00	65.00
C-95	Jug, 5″	125.00	150.00	75.00
C-96	Jug, 7″	150.00	175.00	90.00

Cat.No.	Shape	U.S. $	Can. $	U.K. £
C-402	Plate, octagonal, 5″	50.00	75.00	35.00
C-406	Plate, octagonal, 9″	100.00	125.00	65.00
C-407	Plate, octagonal, 10″	100.00	125.00	65.00
C-130	Teacup and saucer	65.00	80.00	40.00
C-135	Teapot, 2 cup	325.00	400.00	225.00
C-136	Teapot, 4 cup	400.00	475.00	250.00
C-160	Vase, bud	100.00	125.00	65.00
C-163	Vase, spill, 8″	150.00	175.00	90.00
C-162	Vase, trumpet 6″	125.00	150.00	75.00
C-165	Vase, 9″	200.00	250.00	150.00

FESTIVAL

This pattern was introduced in the United States around 1926.

Cat.No.	Shape	U.S. $	Can. $	U.K. £
Fe-17	Bowl, lily 12″	100.00	125.00	65.00
Fe-22	Bowl, octagonal, 7″	250.00	300.00	175.00
Fe-24	Bowl, octagonal, 8″	300.00	350.00	200.00
Fe-53	Coffee pot, 3 cup	550.00	650.00	350.00
Fe-65	Condiment set	165.00	200.00	100.00
Fe-70	Cream and sugar	115.00	150.00	75.00
Fe-75	Demi-tasse	65.00	80.00	40.00
Fe-85	Jam pot	100.00	125.00	65.00
Fe-95	Jug, 5″	200.00	250.00	125.00
Fe-96	Jug, 7″	225.00	275.00	150.00

Cat.No.	Shape	U.S. $	Can. $	U.K. £
Fe-402	Plate, octagonal, 5″	65.00	80.00	40.00
Fe-406	Plate, octagonal, 9″	100.00	125.00	65.00
Fe-407	Plate, octagonal, 10″	125.00	150.00	75.00
Fe-130	Teacup and saucer	75.00	85.00	45.00
Fe-135	Teapot, 2 cup	375.00	450.00	250.00
Fe-136	Teapot, 4 cup	475.00	560.00	300.00
Fe-160	Vase, bud	100.00	125.00	65.00
Fe-163	Vase, spill, 8″	165.00	200.00	125.00
Fe-162	Vase, trumpet 6″	135.00	165.00	75.00
Fe-165	Vase, 9″	250.00	275.00	150.00

FLORIDA

This chintz pattern was advertised in the United States in 1925 and was described as "a wordless song of the tropics." American collectors know this pattern as "Mauve Crown Ducal".

Cat.No.	Shape	U.S. $	Can. $	U.K. £
Fd-17	Bowl, lily 12"	165.00	200.00	100.00
Fd-22	Bowl, octagonal, 7"	400.00	475.00	275.00
Fd-24	Bowl, octagonal, 8"	450.00	550.00	300.00
Fd-53	Coffee pot, 3 cup	850.00	1,100.00	600.00
Fd-65	Condiment set	250.00	300.00	175.00
Fd-70	Cream and sugar	175.00	225.00	100.00
Fd-75	Demi-tasse	100.00	125.00	65.00
Fd-85	Jam pot	165.00	200.00	100.00
Fd-95	Jug, 5"	300.00	355.00	200.00
Fd-96	Jug, 7"	350.00	425.00	225.00
Fd-402	Plate, octagonal, 5"	100.00	125.00	65.00
Fd-406	Plate, octagonal, 9"	160.00	200.00	100.00
Fd-407	Plate, octagonal, 10"	175.00	225.00	125.00
Fd-130	Teacup and saucer	100.00	125.00	65.00
Fd-135	Teapot, 2 cup	575.00	700.00	375.00
Fd-136	Teapot, 4 cup	700.00	850.00	450.00
Fd-160	Vase, bud	160.00	200.00	125.00
Fd-163	Vase, spill, 8"	250.00	300.00	175.00
Fd-162	Vase, trumpet 6"	200.00	250.00	150.00
Fd-165	Vase, 9"	350.00	425.00	450.00

"GREY FRUIT"

Unfortunately we have no information available on this pattern at this time.

Cat.No.	Shape	U.S. $	Can. $	U.K. £
GF-17	Bowl, lily 12"	100.00	125.00	65.00
GF-22	Bowl, octagonal, 7"	225.00	275.00	150.00
GF-24	Bowl, octagonal, 8"	250.00	300.00	175.00
GF-53	Coffee pot, 3 cup	475.00	575.00	300.00
GF-65	Condiment set	150.00	175.00	90.00
GF-70	Cream and sugar	100.00	125.00	65.00
GF-75	Demi-tasse	50.00	75.00	35.00
GF-85	Jam pot	100.00	125.00	65.00
GF-95	Jug, 5"	150.00	175.00	90.00
GF-96	Jug, 7"	175.00	200.00	100.00
GF-402	Plate, octagonal, 5"	50.00	75.00	35.00
GF-406	Plate, octagonal, 9"	100.00	125.00	65.00
GF-407	Plate, octagonal, 10"	100.00	125.00	65.00
GF-130	Teacup and saucer	65.00	80.00	40.00
GF-135	Teapot, 2 cup	325.00	400.00	225.00
GF-136	Teapot, 4 cup	400.00	500.00	275.00
GF-160	Vase, bud	100.00	125.00	65.00
GF-163	Vase, spill, 8"	150.00	175.00	85.00
GF-162	Vase, trumpet 6"	125.00	150.00	75.00
GF-165	Vase, 9"	200.00	250.00	150.00

IVORY CHINTZ

This chintz pattern was introduced into the United States before 1926.

Cat.No.	Shape	U.S. $	Can. $	U.K. £
IC-17	Bowl, lily 12″	125.00	150.00	75.00
IC-22	Bowl, octagonal, 7″	300.00	350.00	200.00
IC-24	Bowl, octagonal, 8″	350.00	425.00	250.00
IC-53	Coffee pot, 3 cup	650.00	775.00	400.00
IC-65	Condiment set	200.00	250.00	150.00
IC-70	Cream and sugar	135.00	165.00	85.00
IC-75	Demi-tasse	75.00	90.00	45.00
IC-85	Jam pot	125.00	150.00	75.00
IC-95	Jug, 5″	250.00	300.00	175.00
IC-96	Jug, 7″	275.00	325.00	175.00

Cat.No.	Shape	U.S. $	Can. $	U.K. £
IC-402	Plate, octagonal, 5″	75.00	90.00	45.00
IC-406	Plate, octagonal, 9″	125.00	150.00	75.00
IC-407	Plate, octagonal, 10″	150.00	175.00	85.00
IC-130	Teacup and saucer	85.00	100.00	50.00
IC-135	Teapot, 2 cup	450.00	550.00	300.00
IC-136	Teapot, 4 cup	550.00	650.00	350.00
IC-160	Vase, bud	125.00	150.00	75.00
IC-163	Vase, spill, 8″	200.00	250.00	150.00
IC-162	Vase, trumpet 6″	165.00	200.00	125.00
IC-165	Vase, 9″	275.00	325.00	175.00

"IVORY FRUIT"

Unfortunately, we have no information on this pattern at this time.

Cat.No.	Shape	U.S. $	Can. $	U.K. £
IF-17	Bowl, lily 12"	100.00	125.00	65.00
IF-22	Bowl, octagonal, 7"	225.00	275.00	150.00
IF-24	Bowl, octagonal, 8"	250.00	300.00	150.00
IF-53	Coffee pot, 3 cup	475.00	575.00	300.00
IF-65	Condiment set	150.00	175.00	85.00
IF-70	Cream and sugar	100.00	125.00	65.00
IF-75	Demi-tasse	50.00	75.00	35.00
IF-85	Jam pot	100.00	125.00	65.00
IF-95	Jug, 5"	150.00	175.00	85.00
IF-96	Jug, 7"	175.00	200.00	100.00

Cat.No.	Shape	U.S. $	Can. $	U.K. £
IF-402	Plate, octagonal, 5"	50.00	75.00	35.00
IF-406	Plate, octagonal, 9"	100.00	125.00	65.00
IF-407	Plate, octagonal, 10"	110.00	125.00	65.00
IF-130	Teacup and saucer	65.00	75.00	40.00
IF-135	Teapot, 2 cup	325.00	400.00	225.00
IF-136	Teapot, 4 cup	400.00	500.00	275.00
IF-160	Vase, bud	100.00	125.00	65.00
IF-163	Vase, spill, 8"	150.00	175.00	85.00
IF-162	Vase, trumpet 6"	125.00	150.00	75.00
IF-165	Vase, 9"	200.00	250.00	125.00

MARIGOLD

This pattern is most often found on vases and rose bowls.

Cat.No.	Shape	U.S. $	Can. $	U.K. £
MgR-17	Bowl, lily 12″	100.00	125.00	65.00
MgR-22	Bowl, octagonal, 7″	250.00	300.00	175.00
MgR-24	Bowl, octagonal, 8″	300.00	350.00	200.00
MgR-53	Coffee pot, 3 cup	550.00	650.00	350.00
MgR-65	Condiment set	165.00	200.00	100.00
MgR-70	Cream and sugar	100.00	125.00	65.00
MgR-75	Demi-tasse	115.00	150.00	75.00
MgR-85	Jam pot	100.00	125.00	65.00
MgR-95	Jug, 5″	200.00	250.00	150.00
MgR-96	Jug, 7″	225.00	275.00	150.00

Cat.No.	Shape	U.S. $	Can. $	U.K. £
MgR-402	Plate, octagonal, 5″	65.00	75.00	40.00
MgR-406	Plate, octagonal, 9″	100.00	125.00	65.00
MgR-407	Plate, octagonal, 10″	125.00	150.00	75.00
MgR-130	Teacup and saucer	70.00	85.00	45.00
MgR-135	Teapot, 2 cup	375.00	450.00	450.00
MgR-136	Teapot, 4 cup	465.00	550.00	300.00
MgR-160	Vase, bud	100.00	125.00	65.00
MgR-163	Vase, spill, 8″	165.00	200.00	100.00
MgR-162	Vase, trumpet 6″	135.00	165.00	85.00
MgR-165	Vase, 9″	225.00	275.00	150.00

" MAUVE CHINTZ "

This pattern was not a controlled pattern and was used by a number of companies.

Cat.No.	Shape	U.S. $	Can. $	U.K. £
MC-17	Bowl, lily 12"	100.00	125.00	65.00
MC-22	Bowl, octagonal, 7"	225.00	275.00	150.00
MC-24	Bowl, octagonal, 8"	250.00	325.00	175.00
MC-53	Coffee pot, 3 cup	475.00	575.00	300.00
MC-65	Condiment set	150.00	175.00	90.00
MC-70	Cream and sugar	100.00	125.00	65.00
MC-75	Demi-tasse	50.00	75.00	35.00
MC-85	Jam pot	100.00	125.00	65.00
MC-95	Jug, 5"	150.00	175.00	85.00
MC-96	Jug, 7"	175.00	225.00	125.00

Cat.No.	Shape	U.S. $	Can. $	U.K. £
MC-402	Plate, octagonal, 5"	50.00	75.00	35.00
MC-406	Plate, octagonal, 9"	100.00	125.00	65.00
MC-407	Plate, octagonal, 10"	100.00	125.00	65.00
MC-130	Teacup and saucer	65.00	80.00	40.00
MC-135	Teapot, 2 cup	325.00	400.00	225.00
MC-136	Teapot, 4 cup	400.00	500.00	275.00
MC-160	Vase, bud	100.00	125.00	65.00
MC-163	Vase, spill, 8"	150.00	175.00	85.00
MC-162	Vase, trumpet 6"	125.00	150.00	75.00
MC-165	Vase, 9"	200.00	250.00	125.00

"PINK CHINTZ"

This chintz pattern was probably introduced into the United States in 1928.

Cat.No.	Shape	U.S. $	Can. $	U.K. £
PC-17	Bowl, lily 12″	100.00	125.00	65.00
PC-22	Bowl, octagonal, 7″	275.00	325.00	175.00
PC-24	Bowl, octagonal, 8″	325.00	375.00	200.00
PC-53	Coffee pot, 3 cup	575.00	700.00	375.00
PC-65	Condiment set	175.00	225.00	125.00
PC-70	Cream and sugar	125.00	150.00	75.00
PC-75	Demi-tasse	65.00	75.00	40.00
PC-85	Jam pot	115.00	150.00	75.00
PC-95	Jug, 5″	225.00	275.00	150.00
PC-96	Jug, 7″	250.00	300.00	175.00

Cat.No.	Shape	U.S. $	Can. $	U.K. £
PC-402	Plate, octagonal, 5″	65.00	80.00	40.00
PC-406	Plate, octagonal, 9″	115.00	150.00	75.00
PC-407	Plate, octagonal, 10″	135.00	165.00	85.00
PC-130	Teacup and saucer	75.00	90.00	45.00
PC-135	Teapot, 2 cup	400.00	475.00	250.00
PC-136	Teapot, 4 cup	500.00	600.00	350.00
PC-160	Vase, bud	115.00	150.00	75.00
PC-163	Vase, spill, 8″	175.00	225.00	125.00
PC-162	Vase, trumpet 6″	150.00	175.00	90.00
PC-165	Vase, 9″	150.00	300.00	175.00

PRIMULA

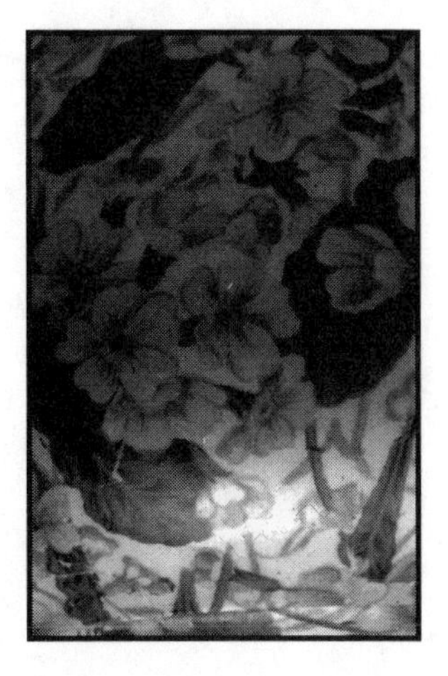

This chintz pattern was introduced in the 1930s.

Cat.No.	Shape	U.S. $	Can. $	U.K. £
PrR-17	Bowl, lily 12″	100.00	125.00	65.00
PrR-22	Bowl, octagonal, 7″	250.00	300.00	175.00
PrR-24	Bowl, octagonal, 8″	300.00	350.00	200.00
PrR-53	Coffee pot, 3 cup	550.00	650.00	350.00
PrR-65	Condiment set	165.00	200.00	100.00
PrR-70	Cream and sugar	115.00	150.00	75.00
PrR-75	Demi-tasse	65.00	75.00	40.00
PrR-85	Jam pot	100.00	125.00	65.00
PrR-95	Jug, 5″	200.00	250.00	125.00
PrR-96	Jug, 7″	225.00	275.00	150.00

Cat.No.	Shape	U.S. $	Can. $	U.K. £
PrR-402	Plate, octagonal, 5″	65.00	80.00	40.00
PrR-406	Plate, octagonal, 9″	100.00	125.00	65.00
PrR-407	Plate, octagonal, 10″	125.00	150.00	75.00
PrR-130	Teacup and saucer	75.00	100.00	45.00
PrR-135	Teapot, 2 cup	375.00	450.00	250.00
PrR-136	Teapot, 4 cup	475.00	550.00	300.00
PrR-160	Vase, bud	100.00	125.00	65.00
PrR-163	Vase, spill, 8″	165.00	200.00	100.00
PrR-162	Vase, trumpet 6″	135.00	165.00	85.00
PrR-165	Vase, 9″	225.00	275.00	150.00

"PURPLE CHINTZ"

This is one of the most popular Crown Ducal chintzes in the United States.

Cat.No.	Shape	U.S. $	Can. $	U.K. £
PuC-17	Bowl, lily 12"	150.00	175.00	85.00
PuC-22	Bowl, octagonal, 7"	375.00	450.00	250.00
PuC-24	Bowl, octagonal, 8"	425.00	500.00	275.00
PuC-53	Coffee pot, 3 cup	800.00	950.00	500.00
PuC-65	Condiment set	250.00	300.00	175.00
PuC-70	Cream and sugar	165.00	200.00	100.00
PuC-75	Demi-tasse	100.00	125.00	65.00
PuC-85	Jam pot	150.00	175.00	85.00
PuC-95	Jug, 5"	275.00	325.00	175.00
PuC-96	Jug, 7"	325.00	400.00	225.00

Cat.No.	Shape	U.S. $	Can. $	U.K. £
PuC-402	Plate, octagonal, 5"	100.00	125.00	65.00
PuC-406	Plate, octagonal, 9"	150.00	175.00	85.00
PuC-407	Plate, octagonal, 10"	175.00	225.00	125.00
PuC-130	Teacup and saucer	100.00	125.00	65.00
PuC-135	Teapot, 2 cup	550.00	650.00	350.00
PuC-136	Teapot, 4 cup	675.00	800.00	450.00
PuC-160	Vase, bud	150.00	175.00	90.00
PuC-163	Vase, spill, 8"	250.00	300.00	175.00
PuC-162	Vase, trumpet 6"	200.00	250.00	125.00
PuC-165	Vase, 9"	350.00	425.00	225.00

ROSE & MOTIFS

This was one of the earliest Crown Ducal chintzes and was introduced in 1918. It has been found on vases and toiletware only.

Cat.No.	Shape	U.S. $	Can. $	U.K. £
RM-95	Jug, 5″	275.00	325.00	175.00
RM-96	Jug, 7″	325.00	400.00	225.00
RM-160	Vase, bud	150.00	175.00	85.00
RM-163	Vase, spill, 8″	250.00	300.00	175.00
RM-162	Vase, trumpet 6″	200.00	250.00	150.00
RM-165	Vase, 9″	350.00	425.00	250.00

The "Florida" Pattern

English Wares of Merit

Crown Ducal Ware

POTTERY for the Gift Department! Pottery that has a vogue. Pottery that is different! Abounds in novelties. A striking example is the colorful

"FLORIDA"

line—a wordless song of the tropics. Gay exotic birds are seen nestling in a wonderful profusion of bright colored flowers against a tan background. Fancy and useful items, Vases in many shapes and sizes, Flower Pots, Bulb Bowls, Tea, Coffee, Breakfast, Dessert, Trinket and Bridge Sets, and Dinnerware.

Only one of many new patterns ready for 1926 Import season.

Maddock & Miller
Incorporated
"The House of Stock"
39-41 West 23rd St.
New York

RIDGWAY POTTERIES LTD.

The firm was founded in 1866 at the Bedford Works in Shelton by Edward John Ridgway and produced both fine and utility earthenwares. The firm had a variety of names and partnerships through the first half of the twentieth century and by 1955 the firm had eight different works in Staffordshire, including Colcloughs and Booths. Ridgway Potteries Ltd. now operates under the Royal Doulton umbrella.

UNKNOWN

This pattern has been seen on tableware items such as casseroles, but little is known about the range of pieces produced.

Photograph not available
at
press time.

Cat.No.	Shape	U.S. $	Can. $	U.K. £
RP-78	Egg cup, large	65.00	75.00	40.00
RP-93	Jug, 6″	250.00	300.00	175.00
RP-106	Plate, 9″	125.00	150.00	75.00

ROYAL DOULTON LTD.

Doulton & Company manufactured drainpipes in the mid-nineteenth century, and from that beginning a huge company has grown which today encompasses Royal Crown Derby, Minton, Shelley, Beswick, Royal Albert and many more. The firm opened their present-day works on Nile Street in Burslem in 1882. The only all-over transfer which might be of interest to chintz collectors was produced in several versions by Doulton around 1913 and was called **Persian**. It was a forerunner of the patterns produced by A.G. Richardson some five years later. The pattern was not used for tablewares, but reserved for rack plates and cabinet pieces. The pattern continued in production until approximately 1940.

PERSIAN

This is an early chintz-type pattern and not yet collected by enough chintz collectors to establish a market.

Cat.No.	Shape	U.S. $	Can. $	U.K. £
Per-107	Plate, 10"	125.00	150.00	75.00
Per-145	Tennis Set	150.00	175.00	85.00

SHELLEY POTTERIES LTD.

In 1853 Henry Wileman became a partner in Foley Potteries and three years later built Foley China Works. Joseph Shelley became a partner in 1872, and the name changed to Wileman & Co. By 1884 Wileman had gone and the firm became a Shelley family business. Although the Shelley backstamp was introduced as early as 1910 it was not until 1925 that Wileman & Co. became Shelley Potteries.

Shelley produced an extraordinary range of teawares in a range of shapes and decorative techniques. Some of the all-over transfers such as **Cloisonne** were used by Shelley as "seconds" patterns and applied to ware which did not meet the factory's high standards. Patterns like **Maytime** and **Melody** however, were offered on a wide range of wares and were advertised both before and after the war.

Although two books have been written on Shelley Potteries only a couple of lines have been devoted to the all-over florals that they produced. The family remained in the business until 1966, when the company was taken over by Allied English Potteries. The owners of Allied acquired Doulton & Company in 1971, and the companies merged to form Royal Doulton Tableware Ltd.

MAYTIME

This pattern was very popular before and after the second world war and was available in both earthenware and bone china.

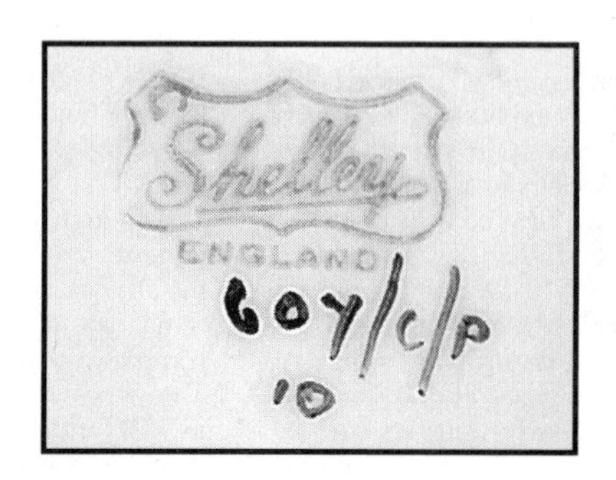

Cat.No.	Shape	U.S. $	Can. $	U.K. £
Mat-55	Coffee pot, 6 cup	450.00	550.00	300.00
Mat-70	Cream and sugar	125.00	150.00	75.00
Mat-98	Pin tray, small	85.00	100.00	50.00

Cat.No.	Shape	U.S. $	Cat. $	U.K. £
Mat-104	Plate, 7″	60.00	75.00	35.00
Mat-130	Teacup and saucer	75.00	90.00	45.00
Mat-137	Teapot, 6 cup	400.00	475.00	250.00

MELODY

Photograph not available
at
press time.

This pattern was very popular before and after the second world war and was available in both earthenware and bone china. Teasets in this pattern were exported in quantity to North America.

Cat.No.	Shape	U.S. $	Can. $	U.K. £
Me-55	Coffee pot, 6 cup	500.00	600.00	325.00
Me-70	Cream and sugar	135.00	165.00	85.00
Me-98	Pin Tray, small	100.00	125.00	65.00
Me-104	Plate, 7"	70.00	85.00	45.00
Me-130	Teacup and saucer	85.00	100.00	50.00
Me-137	Teapot, 6 cup	450.00	550.00	300.00

SUMMER GLORY

This pattern was very popular and was available in both earthenware and bone china. Tea sets in this pattern were exported in quantity to North America.

Cat.No.	Shape	U.S. $	Can. $	U.K. £
SuG-55	Coffee pot, 6 cup	450.00	550.00	300.00
SuG-70	Cream and sugar	125.00	150.00	75.00
SuG-98	Pin tray, small	85.00	100.00	50.00
SuG-104	Plate, 7"	60.00	75.00	35.00
SuG-130	Teacup and saucer	75.00	90.00	45.00
SuG-137	Teapot, 6 cup	400.00	475.00	250.00

WADE CERAMICS LTD.

The original company was founded in 1810 and made pottery fittings for shuttles and textile machinery. The firm was bought by George Wade just after the turn of the century. The Wade Group of Potteries came into existence in the mid 1950s; prior to that time there were a number of individually owned companies with members of the Wade family or their friends in control. The only all-over pattern that Wade appears to have done in the 1920s was the open stock **Paisley** pattern used by many other companies, including Grimwades. In the 1950s the Wade Group offered two chintz patterns among a group of 18 transfer-type patterns available in tea ware and dinner ware on the Orb shape.

The Wade Group's combination of giftwares and industrial products, such as gas refactories and high alumina bodies used in micro-electronic and nuclear fields, have helped them to survive through several recessions in the pottery industry.

"BUTTERFLY CHINTZ"

This pattern was one of two chintz patterns available on a complete range of tablewares in the mid 1950s.

Cat.No.	Shape	U.S. $	Can. $	U.K. £
Bu-103	Plate, 6″	60.00	75.00	35.00
Bu-104	Plate, 7″	75.00	90.00	45.00
Bu-130	Teacup and saucer	75.00	90.00	45.00

THISTLE CHINTZ

This pattern was one of two chintz patterns available on a complete range of tablewares in the mid 1950s.

Cat.No.	Shape	U.S. $	Can. $	U.K. £
Th-103	Plate, 6″	60.00	75.00	35.00
Th-104	Plate, 7″	75.00	90.00	45.00
Th-130	Teacup and saucer	75.00	90.00	45.00

WOOD & SONS LTD.

This factory has manufactured earthenwares and ironstones since 1865. In the twentieth century they had working relationships with many of the leading designers of the day. The company produced such good quality whiteware that a number of firms including A.E. Gray and subsequently Susie Cooper bought in their wares.

As early as 1931 the firm was experimenting with colourful lithograph patterns for their Ivory Ware and may have produced several all-over florals around this time. The association with Susie Cooper and her very different approach to the use of lithos probably steered Wood & Sons away from any involvement in the production of chintz ware. The factory was finally sold in the 1980s but the name was retained.

UNKNOWN

This pattern is rarely found in North America and eagerly sought by collectors.

Cat.No.	Shape	U.S. $	Can. $	U.K. £
WS-103	Plate, 6″	75.00	90.00	45.00

Cat.No.	Shape	U.S. $	Can. $	U.K. £
WS-130	Teacup and saucer	125.00	150.00	75.00

SHAPES

An attractive

"Royal Winton"

adaptation of a popular English Summer Flower

"Delphinium Chintz" No. 9889.

GRIMWADES Limited,

Stoke-on-Trent.

London Showrooms: *Atlantic House, 45-50, Holborn Viaduct, E.C.1.*

Write for Illustrated Price List.

Shapes

From left: Albans (Julia), Albans (Nantwich), Albans (Evesham), Unknown (Estelle)

From left: Raleigh (Eleanor), Raleigh (Marion), Dutch (Cranstone), Dutch (Summertime)

From left: Savoy (Welbeck), Olympic (Florence), Neme (Nantwich). Top right: Fife (Stratford). Bottom right: Lily (Julia)

Shapes

From left: Grecian (Hazel), Grecian (Hazel), Pear (Majestic), Pear (Majestic), Unknown (Hazel), Hampton (Hazel)

From left: Norman(Hazel), Ascot (Hazel), Raleigh (Hazel) Gem (Hazel)

From left: Countess (Royalty), Countess (Clevedon), Sexta (Hazel), Norman (Hazel)

Shapes

Left: Countess Breakfast Set, Raleigh cup (Victorian Rose).
Right: Countess Breakfast Set (Majestic)

From left: Ascot (Sweet Pea), Elite (Hazel), Albans (Summertime),
Rosebud (Welbeck), Albans (Sweet Pea)

Shapes

Ventnor (Peony) | Ventnor (Peony) | Kew Basket

Ascot Jam pot (Florence) | Chelsea Jam pot — missing liner (Summertime) | Rheims Jam pot (Hazel)

Niagara Falls Souvenir Plate (Summertime) | Saville (Hazel) | Bude (Sunshine)

Shapes

From left: Ascot Cream and Sugar (Majestic), Ascot Sugar (Royalty), Athena Cream (Royalty), Large Ascot Cream (Welbeck)

From left: Hector Cream and Sugar (Somerset), Countess Cream and Sugar (Old Cottage Chintz), Ascot Sugar Variation (Welbeck), 2-slice Toast rack (Summertime)

From left: Dane Cheese keep (Evesham), Dane Cheese keep (Delphinium chintz), Ascot square Butter dish (Hazel), Ascot rectangular Butter dish (Welbeck), 4-slice Toast rack (Sweet Pea)

From left: Nut dishes (Summertime), (Cranstone), (Summertime), Egg cup (Summertime), Era (Stratford), Footed Egg cup (Hazel)

Shapes

From left: James Kent— Granville (Rosalynde), James Kent —Diamond (Rosalynde), James Kent — Granville (Rosalynde), Royal Winton —Ascot (Royalty)

From left: James Kent — Granville (Primula), Royal Winton — Perth (Cranstone), Lord Nelson — Coffee Pot (Pansy), James Kent — Granville (Rosalynde)

From left: Royal Winton — Countess (Balmoral), Countess (Marguerite), Albans (Eleanor), Albans (Balmoral)

From left: Lord Nelson Stacking Teapot (Royal Brocade), James Kent Cosy Set (Rapture), Royal Winton Delamere (Peony), Royal Winton Ascot (Joyce-Lynn)

Shapes

From left: Elijah Cotton Ltd. — Lord Nelson Bud Vases (Marina), (Heather), (Rosetime), (Marina)

From left: Grimwades Ltd. — Royal Winton Athena Cup and Saucer, Teapot, Cream and Sugar (Hazel)

From left: Grimwades Ltd. —Royal Winton Etona (Hazel), Unknown (Hazel), Unknown (Hazel), Tudor (Sweet Pea)

Shapes

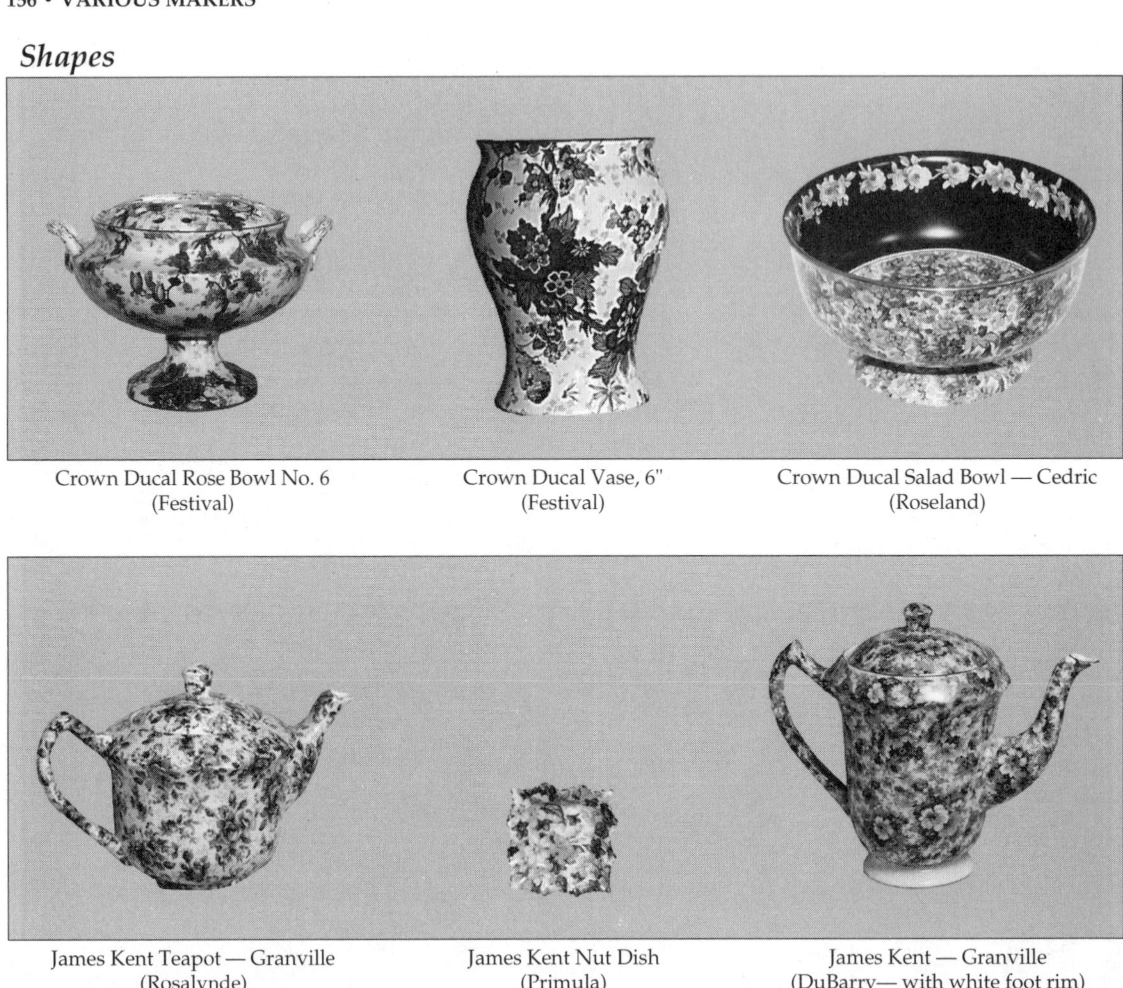

Crown Ducal Rose Bowl No. 6
(Festival)

Crown Ducal Vase, 6"
(Festival)

Crown Ducal Salad Bowl — Cedric
(Roseland)

James Kent Teapot — Granville
(Rosalynde)

James Kent Nut Dish
(Primula)

James Kent — Granville
(DuBarry— with white foot rim)

From left: James Kent Bud Vases (Rapture), (Hydrangea — Black), (Hydrangea — White)

Shapes

Royal Winton — Cambridge (Hazel)

Royal Winton — Rosebud (Welbeck)

Royal Winton — Albans (Summertime)

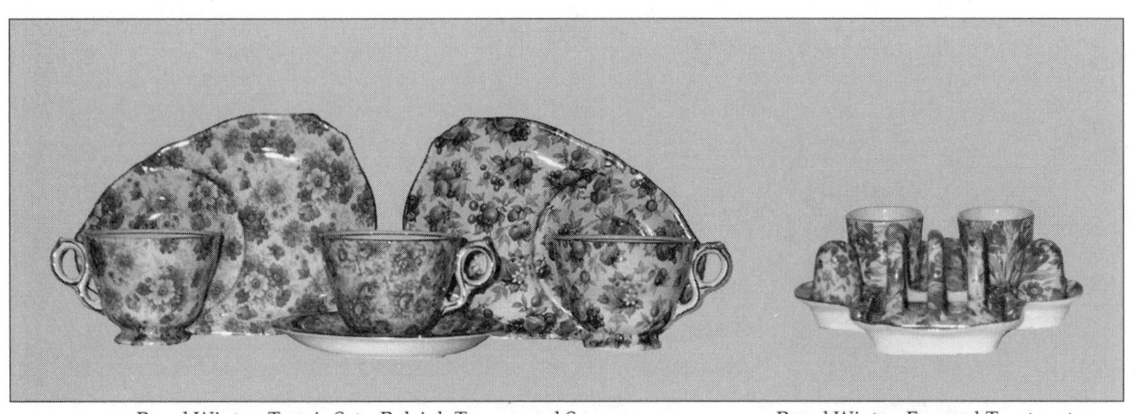

Royal Winton Tennis Sets, Raleigh Teacup and Saucer (Shrewsbury), (English Rose), (Evesham)

Royal Winton Egg and Toast on tray (Springtime)

Crown Ducal Egg, Pepper & Salt on Tray ("Pink Chintz")

Empire — Sugar Bowl (Lilac Time)

Lord Nelson — Bud Vase (Marina)

Royal Winton — Dudley (Marion)

Shapes

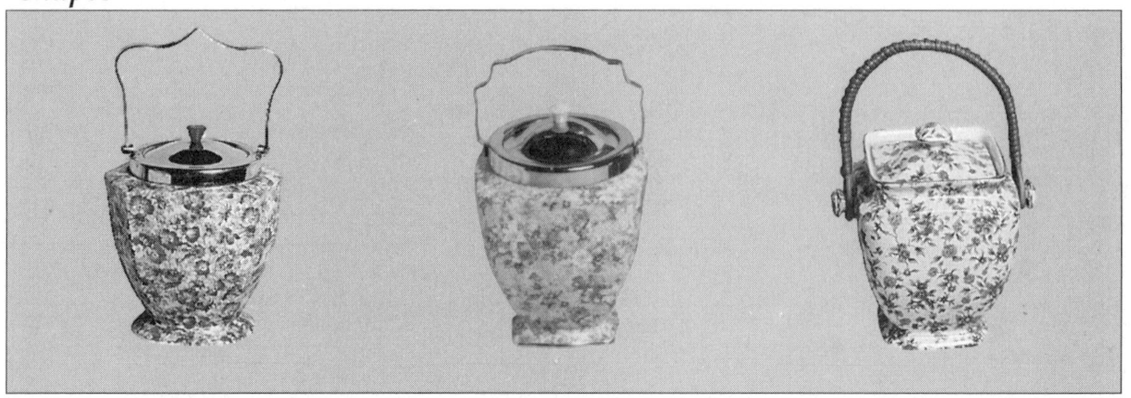

Biscuit Barrel (Royalty) | Biscuit Barrel (Marion) | Rheims Biscuit Barrel (Old Cottage Chintz)

Bedside Set (Stratford) | Era Sauce Boat (Hazel) Rosa Wall Pocket (Esther) | Nita (May Festival)

Lily Bedside Set (Welbeck) | Grosvenor (Old Cottage Chintz) | James Kent — Shaving Mug (Du Barry)

PATTERN INDEX

The Charlton Standards

Royal Doulton Animals

1st Edition, by Jean Dale

Never before listed in one handy reference. All HN, K, D and DA series, plus Royal Adderley, flambé, advertising animals and more.

462 pages; 7" x 9"; softcover;
$24.95 Cdn., $19.95 U.S., £16.95 U.K.
ISBN 0-88968-122-8

Available from your favourite dealer or bookstore, or by calling the Charlton Press on our toll free lines from Canada or the U.S.

Wade, Volume 1–General Issues

2nd Edition, by Pat Murray

From animals to tankards, from figures to commemorative ware, it's all here in the most comprehensive catalogue on Wade.

411 pages; 7" x 9"; softcover;
$24.95 Cdn., $19.95 U.S., £16.95 U.K.
ISBN 0-88968-139-2

Wade, Volume 2–Decorative Ware

2nd Edition, by Pat Murray

For the first time all Wade's flowers, plaques, vases, pots, decorative dishes and more are assembled in one convenient volume.

300 pages; 7" x 9"; softcover;
$24.95 Cdn., $19.95 U.S., £16.95 U.K.
ISBN 0-88968-181-3

FOR TOLL FREE ORDERING
Call
1-800-442-6042
Fax
1-800-442-1542

Chintz

1st Edition, by Linda Eberle and Susan Scott

This eagerly awaited Chintz pricing catalogue covers all major and minor producers of Chintzware.

190 pages; 7" x 9"; softcover;
$19.95 Cdn., $17.95 U.S., £14.95 U.K.
ISBN 0-88968-179-1

The Charlton Press

2010 Yonge St. Toronto, Ontario M4S 1Z9, Canada